DISCARD

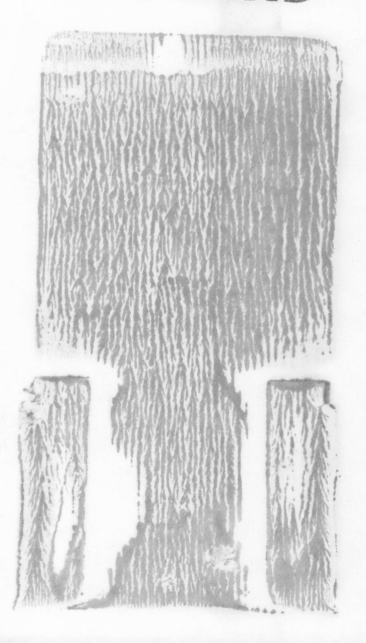

ELECTRICAL AND MAGNETIC PROPERTIES OF METALS

ELECTRICAL AND MAGNETIC PROPERTIES OF METALS

James K. Stanley
Crucible Steel Company of America

AMERICAN SOCIETY FOR METALS
Metals Park, Ohio

Printed in the United States of America

Preface

LONG overdue in our technology is a basic book on the electrical and magnetic properties of metals. In the hope of fulfilling this need, an effort has been made to compile a survey of this increasingly important subject, for engineers and students of science and engineering. Ordinarily, these properties of metals are ignored by our schools, except perhaps in some graduate courses. Scattered, uncoordinated information is available in various handbooks (without background discussion), technical periodicals (usually specialized), or technical books on other subjects (where discussions of materials are often perfunctory).

The objective has been to write a clear, concise account of electrical conduction, electron emission, superconductivity, thermoelectricity, the origin of magnetism, electrical steels, permanent magnets, and related subjects, with indications of how and where these materials and phenomena can be employed. A brief explanation of electron theory and how it is related to the electrical properties of metals is included, as well as a discussion of the theory of magnetism.

The level of presentation assumes some familiarity with mathematics, physics, and chemistry. From this base line the subject is developed.

The book is divided into eight chapters. The first chapter introduces the historical aspects of the subject and takes the reader up to the current ideas of electron theory, and the last chapter attempts to predict developments to be expected in the near future. In between is the treatment of electrical and magnetic properties of metals, from first principles to industrial applications.

Rather complete references are included for those who would care to extend their knowledge of a particular subject.

Because of the widespread use of the cgs emu system, it is

used here, except where otherwise noted. The advantages of the mksa (absolute) system are appreciated and conversion tables in the Appendix can be used by those who prefer absolute units.

I am indebted to the following colleagues at Crucible Steel Company of America: B. R. Banerjee, C. R. Honeycutt, R. S. Fowkes and E. M. Underhill for checking certain chapters of the book; Miss R. Hersch for her editorial assistance; and M. J. Day and W. E. Gregg, executives of the Company, for their interest in this endeavor.

JAMES K. STANLEY

Pittsburgh, Pa.
March 1963

Contents

Chapter 1

Basis for Electrical and Magnetic Characteristics

ELECTRICITY and magnetism are, after mathematics and astronomy, phenomena of ancient record. Although Thales of Miletus (630 to 550 BC) is given credit for observing the attractive power of the lodestone (magnetite), this knowledge probably antedated him. Plato, Aristotle, and Theophrastus mention it in their writings, and as early as 121 AD the Chinese knew that an iron rod, brought near a lodestone, would acquire and retain the property of a natural magnet. They also noted that a freely suspended magnetized rod would set itself approximately in the north-south direction. Use of magnets in navigation goes back to about the eleventh century. W. Gilbert's "De Magnete," published in 1600, summarized the existing information on magnetism at that time. Thales also observed that amber is easily electrified when it is rubbed.

The phenomenological laws describing electricity and magnetism were not discovered until the eighteenth and nineteenth centuries. In 1819, a Danish physicist, H. C. Oersted, discovered that a wire carrying an electric current produces a magnetic field; thus he established the link between electricity and magnetism. Shortly afterward (1822), A. Ampere, a French scientist, found that a spiral or a helix of wire concentrated the magnetic field. It was Ampere who coined the words electromagnetic, electrodynamic, and electrostatic. Coulomb, Volta, Faraday, Henry, among others, contributed much to establishing these sciences. Their work demonstrated that magnetism and electricity are so intimately connected that no intelligent study can be made of one subject without a knowledge of the other.

An understanding of the phenomena in terms of fundamental considerations has evolved in varying degrees only since Maxwell

1

(1831 to 1879), and the development of the electron theory (Thomson, 1856 to 1940) and quantum theory (Planck, 1858 to 1947, and Bohr, 1886 to 1962).

The physics of the solid state had little fundamental meaning until the twentieth century. The keys that opened the door to the new science were the elucidation of the structure of crystals, the explanation (in part) of the conduction of electricity by metals, and the realization that circulating electrons accounted for paramagnetism, diamagnetism and ferromagnetism.*

Crystals, and those converted to gems, were once thought to be exceptional forms of solids. Today, it is known that, while many solids do not appear to be crystalline, they actually are, for example, most rocks and minerals, and all metals. The only noncrystalline solids (the amorphous group) are glasses, pitch, and some rocks (volcanic obsidian). Crystals are homogeneous solids bounded by plane faces. Some are strikingly large and symmetrical. In rocks, the crystals may be hardly apparent unless the rock is fractured and examined. In metals, the crystals are fine (generally microscopic in size) and ordinarily do not have a geometric appearance. External appearance notwithstanding, these materials (rocks, minerals, metals) have an amazing internal symmetry. This geometry is the consequence of the repetition of a fundamental structure called the unit cell.

In 1900, five years after the discovery of the electron (culminating in the work of J. J. Thomson), Drude suggested that these electrons were the agents that conducted electricity. He devised a theory based on the assumption that the electrons in a metal are free, like molecules in a gas. The theory could be used to calculate thermal and electrical conductivity. The ratio between these quantities, the Wiedemann-Franz ratio (which dated back to 1853), could be computed; when compared with experiment, it checked satisfactorily. The theory answered some questions, but it raised more. Nonetheless, Drude's ideas opened the way to an understanding of electrical conduction in solids.

The work of P. Curie (1895) on the measurement of magnetic

---

* Today, solid-state physics not only is concerned with crystallography and structure of metals and alloys, and binding forces, but it also covers properties of homogeneous solids, such as specific heat, thermal and electrical conductivity, intrinsic semiconductivity, superconductivity, magnetic and dielectric properties; furthermore, it also deals with the properties of heterogeneous solids, such as semiconductivity, plasticity, color centers, dislocations, and vacancies.

susceptibility and its variation with temperature was one of the most fruitful researches in the history of magnetism. From this experimental work, Langevin (in 1905) was able to develop a theory to explain paramagnetism and diamagnetism. The theory was based on the notion that the effects were due to circulating electrons. Using the ideas of Langevin, Weiss (in 1907) introduced the rewarding concept of an intrinsic molecular field and was able to explain ferromagnetic characteristics.

Architecture of the Atom

The general structure of the atom — its nucleus of protons and neutrons, and its shells of electrons — is familiar to all scientifically oriented minds. The "solar system" model of the atom is understandable in terms of classical physics, although one must recognize modifications introduced by quantum mechanics. However, the sophistication of quantum and wave mechanics does not lead to a completely satisfactory explanation of many electrical and magnetic phenomena, and even today a comprehensive and fundamental understanding of electrical resistance is lacking. An understanding of ferromagnetism from the fundamental viewpoint is on somewhat firmer ground.

Electrical and magnetic properties of materials are determined by the electronic structure of the atom. The atom has an electrical structure composed of a nuclear charge (positive) about which electrons revolve. The diameter of the atom is of the order of 10^{-8} cm or 1 angstrom unit (symbol, A). The mass of the atom is concentrated in the nucleus, which has a diameter of about 10^{-13} cm. The nucleus is composed of protons, positively charged particles, and neutrons, particles possessing no charge whatsoever. Ordinary hydrogen possesses one proton; deuterium, or heavy hydrogen, has one proton and one neutron. These fundamental particles have almost identical masses, making deuterium twice as heavy as ordinary hydrogen.

The atomic number, Z, of an element, is defined as the total number of positive unit charges on the nucleus; this is equal to the total number of protons. The atomic number is the cardinal number of the corresponding element in the periodic system of elements: For example, $Z = 1$ for hydrogen, and $Z = 2$ for helium.

The atomic weight of an element is also an important quantity.

It is the average weight of an atom of an element measured in units that correspond to one sixteenth of the average weight of the naturally occurring oxygen atom (including the isotopes O^{16}, O^{17}, O^{18}).

For most elements, the nuclei can have different atomic weights (as a result of the number of neutrons present) without change of atomic number or charge. Such atoms are called isotopes. Iron, for example, has seven isotopes; four of them are stable, and three are unstable or radioactive. Tin has sixteen isotopes, and six are unstable or radioactive. The isotopes have identical chemical properties, because these depend on the nuclear charge and not on the nuclear mass. The differences in masses are not large, and therefore are not very important. Hydrogen is the only exception to this statement. Deuterium, or heavy hydrogen, has twice the mass of ordinary hydrogen; the properties of deuterium and hydrogen are noticeably different.

The electrons surrounding the charged nucleus are lightweight, negatively charged particles; the mass of each electron is $1/1813$ of the mass of the unit nuclear weight. An electrically neutral atom contains just as many electrons as the nucleus has unit positive charges.

In many instances, atoms do not exist in electrically neutral states. If the atom loses electrons, it becomes positively charged and is then called a positive ion. The atom can lose any number of electrons — one or all. When it loses one electron, it is a singly charged, positive ion, and when it loses two electrons, it is a doubly charged ion, and so on. Positive ions are stable structures; however, if they come in contact with electrons, they are electrically neutralized. The atom can also gain one or more electrons, and then it becomes a single or multiple-charged negative ion. Negatively charged structures are unstable and tend to expel excess electrons, becoming neutral again. Positive and negative ions exist in the solid, liquid, or gaseous state.

The Periodic System

In 1869, D. I. Mendeleev proposed the periodic law, according to which "the elements arranged according to the magnitude of atomic weights show a periodic change of properties." Mendeleev recognized that the outstanding periodic property of the elements is their valence.

The discovery of the inert gases, such as argon and neon (beginning with 1894), introduced a complication into the system. The position of the inert gases was subsequently resolved by studies of electronic structure. These studies showed that the order of the elements followed the number of electrons in the respective atoms: That is, the elements had characteristic atomic numbers.

The properties of the elements, when arranged in increasing order of their atomic numbers, place them in series of periods of eight families having valences from zero through seven (Table 1). The first series, which consists of hydrogen and helium, can be regarded as a primitive period, inasmuch as hydrogen is the prototype of all elements and helium is the prototype of all inert elements.

The periodic system ends with the so-called actinide series, to which new elements are still being added. The periodic table now has 103 elements, and more will probably be discovered.

The disposition of the electrons about the nucleus is responsible for the periodicity that is so evident in the periodic table. The state of the electrons in an atom can be conveniently described using four quantum numbers.* These numbers are simple integers derived from quantum mechanics that serve to describe physical and chemical facts when they are used in mathematical formulas. These numbers are as follows:

1 The principal or total quantum number, n, with values of 1, 2, 3, 4, and so on, determines the size of the orbit and the energy level in the atom. The symbols corresponding to the numbers are K, L, M, N, and so on. The total number of different combinations in each shell is given as $2n^2$.

2 The orbital angular momentum number, l, is a measure of the angular momentum of the orbital motion of the electron. It can have any of the values of 0, 1, 2, 3, . . . $(n-1)$. Corresponding symbols are s, p, d, f.

3 The spin magnetic quantum number, m_s, measures the electron spin. It can only have values of $+\frac{1}{2}$ or $-\frac{1}{2}$.

4 The magnetic quantum number, m_l, depends on the magnitude of l. It can have integral values between $+1$ and -1, including zero.

* Actually, four quantum numbers are necessary to explain spectroscopic data: n, l, s, and j. Numbers n and l are described in the text. The spin momentum quantum number, s, is due to the rotation of the electron on its axis, and the total angular momentum quantum number, j, is a vector sum of l and s. Two additional numbers are required to describe the behavior of an electron in a magnetic field, namely, m_s and m_l.

Table I. Periodic Table of the Elements

O	I	II	III	IV	V	VI	VII	VIII
								He 2 — 4.003
	H 1 — 1.0080							
	Li 3 — 6.940	Be 4 — 9.013	B 5 — 10.82	C 6 — 12.01	N 7 — 14.008	O 8 — 16.00	F 9 — 19.00	Ne 10 — 20.183
	Na 11 — 22.991	Mg 12 — 24.32	Al 13 — 26.98	Si 14 — 28.09	P 15 — 30.975	S 16 — 32.066	Cl 17 — 35.457	A 18 — 39.994

Long-period section

O	I a	II a	III a	IV a	V a	VI a	VII a	VIII			I b	II b	III b	IV b	V b	VI b	VII b
A 18 — 39.994	K 19 — 39.100	Ca 20 — 40.08	Sc 21 — 44.96	Ti 22 — 47.90	V 23 — 50.95	Cr 24 — 52.01	Mn 25 — 54.94	Fe 26 — 55.85	Co 27 — 58.94	Ni 28 — 58.71	Cu 29 — 63.54	Zn 30 — 65.38	Ga 31 — 69.72	Ge 32 — 72.60	As 33 — 74.91	Se 34 — 78.96	Br 35 — 79.916
Kr 36 — 83.8	Rb 37 — 85.48	Sr 38 — 87.63	Y 39 — 88.92	Zr 40 — 91.22	Cb 41 — 92.91	Mo 42 — 95.95	Tc 43 — (98)	Ru 44 — 101.1	Rh 45 — 102.91	Pd 46 — 106.7	Ag 47 — 107.880	Cd 48 — 112.41	In 49 — 114.82	Sn 50 — 118.70	Sb 51 — 121.76	Te 52 — 127.61	I 53 — 126.91
Xe 54 — 131.30	Cs 55 — 132.91	Ba 56 — 137.36	La to Lu 57 to 71 — 138.92	Hf 72 — 178.58	Ta 73 — 180.95	W 74 — 183.86	Re 75 — 186.22	Os 76 — 190.2	Ir 77 — 192.2	Pt 78 — 195.09	Au 79 — 197.0	Hg 80 — 200.61	Tl 81 — 204.39	Pb 82 — 207.21	Bi 83 — 209.00	Po 84 — 210	At 85 — (211)
Rn 86 — 222	Fr 87 — (223)	Ra 88 — 226.05	Ac 89 — 227	Th 90 — 232.05	Pa 91 — (231.1)	U 92 — 238.07	Np 93 — (237)	Pu 94 — (242)	Am 95 — (243)	Cm 96 — (247)	Bk 97 — (247)	Cf 98 — (251)	E 99 — (254)	Fm 100 — (253)	Mv 101 — (256)	No 102 — (254)	

Right-hand noble gas column (VIII / O):
Kr 36 — 83.8 · Xe 54 — 131.30 · Rn 86 — 222

( ) Mass number of most stable isotope if element does not occur naturally

Rare Earth Metals

	Ce 58 — 140.13	Pr 59 — 140.92	Nd 60 — 144.27	Pm 61 — (145)	Sm 62 — 150.35	Eu 63 — 152.0	Gd 64 — 157.26	Tb 65 — 158.93	Dy 66 — 162.51	Ho 67 — 164.94	Er 68 — 167.27	Tm 69 — 168.94	Yb 70 — 173.04	Lu 71 — 174.99

With the quantum numbers and the very important Pauli exclusion principle, it becomes possible to fix the maximum number of electrons in any atom. The Pauli principle states that only one electron in a given atom can possess a particular set of values for the four quantum numbers n, l, m_s, and m_l.

Table 2. Possible Combinations of the Four Quantum Numbers, n, l, m_l, and m_s

Principal quantum number, n Symbol		Orbital quantum number, l Symbol		Magnetic quantum number, m_l	Spin magnetic quantum number, m_s	Total number of combinations
1	K	0	s	0	$+\frac{1}{2}, \ -\frac{1}{2}$	2
2	L	0	s	0	$+\frac{1}{2}, \ -\frac{1}{2}$	2
		1	p	+1 0 −1	$+\frac{1}{2}, \ -\frac{1}{2}$	6 } 8
3	M	0	s	0	$+\frac{1}{2}, \ -\frac{1}{2}$	2
		1	p	+1 0 −1	$+\frac{1}{2}, \ -\frac{1}{2}$	6 } 18
		2	d	+2 +1 0 −1 −2	$+\frac{1}{2}, \ -\frac{1}{2}$	10
4	N	0	s	0	$+\frac{1}{2}, \ -\frac{1}{2}$	2
		1	p	+1 0 −1	$+\frac{1}{2}, \ -\frac{1}{2}$	6 } 32
		2	d	+2 +1 0 −1 −2	$+\frac{1}{2}, \ -\frac{1}{2}$	10
		3	f	+3 +2 +1 0 −1 −2 −3	$+\frac{1}{2}, \ -\frac{1}{2}$	14

Table 2 gives the total possible combinations of the four quantum numbers. The application of these combinations has been a great aid in studying electrical, magnetic, and chemical properties of the elements.

The information in Table 2 serves as a basis for the periodic system. The periodic table is constructed in the following manner: The addition of an s electron to a nucleus forms the K shell, where $n = 1$, and this results in hydrogen. The addition of two s electrons results in helium, since another electron of opposite spin quantum can be added at the same s level. Additional electrons go into the L shell ($n = 2$). Adding a third electron to the nucleus gives lithium, with the third electron then going into the $2s$ subshell. A fourth electron will also go into the $2s$ subshell, forming beryllium. Electrons then will go into the $2p$ subshell, which can accept six; the group ends with neon. The M shell ($n = 3$) starts with sodium, which has one $3s$ electron, and ends with argon, which has two electrons in the $3s$ and six in the $3d$

Table 3. Shell Distribution of Electrons in the Elements(a)
(Neutral atoms in their ground states)

Atomic number	Symbol	Element	Atomic weight	K 1s	L 2s	L 2p	M 3s	M 3p	M 3d	N 4s	N 4p	N 4d	N 4f	O 5s	O 5p	O 5d	P 6s	P 6p	P 6d
1	H	Hydrogen	1.0080	1															
2	He	Helium	4.003	2															
3	Li	Lithium	6.940	2	1														
4	Be	Beryllium	9.013	2	2														
5	B	Boron	10.82	2	2	1													
6	C	Carbon	12.011	2	2	2													
7	N	Nitrogen	14.008	2	2	3													
8	O	Oxygen	16.000	2	2	4													
9	F	Fluorine	19.000	2	2	5													
10	Ne	Neon	20.183	2	2	6													
11	Na	Sodium	22.991	Ne core 10			1												
12	Mg	Magnesium	24.32	10			2												
13	Al	Aluminum	26.98				2	1											
14	Si	Silicon	28.09				2	2											
15	P	Phosphorus	30.975				2	3											
16	S	Sulfur	32.066				2	4											
17	Cl	Chlorine	35.457				2	5											
18	A	Argon	39.994	2	2	6	2	6											
19	K	Potassium	39.100	Argon core 18						1									
20	Ca	Calcium	40.08	18						2									
21	Sc	Scandium	44.96						1	2									
22	Ti	Titanium	47.90						2	2									
23	V	Vanadium	50.95						3	2									
24	Cr	Chromium	52.01						5	1									
25	Mn	Manganese	54.94						5	2									
26	Fe	Iron	55.85						6	2									
27	Co	Cobalt	58.94						7	2									
28	Ni	Nickel	58.71						8	2									

Shell distribution of electrons

Footnotes on next page

Table 3. Shell Distribution of Electrons in the Elements (Continued)

Atomic number	Symbol	Element	Atomic weight	K 1s	L 2s	L 2p	M 3s	M 3p	M 3d	N 4s	N 4p	N 4d	N 4f	O 5s	O 5p	O 5d	P 6s	P 6p	P 6d
29	Cu	Copper	63.54	2	2	6	2	6	10	1									
30	Zn	Zinc	65.38							2									
31	Ga	Gallium	69.72		Cu⁺ core 28					2	1								
32	Ge	Germanium	72.60							2	2								
33	As	Arsenic	74.91							2	3								
34	Se	Selenium	78.96							2	4								
35	Br	Bromine	79.916							2	5								
36	Kr	Krypton	83.8	2	2	6	2	6	10	2	6								
37	Rb	Rubidium	85.48											1					
38	Sr	Strontium	87.63											2					
39	Y	Yttrium	88.92			Krypton core 36						1		2					
40	Zr	Zirconium	91.22									2		2					
41	Cb	Columbium(b)	92.91									4		1					
42	Mo	Molybdenum	95.95									5		1					
43	Tc	Technetium	98									5		2					
44	Ru	Ruthenium	101.1									7		1					
45	Rh	Rhodium	102.91									8		1					
46	Pd	Palladium	106.7	2	2	6	2	6	10	2	6	10							
47	Ag	Silver	107.880											1					
48	Cd	Cadmium	112.41				Palladium core 46							2					
49	In	Indium	114.82											2	1				
50	Sn	Tin	118.70											2	2				
51	Sb	Antimony	121.76											2	3				
52	Te	Tellurium	127.61											2	4				
53	I	Iodine	126.91											2	5				

(a) Some uncertainty exists about the configurations of the rare earth and actinide elements. (b) Or niobium (Nb).

(Continued on the next page)

Table 3. Shell Distribution of Electrons in the Elements(a) (Continued)

Shell distribution of electrons

Atomic number	Symbol	Element	Atomic weight	K 1s	L 2s	L 2p	M 3s	M 3p	M 3d	N 4s	N 4p	N 4d	N 4f	O 5s	O 5p	O 5d	O 5f	P 6s	P 6p	P 6d	Q 7s
54	Xe	Xenon	131.3	2	2	6	2	6	10	2	6	10		2	6						
55	Cs	Cesium	132.91											2	6			1			
56	Ba	Barium	137.36															2			
57	La	Lanthanum	138.92													1		2			
58	Ce	Cerium	140.13										2					2			
59	Pr	Praseodymium	140.92										3					2			
60	Nd	Neodymium	144.27										4					2			
61	Pm	Promethium	145										5					2			
62	Sm	Samarium	150.35										6					2			
63	Eu	Europium	152.00										7					2			
64	Gd	Gadolinium	157.26										7			1		2			
65	Tb	Terbium	158.93										8			1		2			
66	Dy	Dysprosium	162.51										10					2			
67	Ho	Holmium	164.94										11					2			
68	Er	Erbium	167.27										12					2			
69	Tm	Thulium	168.94										13					2			
70	Yb	Ytterbium	173.04										14					2			
71	Lu	Lutetium	174.99	2	2	6	2	6	10	2	6	10	14	2	6	1		2			
72	Hf	Hafnium	178.58													2		2			
73	Ta	Tantalum	180.95													3		2			
74	W	Tungsten(c)	183.86													4		2			
75	Re	Rhenium	186.22													5		2			
76	Os	Osmium	190.2													6		2			
77	Ir	Iridium	192.2													9		2			
78	Pt	Platinum	195.09													9		1			

Xenon core 54 (applies to elements 55–71)

Lutetium+++ core 68 (applies to elements 72–78)

(c) Or wolfram.

Table 3. Shell Distribution of Electrons in the Elements (Continued)

Shell distribution of electrons

Atomic number	Symbol	Element	Atomic weight	K 1s	L 2s	L 2p	M 3s	M 3p	M 3d	N 4s	N 4p	N 4d	N 4f	O 5s	O 5p	O 5d	O 5f	P 6s	P 6p	P 6d	Q 7s
79	Au	Gold	197.0	2	2	6	2	6	10	2	6	10	14	2	6	10		1			
80	Hg	Mercury	200.61							← Gold core 78 →								2			
81	Tl	Thallium	204.39															2	1		
82	Pb	Lead	207.21															2	2		
83	Bi	Bismuth	209.00															2	3		
84	Po	Polonium	210															2	4		
85	At	Astatine	211															2	5		
86	Rn	Radon	222	2	2	6	2	6	10	2	6	10	14	2	6	10		2	6		
87	Fr	Francium	223							← Radon core 86 →											1
88	Ra	Radium	226.05																		2
89	Ac	Actinium	227																	1	2
90	Th	Thorium	232.05																	2	2
91	Pa	Protactinium	231.1														2			1	2
92	U	Uranium	238.07														3			1	2
93	Np	Neptunium	237														5				2
94	Pu	Plutonium	242														6				2
95	Am	Americium	243														7				2
96	Cm	Curium	247														7			1	2
97	Bk	Berkelium	247														8			1	2
98	Cf	Californium	251														9			1	2
99	E	Einsteinium	254														10			1	2
100	Fm	Fermium	253														11				2
101	Mv	Mendelevium	256														13				2
102	No	Nobelium	254														14				2
103	Lw	Lawrencium	257														14				2

(discovered 1961)

(a) Some uncertainty exists about the configurations of the rare earth and actinide elements.

subshells. Beginning with potassium, the $4s$ and $4p$ subshells become filled, and electrons are added until krypton is reached. It is of interest and practical significance to note that the $3d$ subshell fills after the $4s$ is established. In this manner, the periodic system of the elements is built up (Table 1). The rare gases are in effect key elements in the periodic table, for they represent completed electron shells. They are alike in having a completed group (helium has two, and neon, argon, krypton, xenon and radon have eight) in their outermost shells, and all are chemically inert.* The shell distribution of electrons, together with the atomic numbers and the atomic weights, is given in Table 3.

A convenient shorthand notation is used to write down the electronic constitution of an atom. The principal quantum number, n, has corresponding symbols of $K, L, M, N, \ldots$ which also identify the x-ray levels. Likewise, the orbital quantum number, l, has corresponding symbols of $s, p, d, f, \ldots$ With the use of integers, letters, and superscripts, the number of electrons can be indicated.

Thus, $1s^2$ signifies the K level for $n = 1$, the s state for $l = 0$, and the superscript indicates the number of electrons involved. The symbol $1s^2$ is for helium; those for iron would be $1s^2, 2s^2, 2p^6, 3s^2, 3p^6, 3d^6, 4s^2$.

The number of electrons in the outermost shell determines the valence and many chemical properties. Valence is defined as the ability of atoms to unite with one or more other atoms. Some atoms are either electron donors or electron acceptors. Only the inert gases, such as helium and argon, have no power of chemical combination, because the stability of the electronic groups is so great that it cannot be increased by interaction of other atoms. The alkali metals, lithium, sodium and potassium, are alike in having one electron in the outermost shell. Beryllium, magnesium and calcium have two electrons in the outermost shell. Elements like chlorine and fluorine have seven electrons in the outermost shell. Atoms of one element will combine with atoms of another element, because in so doing they rearrange their electrons in a more stable configuration. For example, when a sodium atom comes near a chlorine atom, the electron of the metal is strongly attracted to the halogen atom and takes up a new orbit in which

---

* The preparation of xenon compounds (xenon tetrafluoride and difluoride, and xenon-platinum hexafluoride) has been reported. The explanation for this reaction phenomenon is obscure.

Table 4. Illustration of Valency

	O	F	Ne	Na	Mg	Al
			—Element—			
Atomic number..	8	9	10	11	12	13
Ion.............	O^{--}	F^-	Ne^0	Na^+	Mg^{++}	Al^{+++}
Electrons in ion..	10	10	10	10	10	10

it spends most of the time about the halogen. This type of chemical bond is very strong. When nonmetals combine with metals, the nonmetals borrow electrons from the metals; this tends to fill the vacant levels of the nonmetals. As soon as the incompleted shells of the nonmetals are filled, they become saturated, in the sense that the pattern of filled orbits resembles those of the rare gases.

Valence is illustrated for several elements in Table 4.

The special magnetic characteristics of some elements are due to the presence of incomplete inner shells of electrons. The elements having partly filled *d* shells are usually ferromagnetic and include the useful metals, iron, nickel and cobalt.

The transition elements have one or two electrons in the outermost (valency) group of the isolated atom, and no stable arrangement (not 2, 8 or 18, but a number between 8 and 18) in the inner group. A group of this size does not hold electrons firmly, and one or two of them can be detached by chemical action. For example, iron has the electron grouping 2, 8, 14, 2. It can lose its two outermost electrons in the usual way to form the bivalent cation (ferrous) Fe^{++} (2, 8, 14). However, by a more energetic treatment, a third electron can be detached from this ferrous ion, leaving the trivalent ferric cation Fe^{+++} (2, 8, 13). In this particular element, there are just these two valencies. In other metals such as manganese (2, 18, 13, 2), the stripping of electrons can occur to such an extent that there are valencies of 2, 3, 4, 5, 6, and 7, until the inert core of argon is reached. In the transitional elements, valencies vary by single units.

The Solid State

The solid state comprises crystalline and amorphous substances. Crystalline materials, such as rocks, minerals and ice, have well-formed symmetrical arrangements of atoms. Metals, either as elements or alloys, are also crystalline, although this is not normally evident. Amorphous substances, such as glasses, fused quartz, and metallurgical slags, are without a regular internal structure, and can be regarded as supercooled liquids.

Solid-state physics is largely the study of crystals and their properties; considerable knowledge, however, is being developed on the amorphous state—for example, the physics of glass. The amorphous state notwithstanding, the following discussion will be restricted to metals, their constitution, and their electrical and magnetic properties.

The analysis of the crystal structure involves determination of the type of symmetry, calculation of the distances in the lattice structure, and determination of the number of atoms in a unit cell. The discovery by Friedrich, Knipping and Laue (1) that crystals will diffract x-rays put earlier crystallographic theories on a firm basis. Using x-ray techniques, the Braggs (father and son) (2) laid the foundation for the physics of the solid state.

A space lattice is thought of as a three-dimensional latticework of imaginary lines connecting the atoms. The unit cell is the

Table 5. The Seven Crystal Systems

System	Crystallographic elements
1 Cubic (or isometric or regular)	Three axes at right angles — all equal
2 Tetragonal	Three axes at right angles — two equal
3 Hexagonal	Three axes coplanar at 60° — these three equal. Fourth axis at right angles to the others.
4 Orthorhombic (or rhombic)	Three axes at right angles — all unequal
5 Monoclinic	Three axes, one pair not at right angles — all unequal
6 Triclinic (or anorthic)	Three axes not at right angles — all unequal
7 Rhombohedral (or trigonal)	Three axes equally inclined, not all at right angles — all equal

smallest prism that possesses the characteristic symmetry of the crystal. Every unit cell in a space lattice is identical in shape and orientation with every other.

All crystalline substances can be grouped into seven crystal systems, each possessing certain relations as to equality of angles and lengths of the coordinate axes (Table 5). From these seven systems there are only 14 space lattices (Fig. 1). A total of 230 different groups can be derived from these 14 space lattices.

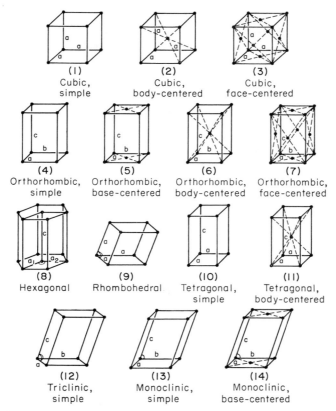

Fig. 1. Unit cells of the 14 space lattices. A total of 230 different standard groups can be derived from these 14 space lattices. Most of the metals crystallize in one or more of the common structures: body-centered cubic, face-centered cubic, hexagonal close-packed. (After Barrett)

In order to use crystallographic information, it is necessary to have a method for describing the faces or planes of a crystal, as well as the directions in the crystal or space lattice. Such knowledge is of great importance in the description of preferred orientations in grain-oriented magnetic materials, particularly the silicon steels.

The Miller indices are used universally as a basis for a system of notation for planes and faces of a crystal. The indices are based on the reciprocals of intercepts of a plane on the three crystal axes, x, y, and z, which are the edges of a unit cell.* The intercepts are measured in unit distances along the three axes. By way of example, if a plane intersects the x-axis at a positive unit distance a and is parallel to the y and z axes (intersection at infinity), the intercepts are, 1, ∞, ∞; the reciprocals become 1/1, $1/\infty$, $1/\infty$, and the Miller indices are (100). A plane cutting all three axes at unit distances a, b and c has intercepts 1, 1, 1, similar reciprocals, and hence Miller indices of (111). If a plane cuts an axis on the negative side of the origin, the index will be negative and is indicated by placing a minus sign over the index, ($\bar{1}$11). A specific plane is enclosed by parentheses (100), and a family of similar planes that are equivalent in the crystal is indicated by brackets {100}.

The indices of a direction are not reciprocals. They can be described as the lattice coordinates of a point on a line in the given direction through the origin. Another way of considering indices of direction is to imagine that a point at the origin of coordinates must move in a certain direction by means of a motion parallel to the three axes, x, y and z. This is accomplished by moving along the x-axis a distance u times the unit distance a, along the y-axis a distance v times the unit distance b, and along the z-axis a distance w times the unit distance c. If u, v and w are the smallest integers that will give the motion, they are the indices of direction. An index of direction is written with square brackets [111], and a family of equivalent directions with carets <111>. By way of example, the [111] direction is obtained by moving a point along the x-axis a unit distance a, parallel to the y-axis a unit distance b, and parallel to the z-axis a unit distance of c. The indices of this final point are the indices of direction. The x-axis has indices of [100], the y-axis [010], and the z-axis [001].

Even though the cubic structure is the simplest of the crystal systems, it has three modifications: simple cubic, body-centered cubic, and face-centered cubic. The cubic system is the only one

* Miller indices of a plane are established in the following manner:
  1 Find the intercepts on the x, y and z axes in multiples or fractions of the unit distances on each axis
  2 Take reciprocals of these numbers
  3 Reduce to the three smallest integers having the same ratio
  4 Enclose in parentheses to indicate planes, (hkl)

in which each direction is perpendicular to a plane of the same indices.

Most metals crystallize in one or more of the three common structures: body-centered cubic (bcc), face-centered cubic (fcc), and close-packed hexagonal (cph). These common structures have high coordination in that each atom is surrounded by 12 or 8 near neighbors, and hence there is a close packing of atoms.

As atoms approach each other in the assembly of a metallic crystal, the inner electrons are essentially unaffected, because they are under the predominant influence of the nucleus. However, the condition of the valence electrons is very significantly altered. It is the valence electrons that produce the binding forces characteristic of the metallic crystal. Also, valence electrons are responsible for electrical conductivity. A lattice of ions, it is currently believed, is held together by valence electrons that move freely through the structure and pull the ions together, until their electron clouds overlap and start to repel each other.

The magnetic properties of the free atom, as well as aggregates of them (as in a lattice), arise from the angular momentum of the electron as it moves in an orbit and as it spins on its own axis.* The interactions between spinning electrons and between spin and orbital motions, explainable only by quantum mechanics, are responsible for magnetic properties of matter.

Atoms in a crystal are held together by four different types of forces or bonds: ionic, covalent or homopolar, metallic, and Van der Waals' (4). Crystals with ionic, covalent, and Van der Waals' bonds are essentially nonconductors of electricity, because the electrons are locked into certain quantum states. Only with the metallic bond, where there are mobile electrons, is there electrical conductivity. The metallic bond is one in which the number of quantum states is greater than the number of electrons to fill them — a situation that results in electronic conduction.

In ionic bonds, electrons have moved from one type of atom to another. Ions are thus formed, and the attraction between the ions is electrostatic in nature. The classical example of sodium chloride is useful here. Sodium chloride was the first solid whose structure was analyzed crystallographically, and the first whose binding energy was accounted for on physical principles (5).

---

* Admittedly, electrical and magnetic phenomena exist in gaseous and liquid metals, but consideration of these is perhaps best reserved for electron physics and physical chemistry, respectively.

The metallic bond is formed by the interaction of the negative electron gas of the valence electrons and the positive ions. The valence electrons are able to move in the metal, but they are subject to the influence of the periodic electrostatic field that is formed by the positive metal ions on lattice points.

In covalent or homopolar bonds, the linking force is built up by the sharing of electrons; each atom contributes one electron to the bond. A bond between two atoms requires the sharing of two electrons. Double or even triple bonds between two atoms exist. This type of bond is common in organic chemistry. Some inorganic crystals with this type of bond are diamond, silicon, germanium, and gray tin. The stability of the covalent bond tends to diminish with increasing atomic number. An explanation of this type of bond is one of the successes of quantum mechanics.

Van der Waals' force, also known as polarization force, is due to the interaction of the electrons of an atom at comparatively great distances. In the solid and liquid states, diatomic H_2, O_2, N_2 molecules are held together by Van der Waals' force.

A metal can be either an element or an alloy. For many years, it has been customary to define a metal as a material having good thermal and electrical conductivity, and comparatively good mechanical properties, ductility, and luster. It is no longer necessary to define a metal in terms of its properties, for now a metal can be defined in terms of the nature of its bonds. (A semimetal has poor electrical conductivity, because of the covalent nature of the bonds. Bismuth and antimony are typical semimetals.)

The so-called ordinary metals possess metallic bonds, whereas the nonmetals possess covalent bonds. The covalent binding joins atoms in layers. This results in brittleness and a tendency toward easy cleavage. In metals, although there is a tendency to share electrons, there is an insufficient number of them to go around. There are several consequences of this situation: For one thing, there are no directional properties associated with the bonds as in covalent bindings; also, because the valence bonds are shared among several pairs of atoms, they are not as strong as real homopolar valences. The fewer electrons an atom has to share with its neighbors, the weaker are its bonds. The alkali metals, for example, with only one electron outside closed shells, are the weakest metals mechanically and have low melting points. Elements such as iron, platinum, molybdenum, and tungsten have the strongest bonds. Electrons holding the metals together are not localized between any atoms, but are free to move around in the lattice. This freedom of motion of the electrons results in good electrical conductivity, perhaps the most distinguishing feature of metals.

The interatomic distances in the lattice are greatest for the alkali elements, smaller for the alkaline earths, decrease somewhat further with a few more elements, and then remain essentially constant. This situation is due to the fact that the alkali elements, having the fewest electrons for sharing, are the most loosely bound. One other consideration is important: There is a natural increase in ion size with higher atomic numbers, say from lithium at 3.03 A to cerium at 5.25 A. The tendency is less marked for the heavier elements, because the ions are more closely bound. Within each group of elements in the periodic table, the heavier ions tend to be smaller than lighter ions, because the higher positive charge on the heavier nuclei attracts the surrounding electron shells more strongly. The constancy of the interatomic distance appears to hold even as the crystal structures change.

Rather complicated crystal structures exist at the end of the periods in the periodic table. These structures (for example, germanium and tin) appear to have bonds more of the covalent type than of the metallic type. In the series consisting of diamond, silicon, germanium and tin, there is a change from the stronger covalent bonds of the diamond to the metallic, mechanically weaker tin. Crystals of arsenic, antimony, and bismuth cleave easily, because of their layered structures, the result of covalent binding, so that they are really very brittle. In these materials, electrical conductivity is fairly good in directions parallel to the layers, but is very poor in the direction normal to the layers. Selenium and tellurium have structures in which the ions form chains, each ion being joined to its two neighbors; the chains form helices, similar to a clock spring. Electrical conductivity is good in the direction of the chain, but poor perpendicular to it.

Crystal Structures

Elements. In the periodic table, elements of the same group tend to have similar structures; the alkali metals, lithium, sodium, potassium, cesium, and rubidium, are body-centered cubic; beryllium, magnesium, zinc, and cadmium are close-packed hexagonal; and copper, silver, and gold are face-centered cubic. The face-centered cubic and the close-packed hexagonal crystals contain atoms in closest packing.

Many elements exhibit polymorphism: That is, they assume different crystallographic structures when temperature or pressure is varied, or when certain thermal and mechanical treatments are used. The transformation is reversible and is generally accompanied by hysteresis effects. Pure iron up to 910 C (1670 F) is body-centered cubic; from 910 to 1400 C (2550 F), it is face-centered cubic; above 1400 C, it is again body-centered cubic. Manganese has three transformations — four crystallographic forms: alpha to beta at 727 C (1340 F), beta to gamma at 1095 C (2000 F), and gamma to delta at 1133 C (2071 F). Tin has a metallic gray tetragonal beta structure at ambient temperatures, but will form the nonmetallic gray cubic alpha form at 13 C (56 F). This reaction is very sluggish, but can be accelerated by neutron irradiation. Other elements displaying polymorphism are cobalt, zirconium, titanium, thallium, lithium, lanthanum, scandium, and uranium. Metallic selenium can occur in the crystalline, as well as the vitreous or amorphous form. Two monoclinic and two hexagonal forms of selenium are known.

Solid Solutions. The lattices of many elements can accommodate atoms of other elements in two different situations without losing the identity of the solvent atom. In the system copper-gold, gold can be added to copper without changing the crystal structure of copper; gold atoms substitute for copper on the fcc lattice points. This is the substitutional solid solution. If the two elements (copper and gold) can be substituted in all proportions, they are said to form a continuous series of solid solutions.

In the iron-carbon system, carbon can dissolve in either the alpha (bcc) form, 0.02% max at 725 C (1335 F), or in the gamma (fcc) form, 2% max at 1130 C (2065 F). The solid solution here is interstitial. In this kind of solution, atoms of small radii can be accommodated within the interstices of the solvent lattice. The substitutional solid solution can be distinguished from the interstitial type by density comparisons (6).

The atomic size factor and the type of crystal structure of the alloying elements are the most important considerations in determining the structure of an alloy. Lesser factors are the effects of valence, electrochemical factors, and electron-atom ratios (7, 8).

A continuous series of solid solutions is found only among atoms of like crystal structure and only when the atoms are not too different in size. For certain systems, it is possible to say that if the atomic diameters of two metals differ more than about 15%, the primary solid solution is restricted. If the size factor is favorable — less than 15% — wide ranges of solid solutions are formed. Another factor influences solid solutions even if the size factor is favorable: If two metals differ widely in electrochemical characteristics — if one is more electropositive than the other — a tendency may exist to form intermediate phases or intermetallic compounds.

The electronegative valency, or the chemical-affinity effect,* also affects solubility. The more electronegative the solute element and the more electropositive the solvent, and the reverse, the greater is the tendency to form intermetallic compounds and the greater is the tendency to restrict solid solubility. In the periodic table (Table 1), the electronegativity of the elements increases from left to right in any period, and from bottom to top in any group. Sulfur, selenium, and tellurium of group VIb form the sulfides, selenides, and tellurides with electropositive elements and limited solid solutions of these elements in more normal metals. In group Vb (P, As, Sb, Bi), the elements have a somewhat less electronegative nature, but the alloy behavior is similar to group VIb elements.

The relative-valency effect, which also governs solubility, occurs when a metal of lower valency tends to dissolve a metal of higher valency more readily than *vice versa*. For instance, in the magnesium-gold system, magnesium (valence 2) dissolves less than 0.2 at. % Au (valence 1), but gold dissolves 20 to 30 at. % Mg.

A solid solution is usually considered as random or disordered. However, it is likely that these solutions for most systems show short-range order — an order that is not maintained over long atomic distances. Long-range order, where the regular arrangement of the solute atoms exists over distances that are large in comparison with the unit cell, leads to superlattice formation.

An interstitial solid solution is expected only when one atom is very much smaller than the other. Solution of carbon, nitrogen,

---

* C. S. Barrett (3) prefers to use the term "chemical-affinity effect" to emphasize the role of affinity between unlike atoms, and, at the same time, avoid confusion with the relative-valency effect.

boron, and hydrogen in iron results in interstitial solid solutions. The radii of atoms forming solid solutions are all under 1.0 A:

$$
\begin{array}{ll}
\text{Hydrogen} \ldots & 0.46 \text{ A} \\
\text{Boron} \ldots & 0.97 \text{ A} \\
\text{Carbon} \ldots & 0.77 \text{ A} \\
\text{Nitrogen} \ldots & 0.71 \text{ A}
\end{array}
$$

When these atoms dissolve interstitially, there is always an expansion of the lattice.

The nature of the interstitial solid solution of carbon in iron apparently is rather complex in light of the following experiment: When heavy currents (dc) are passed through wires or rods of steel at high temperature (in the austenitic condition), there is a migration of carbon (9) toward the cathode (negative terminal). An examination of the data suggests that carbon dissolved in austenite exists in the form of C^{4+} ions. This view has been criticized by Hume-Rothery (10), and it appears more likely that carbon atoms are bound by forces similar to covalent linkages (11).

Superlattice Formation (6, 12). In some systems, the high-temperature solid solution shows a random structure (or more probably short-range order), but when the material is slowly cooled or is annealed at a lower temperature, the structure undergoes an atomic rearrangement without any change in crystal structure and with little or no deformation. This ordered structure, due to long-range ordering, is called a superlattice. The gold-copper system is a classical one for showing ordering in the region of 25 (Cu_3Au) or 50 (CuAu) at. % Au. Critical temperatures are those above which the alloy is disordered and below which it is ordered; the ordering temperature for Cu_3Au is 400 C (750 F).

In systems forming superlattices, the size factor is on the borderline of the favorable zone — neither too favorable nor too unfavorable. Superlattices form at compositions at or close to the formulas AB or AB_3.

Intermediate Phases. Intermediate compounds in general are characterized by brittleness, high hardness, high electrical resistance, and complex atomic arrangements. There are, of course, exceptions: In the system titanium-nickel, the phase TiNi is reasonably ductile.

Although the term "compound" is inappropriate in discussing alloy structure, intermediate phases can be intermetallic compounds only if they have a narrow range of homogeneity, approximate stoichiometry, and if atoms of one specie occupy identical lattice sites. Intermediate phases may also be solid solutions. This type of solid solution may have either restricted or wide ranges of homogeneity. Intermediate phases, therefore, can cover the range from solid solution to compounds, which can have ionic, covalent (homopolar), and metallic binding. Ionic bonds occur where the electrochemical factor is high (Mg_3Sb_2, Mg_2Si, Mg_2Sn, Cu_2Se, Cu_2S, Sn_2Pt, MnTe, and PbSe). Covalency compounds are formed by shared electrons, and hence normal valency holds for them (BeS, alpha CdS, alpha ZnS, HgS, InSb, AlAs, HgSe, and GaSb). Metallic binding is evident in phases such as FeS, NiS, FeSn, CoSb, MnAs, NiAs, NiBi, and MnBi. In addition, wide homogeneity ranges exist.

In alloy systems, the intermediate phases do not obey the normal valencies of the elements. This is because most phases have metallic binding. The structure of an intermediate phase depends not only on the nature of the individual atoms, but also on the number of valency electrons and atoms. Intermetallic phases of this type are sometimes referred to as electron compounds.

Hume-Rothery (13) has given considerable attention to the fundamental principles for electron compound formation. Electron-atom ratios tend to be characteristic constants for structurally analogous phases. For instance, in the beta-brass structure, the bcc phase will have an electron-to-atom ratio of 3:2; in gamma brass, the cubic complex phase will have a ratio of 21:13; and in epsilon brass, the cph structure will have a ratio of 7:4.

Interstitial compounds, such as hydrides, carbides, borides, and nitrides, are a group consisting of a metallic element and a small nonmetallic element. Hydrogen, boron, carbon, nitrogen, and sometimes oxygen, phosphorus, and sulfur can be accommodated in the interstices of the metal lattice; the metallic properties of these compounds are frequently preserved, indicating that they are held together by metallic bonds. Tendencies toward covalent and even ionic bonding among certain atoms are possible.

Hagg (14) has systematized the structures of the interstitial compounds. If the ratio of the relative size of the transition (R_M) metal and metalloid atoms (R_X) is considered, an R_X/R_M ratio of less than 0.59 is found in simple crystal structures, and a ratio greater than 0.59 is found in complex crystal structures. Ratios of 0.59 are lattices of fcc, cph, or sometimes bcc. Some interstitial compounds of formula MX (fcc) are ZrN, CrN, TiN, ZrC, TiC, VC, ZrH, and TiH. Compounds M_2X (cph) are Fe_2N, Cr_2N, W_2C, Ta_2C, and Ti_2H. When the R_X/R_M ratio is more than 0.59, the more complex compounds are obtained: carbides of chromium, manganese, iron, cobalt and nickel, and borides of iron.

Imperfections in Crystals (15, 16)

Many properties of crystals cannot be explained by the periodicity associated with the ideal crystal. Important properties associated with imperfections in the lattice are electrical conductivity, magnetism, and mechanical strength. Crystalline materials contain many flaws and irregularities; indeed, the ideal crystal is very rare. Some of these imperfections * according to Haven (17) are as follows:

1 Vacancies are empty lattice sites from which an atom is missing.
2 Dislocations ** are fundamental lattice defects. A simple form of dislocation can be considered as a lattice plane forced hypothetically between existing lattice planes. Near the edge of the interposed lattice plane, the crystal is severely deformed. If interstitial atoms are present, they tend to segregate preferentially into such regions.
3 Grain boundaries represent the surfaces of the grains composing crystalline solids. At these boundaries, there is an abrupt change in crystal orientation.
4 Foreign atoms, substitutional or interstitial, are also to be considered as lattice imperfections.

Darwin (18) was one of the first to point out that actual crystals diffract x-rays as if they were composed of small imperfect blocks 10^{-4} to 10^{-6} cm on edge. These blocks varied within a degree or so in orientation with respect to their neighbors. Burger (19) has described a lineage (mosaic) imperfection structure that results from the dendritic and branching growth of the solidifying crystals.

In some metals, notably aluminum, that have been slightly deformed and then annealed, dislocations migrate together into surfaces that become subgrain boundaries. This subdivision of a grain is referred to as "polygonization."

---

* Haven also considers electron holes, color centers, excitons, phonons, and even thermal agitation as forms of lattice imperfections.
** Barrett (reference 3, p. 393) devotes an excellent chapter to dislocation theory.

Conduction of Electricity and the Electron Theory of Metals

Any theory of electrical resistivity or conductivity must explain the following experimental observations:

1 According to Ohm's law, the current density in the steady state is proportional to the field strength (voltage).
2 The specific resistivity of metals at room temperature is about 10^{-5} ohm-cm.
3 Above the Debye characteristic temperature,* the resistivity of metals increases linearly with temperature.
4 At low temperatures, but above about 20 K, the resistivity of many metals is proportional to T^5. At liquid-helium temperatures, some metals exhibit a minimum in the resistivity-versus-temperature curve.
5 For most metals, the resistivity decreases with increasing pressure.
6 The resistivity of a metal containing small amounts of impurities varies with temperature in the following manner (Matthiessen's rule):

$$\rho = \rho_0 + \rho(T) \tag{1}$$

where ρ_0 is a constant that increases with impurity content and $\rho(T)$ is the temperature-dependent part.
7 The resistivity of alloys that exhibit order-disorder transitions shows pronounced minimums corresponding to ordered phases.
8 Above the Debye characteristic temperature, the ratio of thermal to electrical conductivity is proportional to temperature, the constant of proportionality being approximately the same for all metals (Wiedemann-Franz law).
9 A number of metals exhibit the phenomenon of superconductivity (resistivity disappears near absolute zero). Examples are magnesium, zinc, mercury, aluminum, cadmium and lead, and many intermetallic compounds.

Even though modern theory is not capable of explaining all the enumerated and other aspects of conduction in solid metals, let alone in gases and liquids, it does give an insight into some of the important features of conduction in the solid state. The story, certainly oversimplified, begins with the discovery of the electron.

---

* The Debye characteristic temperature is a parameter having the dimensions of temperature that appears in Debye's theory of specific heat. The characteristic temperature, Θ, is defined as follows:

$$\Theta = h\nu/k \tag{2}$$

where ν is the maximum frequency of thermal vibrations of the lattice, h is Planck's constant, and k is Boltzmann's constant.

Associated with this scientific saga are the names of W. Crookes, H. A. Lorentz, A. Schuster, P. E. A. Lenard, W. Wien, H. R. Hertz and M. Faraday. Their researches, all before the advent of the twentieth century, culminated in the work of Thomson (20). He was able to show that the mysterious cathode-ray particles were negatively charged, were much lighter than atoms of any element (about 1/2000 of the weight of the hydrogen atom), and could be produced from many kinds of matter. Thomson had discovered the electron; he was shortly to appreciate that the cathode-ray particles were the electrons of the existing electron theories.

The magnificent researches of Millikan (21) showed that the charge on the electron is constant, confirming the suspicion that the electron was an ultimate fundamental particle.

The usual model employed in visualizing conduction in metals assumes that, as electrons move through the crystal lattice under the influence of an applied voltage, they will collide with ions in the lattice. This impedance to electron flow is the electrical resistance of the material. It is, of course, common knowledge that the resistance increases with temperature. The model explains the temperature effect on this basis: The ions on the lattice points oscillate over wider distances as the temperature increases and thereby interfere more strongly with the motion of the electron. The earliest attempts to explain these observations were those of Drude (22) and Lorentz (23).

Drude and Lorentz assumed that the outer electrons of an atom formed an "electron gas" that moved through a lattice of positively charged ions. The theory had considerable success in accounting for electrical conductivity of metals and explaining the Wiedemann-Franz law, but it failed to account for the difference between a conductor and an insulator.

Tolman and Stewart (24) were able to prove experimentally (1917) that the conduction of electricity in metals was due to electron motion.

Sommerfeld (25), applying quantum mechanics, postulated that the valency electrons belonged to the entire crystal structure and that the electrons occupied well-defined energy states when a solid formed. The lower energy levels (those for closed electron shells) are not affected or are only slightly affected by the lattice formation. The Sommerfeld model was successful in explaining the specific heats of metals. Sommerfeld's theory, however, still failed to explain the difference between conductors and nonconductors, the origin of magnetic properties, or the relation of crystal structures of metals and the valence electrons.

The original Drude theory of conduction postulated a collision mechanism, in which the motion of the electron, under the influence of an applied field, was destroyed. Otherwise, the electron could accelerate indefinitely in the presence of the field. In this classical prequantum Drude theory, the conductivity of metals depended on three quantities: The number of free electrons per unit volume of metal, N, their average velocity, v, and their mean free path, l. It follows, then, that an electron of charge e and a mass m in the presence of a field X will have a mean velocity v given by the following relation:

$$v = \frac{eX\tau}{2m} = \frac{eX}{2m}\left(\frac{l}{v}\right) \tag{3}$$

where τ is mean time.

If, then, N electrons per unit volume are present, the current density (amount of electricity moving over a unit area in unit time) is as follows:

$$Nev = \frac{Ne^2Xl}{2mv} \tag{4}$$

The electrical conductivity, σ, is as follows:

$$\sigma = \frac{Nev}{X} = \frac{Ne^2l}{2mv} \tag{5}$$

The analysis gives results of the right order of magnitude for simple metals at normal temperatures. However, it does not account for the effect of temperature, the wide variation of conductivity among metals and alloys, nor the effect of impurities, particularly for those of the semiconductor variety. Furthermore, the analysis offers no clue to the enormous gap between insulators and metals. A similar relationship is derived from quantum mechanical considerations. However, the treatment gives different values of N, v, and l.

Current theories assume that scattering of electrons is isotropic. Semiempirical calculations show that the mean free path of the electrons is of the order of several hundred angstroms. Before the development of the band theory, this large mean free path presented a great difficulty: Electrons were assumed to bounce around in the spaces between ionic cores. Such a model led to mean free paths of a few angstroms, and difficulties were also encountered in explaining the effect of temperature and pressure, and the influence of impurities.

It is now thought that the electron, due to its wave nature,* can pass through a perfect crystal without suffering any resistance. The wave vector of an electron moving in a perfect periodic potential (such as represented by a lattice) remains unchanged in the absence of an external electric field. It follows that, if all nuclei were at rest, the mean free path for electron scattering would be infinite. Hence, the actual course of resistivity must be sought in deviations from periodicity of the potential in which the electrons move.

Deviations from periodicity of the potential causing resistivity may be the result of: (a) lattice vibrations; (b) lattice defects (vacancies, dislocations); (c) foreign impurity atoms; and (d) grain boundaries and substructures.

The modern theory of conduction in solids will be outlined here. In monovalent metals, each atom contributes just one electron to the total number of free electrons, so that N will be equal to the number of atoms per unit volume.

From classical physics, which treated electrons as a perfect gas, the mean velocity, v, of the electrons is 1.2×10^7 cm per sec at room temperature; this comes from the mean kinetic energy which is $3kT/2$ for a perfect gas. Sommerfeld (25) concluded that the mean velocity of the electrons has a considerably larger value than that obtained from classical physics. His conclusions are based on the following considerations: The velocity of the electron is related to its de Broglie wave length, λ, by the formula:

$$\lambda = \frac{h}{mv} \tag{6}$$

For an electron confined within a metal of length L, the associated de Broglie wave must have the form of a standing wave. The wave length must have one of the discrete values of the following form:

$$\lambda = \frac{2L}{n} \tag{7}$$

where n is an integer. With appropriate substitutions, the energy

---

* It is necessary to keep in mind that the older concept of the electron as a mere electrical particle has given way to the recognition that the electron has wave characteristics: a frequency and a wave length.

of the electron may then be written as in equation (8) below:

$$E = \frac{1}{2}mv^2 = \frac{n^2h^2}{8mL} \tag{8}$$

For values of L of 1 cm, the values of energy will be so close to each other (as necessary for quantization of energy) as to be practically indistinguishable from a continuous series of values (consequence from classical consideration). However, quantization of energy is required, mainly from consideration of the Pauli exclusion principle.* At absolute zero, all electrons will be in states of as low energy as possible. From equation (7), only two electrons will have the lowest energy corresponding to a wave

Table 6. Effect of Temperature on Conductivity and
Mean Free Path in Silver

Temperature, K	Conductivity, mhos per cm $\times 10^{-5}$	Mean free path, l, cm $\times 10^{-4}$
4.2	$(960)^3$?	(163)
76	36	6
273	6.8	1.14

length of $2L$. Then if the total number of electrons is N, the electrons will have all wave lengths from $2L$ to a minimum of $4L/N$. With one electron per atom, this is equal to four times the interatomic distance a. Thus, the velocities have all values from virtually zero to $h/4ma$. If $a = 2 \times 10^{-8}$ cm, the velocity corresponds to 9×10^8 cm per sec.

That the conduction electrons have a series of energies lying in a range of several electron-volts is proved by observations of soft x-ray emission bands. Because the spread of energies, indicated by x-ray quantum being emitted through one of the electrons making a transition to the K or L-level, an emission band instead of an emission line is observed.

From the observed conductivity of silver and the use of N and v established as shown, substitution in equation (3) gives the mean free path of the electron. The mean free paths are very long, far greater than the interatomic distances. Such long paths could not be explained by classical physics, but are readily rationalized by wave mechanics. Table 6 gives some estimates of the free path of the electrons in silver.

* No more than two electrons can be in any one quantized state.

In the quantum model, electrons are assumed to be moving in a periodic field having the period of the lattice. To calculate the distance an electron will move without being scattered, we must apply the methods of wave mechanics and picture a plane de Broglie wave moving through the lattice with a wave length somewhat greater than the interatomic distance. Each positive ion scatters a wavelet, but, because of the periodicity of the structure, these wavelets build up a new plane wave front, and there is no resultant scattering of the wave. The important fact then is that, in a perfectly crystalline metal in which the ions are at rest in their positions of equilibrium, there is no scattering of the electrons, and hence there is no resistance to the electrons whatsoever.

Resistance in a pure metal arises from the fact that, at any finite temperature, the ions are not at rest in their positions of equilibrium, but are vibrating thermally around them. The period of the atomic vibrations is about 10^{-12} sec and is large in comparison to the period of de Broglie waves, which is of the order of 10^{-16} sec. Incoherent scattering of the electrons will take place because of the vibrations. The scattering, and hence the resistance, will increase as the vibration of the ions increases as the temperature is raised.

This model will not explain superconductivity. Actually, there is yet no satisfactory quantum theory of superconductivity. Theories exist, but all are too controversial, and hence they do not enjoy wide acceptance.

Band Theory of Solids (26). The free-electron theory of metals gives a good insight into some properties, but for others it is quite uninstructive. For example, it does not distinguish between excellent conductors, fair conductors, semiconductors and insulators. The basic assumption of the free-electron theory is that the outer electrons can be stripped from the atoms, and that these electrons can be poured, figuratively, into the remaining lattice of ions. The actual situation is not as simple as this. Differences in conductivity are explicable only when the interaction of electrons with the periodic field of the lattice is considered. The band theory helped to explain the wide range in electrical resistivity found in different materials (from 10^{-8} ohm-cm for pure metals at low temperatures to 10^{22} ohm-cm for a well-dried insulator).

The origin of the bands can be explained as follows: Atoms in a gas possess a set of discrete electron energy levels that are characteristic of the free atom. When these atoms are brought close together, as in a crystalline solid, the presence of neighboring atoms on the lattice affects the behavior of the electrons, and their energy levels are no longer unique. Interactions of the electrons give rise to bands of energy levels. A band will arise from a single energy level in the free atom. Figure 2 shows the development of energy levels in sodium as the isolated atoms form a crystalline solid.

Because the crystalline solids are usually used at ambient temperatures and at atmospheric pressure, the average lattice spac-

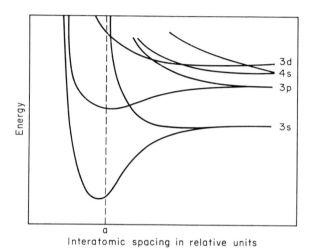

Interatomic spacing in relative units

Fig. 2. Behavior of the atomic levels of sodium as the atoms are brought together to form a crystalline solid. The vertical dashed line gives the lattice spacing of solid sodium metal. (After Slater)

ing *a* remains reasonably constant. At this spacing, there will be a particular configuration of bands for insulators, intrinsic (pure) semiconductors, and metals; this situation is shown diagrammatically in Fig. 3. The ordinate represents electron energy.

The valence and conduction bands may remain separated or they may overlap. When the bands are separated, a gap that is empty of allowed energy levels (forbidden to electrons except under unusual conditions) occurs. This gap is called the forbidden gap, and its width determines whether or not a particular material is a conductor, semiconductor, or insulator. The upper conduction band can be empty or partially filled, and the valence band can be partially or completely filled. It is the conduction and valence bands and the forbidden energy band that are of interest

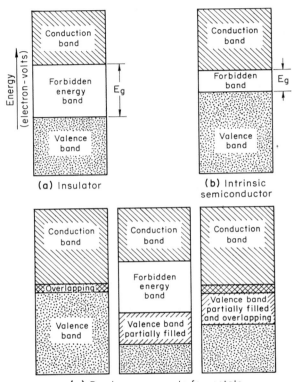

(c) Band arrangements for metals

(a) In an insulator, the valence band is completely filled with electrons; conduction of electricity by electrons is impossible. An energy gap of several electron-volts exists between valence and conduction bands.

(b) In an intrinsic semiconductor, the energy gap is smaller than in an insulator.

(c) In a metal, three situations can exist: Conduction of electricity can occur when the valence band overlaps the conduction band; when the valence band is partially filled, even though this is a forbidden band; and when the valence band is partially filled, but still overlaps the conduction band.

Fig. 3. *Energy level diagrams for insulators, intrinsic semiconductors, and metals*

in electrical conduction. Bands of filled electronic shells closer to the nucleus do not normally contribute to conduction.

Conduction in metals can occur in several ways (Fig. 3,c). It can occur when the valence band is partially full; it can occur when bands overlap. In doped semiconductors, conduction occurs because impurities create extra levels between the valence and conduction bands.

In a metal where the valence band is only partially full, the conduction is by electron motion in valence-band levels. Such substances exhibit low electrical resistivity and would be perfect conductors were it not for the imperfections in the periodicity of the lattice induced by thermal forces. If an atom contributes one valence electron to the band (for example, copper, silver, gold and the alkali metals), the band will be half full * and the solid will possess the characteristic properties of a metal.

If each atom contributes two valence electrons, the band will be exactly full, provided that no other bands overlap it in energy. If there are no overlapping bands, the band will not contribute to electrical conductivity. If all states in the band are full, an applied electric field cannot cause the electrons in the band to change their states, and, therefore, they cannot be accelerated.

The alkaline earth metals, which are divalent, are not insulators, because the bands overlap. In this way a band that might be exactly filled in the absence of overlapping bands is not entirely filled, and a band that might be vacant in the absence of overlap is partly filled. Because of overlapping, it is possible for some electrons to be promoted to higher levels without overcoming an energy gap, and the solid becomes a conductor. This is the situation for zinc and magnesium. The higher resistances of the divalent metals, in comparison with the monovalent ones, is due to the small effective number of free electrons.

In a solid with a very wide forbidden gap, the thermal energy is insufficient to excite electrons across the gap and the conduction band is always empty. Because no unoccupied levels are available, there can be no movement of electrons as there is no level into which they can jump. Such solids are called insulators. Diamond is an insulator; it has four valence electrons, and the bands are separated by a large energy gap (5 ev). The important

* This is a consequence of the Pauli principle, which states that only two electrons may occupy an energy state and they must have opposite spins.

semiconductors, silicon and germanium, have the same valence and structure as a diamond, but the gap is considerably smaller than in diamond (about 1 ev *).

In those materials in which there is a small energy gap between a filled valence band and the conduction band and electrons can jump from one to the other, the solid is called an intrinsic semiconductor. In these substances, conduction occurs by thermal excitation of electrons from the valence to the conduction band. Electrons excited to the higher conduction-band levels can then move from atom to atom in the presence of an applied field. The conductivity of a semiconductor depends strongly on temperature, because of the need to excite electrons into the conduction band. The higher the temperature, the greater the number of electrons excited and consequently the lower the electrical resistivity — the reverse for metals. The jumping of electrons to the conduction level leaves vacancies or holes.

After electrons are excited to the conduction band, the empty state left in the valence band also contributes to conduction. In a nearly filled valence band, conduction occurs by an electron filling a hole, another electron filling the hole just created, and so on. Under the influence of a field, the motion of holes is always opposite to the motion of the electrons that fill them. The inertia of the motion of a hole is related to the electrons that fill it; the hole acts as if it had a mass. The hole also acts as if it had a positive charge. This concept has been a very fruitful one in semiconductor physics.

In semiconductors, when electrons are raised to the conduction band by light or thermal radiation, holes are simultaneously created. This mechanism is referred to as production of hole-electron pairs. In such an instance, the intrinsic conductivity is given as the following relationship:

$$\sigma = ne\mu_n + pe\mu_p = n_i e(\mu_n + \mu_p) \qquad \text{mhos per cm} \qquad (9)$$

where $n_i = n = p =$ number of hole-electron pairs, $\mu_n =$ electron mobility, $\mu_p =$ hole mobility.

Pure, or intrinsic, semiconductors, however, are of theoretical

* The electron-volt is a convenient unit of energy for calculations in electronics, and is equivalent to 1.602×10^{-19} joule or 1.602×10^{-12} erg. When an electronic charge, e, is transferred from an electric potential V_1 to V_2, its potential energy changes by an amount equal to $e(V_1 - V_2)$. If the charge e is 1.602×10^{19} coulombs, and if the potential difference between V_1 and V_2 is 1 v, the corresponding change in energy is 1 ev.

interest only. More interest and commercial exploitation center around effects produced in semiconductors by deliberate, controlled addition of impurities or carriers, generally in a concentration of about one part in 10^8. Were it not for the impurity semiconductors, most semiconducting devices would not exist.

For example, in silicon, one atom of boron to 10^5 atoms of silicon increases the electrical conductivity of silicon by a factor of 1000. The impurity levels may act either as "acceptors" or "donors." With acceptors, the levels are empty at the absolute zero of temperature and, as the temperature rises, receive electrons from the s band and hence are known as p-type semiconductors. With donors, the impurity levels are full at zero temperature, and, as the temperature rises, the impurity levels can supply electrons to the higher level conduction band and give rise to electron conduction; these are n-type semiconductors.

Besides thermal excitation, semiconductors can be excited by electromagnetic radiation or by bombardment with nuclear particles. Nuclear radiation is very effective in altering semiconductors. Bombardment of germanium with slow neutrons will develop gallium in occasional lattice sites, and p-type properties will result. Fast neutrons produce some arsenic atoms, and n-type properties result. In silicon, slow neutrons produce donor centers (phosphorus), and fast neutrons, acceptor centers (aluminum).

Origin of Magnetism

Any complete theory of the magnetism of matter, excluding consideration of terrestrial and cosmic phenomena, will have to account for the following magnetic classifications and some of their important characteristics:

1 *The diamagnetism of gases, liquids and solids.* Faraday noted that certain gases, liquids and solids suspended in a homogeneous magnetic field were repelled from the strongest part of the field to the weakest, and that needles and tube containers of gases and liquids turn their axes perpendicular to the field. He called these substances diamagnetic. The susceptibility * of these

---

* The susceptibility per unit volume, K, is defined as a measure of the increase in magnetic moment caused by the application of a field, H, and is given as $K = I/H$, where I is the intensity of magnetization. Permeability, μ, represents the increase in flux B caused by the presence of the magnetic material and is given as $\mu = B/H$, where B is the magnetic induction. The susceptibility is related to the permeability in the following manner: $K = (\mu - 1)/4\pi$.

materials is negative, and the permeability is less than 1. Examples of diamagnetic substances are the rare gases, He, Ne, A, Kr and Xe, liquids such as H_2O, Br, I, Hg and benzene, and solids such as Bi, Na, K, Mg and Ca.

   a The diamagnetism of some substances (for example, S, Si and Au) remains constant with changes in temperature, while others (bismuth and copper) show temperature dependence.

2 *The paramagnetism of gases, liquids and solids.* Faraday noted that these materials suspended in a homogeneous field moved from a weaker to a stronger portion of the field, and needles or rod containers aligned themselves parallel to the nonuniform field. The susceptibility of these materials is positive, and the permeability is just slightly greater than 1. Examples of paramagnetic gases are O_2 and NO, of liquids, aqueous solutions of simple compounds of elements of the first transition group, calcium to copper, and of such solids as the rare earth elements from cerium to lutetium.

   a The paramagnetism of some substances increases with temperature (barium and rhodium), decreases with temperature (O_2, Pd, Ni and Fe above the Curie temperature) or remains independent of temperature (Na, Li, Sn and Rb).

   b Antiferromagnetism is a special case of paramagnetism. With these substances, the susceptibility increases with temperature to a critical temperature; above the critical temperature, the susceptibility decreases. Examples are Cr, alpha Mn, MnO, FeF_2, $CoCl_2$, NiO and Cr_2O_3.

3 *The ferromagnetism of some materials such as iron, cobalt, nickel, and their alloys.* These materials are strongly attracted to a magnet or an electromagnet. The ferromagnetic substances have exceedingly high and variable susceptibilities, and very high and variable permeabilities (over one million in some instances).

   a When the magnetic induction, B, is plotted against the magnetic field, H, a magnetization curve is obtained. The ratio of B/H at any point on this curve is called the permeability, μ. The magnetic phenomena leading to this curve are not reversible, and, hence, the curve is not retraced when the field, H, is reduced.

   b Because the magnetization curve is not retraced when the field, H, is reduced, the induction, B, will lag behind the field, giving rise to hysteresis phenomena. It is possible to develop a symmetrical curve about the origin of the B and H coordinates when H is cyclically changed ($+H_{max}$ to $-H_{max}$). The resulting loop is known as a hysteresis loop and represents an energy loss as heat. From the loop, two important quantities are obtained: the coercive force, H_c, which is the value of

H for $B = 0$, and the remanence or residual induction, B_r, which is the value of B for $H = 0$.

c When the magnetic field, H, is increased to high values, the intensity of magnetization, I, and the intrinsic induction, B-H, approach a limiting value known as saturation.

d The ferromagnetic behavior mentioned under a, b, and c vanishes when the material is raised to a certain temperature called the Curie temperature or point. Above this temperature, the material shows a paramagnetic behavior.

e Ferromagnetic substances show minute changes of a few parts per million in dimensions (either plus or minus) when magnetized. These dimensional changes are a function of the field strength. The phenomenon is known as magnetostriction.

f In ferromagnetic single crystals and in polycrystalline materials with preferred orientation, the magnetic properties depend on the direction in which they are measured. Directions of easy and difficult magnetization are the lower indice crystallographic directions. For example, $<100>$ are the easy directions for iron, while the $<111>$ are the difficult ones.

g Young's modulus of elasticity, E, changes with magnetization. With magnetization, increases in E of over 35% have been reported.

h In an elastically vibrating system, there is an energy loss, and damping in such a system is generally larger when the material is magnetized than when it is not.

i The specific heat of a ferromagnetic material is higher than of a diamagnetic or paramagnetic one. Above the Curie temperature, the specific heat behavior is normal.

j In a ferromagnetic material, there is an increase of a few per cent in the electrical resistivity with magnetization when the current and magnetic field are parallel, and a decrease in resistivity when they are at right angles to each other.

Although considerable progress has been made in understanding the fundamental aspects of the magnetism of matter, there are still many magnetic phenomena that remain to be satisfactorily explained. Considerable progress has been made by considering by itself each type of magnetic matter, or even its subdivisions. A common denominator to all magnetism is slowly becoming evident.

Diamagnetism and Paramagnetism. Langevin, in his celebrated paper on magnetism (27), considered an atom with a single charge, e, and a mass, m, traveling with a velocity, v, in a circular orbit of radius, r. The moving charge creates a current that in turn gives rise to a magnetic moment.* The application of a magnetic field, H, will create an electromotive force in the orbit, and this electromotive force will cause the electron to change its velocity with a corresponding change in the magnetic moment. If the atom contains many electron orbits, oriented in many directions to the magnetic field, it is still possible to estimate by mathematical analysis, the magnetic moment of the complex system. Langevin's ideas are applicable to all atoms, whether they are diamagnetic or paramagnetic. Often, the diamagnetism is not apparent because, if any paramagnetism is present, it masks the diamagnetic component. Although somewhat modified now, the Langevin concept has not suffered severely as a result of quantum mechanical treatment.

Strong paramagnetism is found in gases, liquids and solids. This paramagnetism is caused by the permanent magnetic moment of the atoms, because some of the electron shells are incomplete and the resultant moment is large in comparison to the spin of the outer electrons or the diamagnetic moment of closed shells. The iron group and the rare earth group of elements show this strong paramagnetism. Weak paramagnetism in the solid state is explained by the effect of the magnetic field on the spins of the conduction electrons; metallic sodium is an example.

There exists a special class of paramagnetic substances known as antiferromagnetic materials. Their susceptibilities increase with increasing temperature to a critical temperature, above which the susceptibilities decrease. In antiferromagnetism, exchange forces maintain neighboring atoms antiparallel below the critical temperature, while above the critical temperature, the magnetic moments are parallel.

Ferromagnetism. While Langevin was successful in elucidating diamagnetism and paramagnetism, he could not explain ferromagnetism — the magnetization curve and the approach to saturation. It remained for Weiss (28) to develop the fundamental ideas underlying ferromagnetism. Weiss postulated an internal field that would cause the elementary carriers (electrons) to lock

---

* Magnetic moment can have several connotations. In one case, the moment is the pole strength times the interpolar distance. In another, the moment of a current loop or a magnetized body is a measure of the magnetizing force, H, produced by the current or magnetized body. The meaning intended here is that the magnetic moment of a magnetized body is the vector summation of the magnetic moments of the intrinsic spin of the particles and their orbital motion within the system.

together. He realized that magnetic or electrostatic forces alone could not assist in aligning the elementary carriers. However, he could not account for the origin of the necessary internal field. The concept of the internal field, however, did account for some important features of ferromagnetism, such as saturation in weak fields, temperature dependence, and Curie temperature. It was apparent to Weiss that a material with a large internal field should be spontaneously magnetized at room temperature. But, how could it be magnetized if the net external effect were zero? Then, he visualized the domain, a small spontaneously magnetized region that is now easily observed. The directions of intrinsic magnetization of the domains would be randomly distributed, so that the external effect could not be easily perceived. The concept of domains then made it possible to explain the magnetization curve and the hysteresis loop. Domains are very real and can be seen. They are regions spontaneously magnetized to saturation and contain 10^{10} to 10^{15} atoms. Why spontaneous magnetization is confined to small regions is not clear.

So much for an explanation of the gross features of ferromagnetism, but what about the origins of ferromagnetism? As stated, the elementary magnets are the electrons that spin on an axis through their centers. In the presence of a magnetic field, the electrons take one of two orientations: The magnetic moment caused by the spinning electron is directed parallel to the field or antiparallel (opposite) to it. Where there are two oppositely directed electrons in a shell, their moments cancel, and only a small magnetic moment in one direction can arise, as in diamagnetism. This is the situation for many elements. The origin of ferromagnetism, or the large magnetic moment in iron, nickel and cobalt, is explained on the basis of spin unbalance. These ferromagnetic

Table 7. Spin Unbalance as a Consequence of the Disposition of Electrons in the $3d$ and $4s$ Shells

Element	Total electrons in 4s and 3d	Electrons in			Unpaired electrons in 3d shell
		4s	+3d	−3d	
Chromium......	6	0.6	2.7	2.7	0
Manganese......	7	0.6	3.2	3.2	0
Iron............	8	0.6	4.8	2.6	2.2
Cobalt.........	9	0.7	5	3.3	1.7
Nickel.........	10	0.6	5	4.4	0.6
Copper.........	11	1.0	5	5	0

elements contain partly filled $3d$ shells. The $3d$ band of levels can accommodate 10 electrons per atom: 5 with plus spins ($+3d$) and 5 with minus spins ($-3d$). In general, as many as possible of the electrons have plus spins; the remainder, minus. In iron, with eight electrons distributed in the $4s$ and $3d$ shells, a distribution is calculated to give 0.6 electrons in the $4s$, and 4.8 in the $+3d$ and 2.6 in the $-3d$. The resulting spin balance is 2.2. It is this unpairing that is responsible for large magnetic moment (see Table 7). The number of unpaired electrons is altered by solid-solution formation.

The unpaired electrons of one atom bring about alignment of neighboring atoms by an exchange-energy interaction. This ordering tendency is opposed by thermal agitation of the ions on the lattice, and, at the Curie temperature, the thermal agitation is sufficiently great so as to destroy the ordering resulting from exchange energy. The alignment of the magnetic moments exists over large microscopic regions in a ferromagnetic material; these regions are known as domains.

Heisenberg (29) showed that the exchange energy as a result of spin-spin interaction of electrons is identical with the Weiss internal field. The forces between electrons at atomic distances are such that the force tending to hold the electron spins parallel increases to a maximum as the electrons approach each other and then decreases until the spin axes are held antiparallel. In ferromagnetic materials (Fe, Ni, Co, Gd), the lattice spacing is of the order of the optimum separation for good coupling.

If the idea of angular momentum and magnetic moment, which appear almost inseparable, is extended to the spinning electron, it becomes evident that intrinsic magnetization is an attribute of ferromagnetic elements. If the orbital electron has a charge, e, and a mass, m, it can be shown that the ratio of angular momentum to magnetic moment is $2m/e$. The connection between angular momentum and magnetic moment received experimental verification by Barnett (30) in 1914, when he demonstrated "magnetization by rotation." Barnett, however, obtained for the ratio of the angular momentum to magnetic moment only one half the $2m/e$ value for the electron as predicted by theory. Similar mystifying results (m/e) were obtained by others. The anomalous data were resolved by Goudsmit and Uhlenbech (31) in 1925. They suggested that electron-spin momentum was quantized in half Bohr units. This experimental work confirmed the theoretical consideration of Heisenberg and of Dirac, and established conclusively that the spinning electron was the origin of ferromagnetism.

The behavior of domains is important in understanding ferromagnetic phenomena. In the unmagnetized material, the directions of the magnetization of the domains are aligned along axes of easy magnetization in such a manner that the resultant magnetic moment of the body is zero. The domain walls, or boundaries that separate one domain from another, are regions representing a change in the direction of spins. The application of an external field causes the spins at the boundary to turn so that one domain can grow at the expense of another. This displacement of the boundary, known as a translational process, causes the domains to become aligned, in general, along the easy directions nearest to the field. The translational process is associated with the turning of spins through a large angle — 90 or 180° for iron. If the field is in an easy crystallographic direction, saturation is obtained in a weak field. If the field is in another direction, the approach to saturation can still be made only if a sufficiently strong field is applied. Under these conditions, a gradual turning of the spins from an easy direction toward the field direction takes place. This is a rotational process.

The nucleus of an atom also has a magnetic moment. However, such moments do not have any important effect on the magnetic properties of materials. Information on nuclear moments is helpful primarily in understanding nuclear structure.

Chapter 2

Conduction in Solids

ALL SUBSTANCES conduct electricity (electrical charges) but to various degrees. Although it is proper to refer to the conductivity of a substance, by usage its electrical resistivity (the reciprocal of conductivity) is the more important physical quantity.* Materials can be divided into three classes on the basis of the magnitude of their electrical resistivity at room temperature: conductors, semiconductors, and dielectrics (insulators).

Conductors may have an electrical resistivity from 1.59×10^{-6} ohm-cm (silver) to about 400×10^{-6} ohm-cm (99 Bi – 1 Sn). The conduction is electronic in that a charge is transmitted by the motion of electrons (a current) moving through the crystal lattice under the influence of a voltage. The impedance to electron motion constitutes the electrical resistance of the conductor. The temperature coefficients of electrical resistivity are positive and approximately linear with temperature. Thus, as the temperature increases, resistivity increases.

General Aspects of Electrical Resistivity of Metals

There are four methods of altering the physical and mechanical properties of metals, including electrical resistivity. Three, known since the Bronze Age, are (a) the introduction of alloys or the presence of impurities; (b) plastic deformation — hot, warm or cold; (c) heat treating by slow cooling or quenching. The fourth method, of recent origin, is irradiation with high-energy nuclear particles, mainly neutrons. The effect of these factors will be discussed later in this chapter.

* An exception to this statement is the reference to the International Annealed Copper Standard (IACS) conductivity in Chapter 4.

The semiconductor made a brief appearance in the early days of radio as a crystal in the primitive radio receiver. Its reappearance in modern technology is leading to amazing developments in physics and engineering. Semiconductors, which include lead sulfide, silicon carbide, silicon, germanium, cuprous oxide, and selenium, may have resistivities from 10^{-3} to 10^{+9} ohm-cm. The

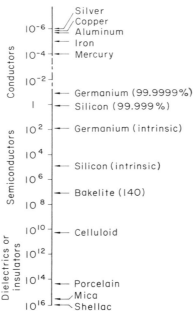

Fig. 4. Relative resistivities of conductors, semiconductors and insulators

resistivity of the elements is extremely sensitive to impurities, and, in the chemical compounds, it is very sensitive to small departures from stoichiometric ratios. The temperature coefficients are generally strongly negative, and they are not linear with temperature. Conduction is electronic.

Dielectrics or insulators can have a resistivity from about 10^{10} ohm-cm to the limit of measurements, about 10^{20} ohm-cm. Examples are cellulose, insulating oils, polystyrene, glass, mica, and fused quartz. The conductivity of these materials is due chiefly to the migration of ions. Figure 4 compares the relative resistivities of conductors, semiconductors, and dielectrics.

Electrical resistivities and temperature coefficients of resistivity of the elements, in relation to their atomic weights and number, are given in Fig. 5 and 6, respectively.* Note the roughly periodic variation of these electrical properties, which corresponds to the complexity of the outer electronic configurations of the atoms as they increase in atomic weight. Table 8 gives the

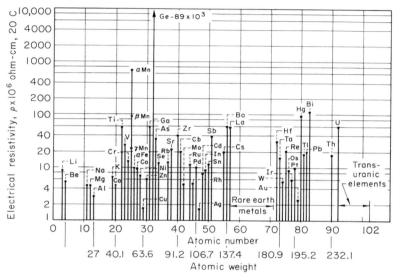

Fig. 5. Electrical resistivities of the elements at 20 C (68 F)

electrical resistivity and the temperature coefficient for the rare earth elements, which are omitted from Fig. 5 and 6.

Resistance and Resistivity. The practical unit of resistance is the ohm. The international ohm is represented by the resistance of a column of mercury of uniform cross section at 0 C, when its length is 106.300 cm and its mass is 14.4521 g. This unit is intended to represent an electrical resistance of 10^9 cgs units.** A convenient subdivision is the microhm, one-millionth part (10^{-6}) of an ohm; a convenient multiple is the megohm, a million ohms (10^{+6}).

---

* Data from International Critical Tables and International Annual Tables of Constants. Charted in this form by P. H. Brace and W. Hurford of the Westinghouse Research Laboratories (1947).
** See Appendix, page 362.

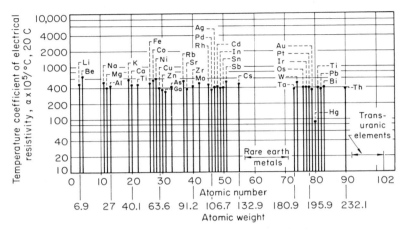

Fig. 6. Temperature coefficients of electrical resistivity of the elements at 20 C (68 F)

The resistance of a metallic conductor depends on its dimensions and its electronic structure according to the equation

$$R = \rho \frac{l}{A} \tag{10}$$

where R is the resistance in ohms, l is the length in feet or centimeters, A is the cross-sectional area in circular mils or square centimeters, and ρ is a material constant called the specific resistivity, electrical resistivity, or volume resistivity in ohms per circular mil-foot or ohm-centimeters.* The specific resistivity is equal to the resistance when l and A define a unit cube.**

The volume resistivity, ρ, can be expressed in different systems of units. It is customary, however, to use the cgs system, so that if l is in centimeters, A in square centimeters, and R in ohms, the resistivity will be given in ohm-centimeters. Some typical resistivity values of metals are given in Table 9.

The atomic resistivity is another useful, convenient quantity that facilitates a comparison of the electrical properties of metals under similar conditions. The atomic resistivity is the resistance for unit potential difference of a cube containing Avogadro's

---

* See Appendix, Dimensions of Resistivity, page 361.
** Table 18 illustrates a point that is sometimes missed. The change in dimensions of a metal can cause large variations in resistance, but the specific resistivity need not change. In Table 18, the plastic strain affects the resistivity slightly.

**Table 8. Electrical Resistivities and Temperature Coefficients
of Electrical Resistivity of the Rare Earth Elements**

Symbol	Element	Atomic number	Atomic weight	Electric resistivity, microhm-cm at 0 C (32 F)	Temperature coefficient per °C at 0 to 20 C
Ce	Cerium	58	140.13	75	0.00048
Pr	Praseodymium	59	140.92	68	0.00095
Nd	Neodymium	60	144.27	64	0.00091
Pm	Promethium	61	145	...	...
Sm	Samarium	62	150.35	88	0.00082
Eu	Europium	63	152.00	90	...
Gd	Gadolinium	64	157.26	140.5	0.00098
Tb	Terbium	65	158.93	...	...
Dy	Dysprosium	66	162.51	56	0.00066
Ho	Holmium	67	164.94	87	0.00095
Er	Erbium	68	167.27	107	0.00111
Tm	Thulium	69	168.94	79	0.00108
Yb	Ytterbium	70	173.04	30	0.00072
Lu	Lutetium	71	174.99	79	0.00133

number of atoms. Therefore, there is the same number of atoms in a cross section, and the potential drop per atom is the same. The atomic resistivity is equal to the volume resistivity multiplied by the cube root of the ratio of the density to the atomic weight.

Much engineering work requires the use of wires of circular cross section; hence, it is convenient to use the unit of area called the circular mil. It replaces measurements in square inches. In the circular mil, the area, A, becomes $\pi d^2/4$, where d is the diameter of the wire, so that the expression (equation 10) becomes

$$R = \frac{4\rho l}{\pi d^2} = \rho' \frac{l}{d^2} \tag{11}$$

Actually, ρ' is modified to permit the expression of d in mils (thousandths of an inch) and l in feet. The d^2 factor is still considered an area, the unit of which is the circular mil. The area of a circle whose diameter is n mils is merely n^2 circular mils. A square inch of wire contains 1,273,240 circular mils, and 1 circular in. is equal to one million circular mils. Table 9 also gives the resistivity of various materials in ohms per circular mil-foot.[*]

The reciprocal of resistance, R, is the conductance, G. The reciprocal of resistivity, ρ, is the conductivity, σ; the reciprocal of

---

[*] This value can be obtained by multiplying the resistivity in ohm-centimeters by the factor 6.015×10^6.

the ohm is the mho. One may write, that the conductance, G, is as follows:

$$G = \frac{\sigma A}{l} \tag{12}$$

Little use is made of the constant, σ, in the study of metals (see the section on conductors in Chapter 4).

The current density, i, for direct current is assumed to be uniform in a metallic conductor and is defined by the relation:

$$i = \frac{I}{A} \text{ amperes per unit area} \tag{13}$$

Table 9. Volume Resistivities and Temperature Coefficients of Some Metals

Material	Resistivity at 20 C (68 F) Microhm-cm	Resistivity at 20 C (68 F) Ohms per cir mil-ft	Temperature coefficient per °C at 20 C (68 F)
Aluminum (99.996%)	2.6548	15.98	0.00429
Aluminum (annealed)	2.828	17.02	0.0039
Aluminum (hard drawn)	2.92	17.58	0.0038
Bismuth	115.0	692.30	0.0045
Copper (spectrographically pure)	1.6730	10.06	0.0068
Copper (annealed standard)	1.724	10.37	0.00393
Copper (hard drawn)	1.77	10.66	0.00382
German silver (18% Ni)	33.8	203.5	0.00031
Gold	2.44	14.7	0.0034
Iron (99.99 + %)(a)	9.71	58.45	0.00651
Iron (99.98%)	10.0	60.2	0.005
Iron (hard cast)	75 to 100	. . .	0.001 to 0.00074
Lead (99.73 + %)	20.648	124.30	0.00336
Magnesium (99.80%)	4.46	26.97	0.01784
Manganin (84% Cu)	44	265	0.000006
Mercury	95.8	577	0.00089
Nickel (99.95% Ni + Co)	6.84	41.18	0.0069
Nichrome (66% Ni)	100	602	0.0004
Phosphor bronze	8.37	50.4	0.004
Platinum (99.99%)	10.6	63.81	0.003923
Silver (99.78% pure)	1.59	9.56	0.0041
Steel (hard)	45	271	0.00161
Steel (soft)	11.8	71	0.00423
Steel (wire)	10.7 to 17.5	. . .	0.006 to 0.0036
Tantalum	15.5	93.3	0.0031
Tin (99.95%)	11.5	69.2	0.00447
Tungsten	5.51	33.3	0.0045
Zinc	5.916	35.61	0.00419

(a) The electrical resistivity of gamma iron is 115 microhm-cm at 910 C (1670 F) and 119 microhm-cm at 1110 C (2030 F).

Platinum, tungsten and copper show no deviation from Ohm's law ($I = E/R$) up to current densities of 5 to 8 × 10⁶ amp per sq cm; whereas bismuth, at densities of 0.5 to 1 × 10⁶ amp per sq cm, shows deviations of 20 to 30% (32).

Skin Effect. For alternating current, the current is no longer uniformly distributed over the cross section, because there is a tendency for the current density to be greater near the surface of the conductor than at the center. This crowding of the current to the outer surface, which is due to the magnetic effect of the moving electrons, is called the skin effect. Because the center of the conductor is not fully utilized, the conductor as a whole exhibits more resistance to alternating than direct current, since the effective cross section is reduced. As the frequency or the conductor size, or both, increases, the ratio of alternating-current to direct-current resistance becomes progressively larger. This ratio, in terms of a quantity X, for nonferrous conductors is given as in equation (14) below:

$$X = \pi d \sqrt{\frac{f}{500\rho}} \tag{14}$$

where d is the diameter of the wire in centimeters, f is the frequency in cycles per second, and ρ is the resistivity of the conductor in microhm-centimeters. Table 10 indicates the skin effect factors, R_{ac}/R_{dc}, for various values of X.

Table 10. Skin Effect Factors

X	R_{ac}/R_{dc}	X	R_{ac}/R_{dc}
1.0	1.005	10.0	3.975
2.0	1.078	14.0	5.209
3.0	1.318	20.0	7.328
4.0	1.678	24.0	8.741
5.0	2.043	30.0	10.860

Wiedemann-Franz Ratio. The ratio of the thermal conductivity to the electrical conductivity, knowledge of which goes back to 1853, is called the Wiedemann-Franz ratio (33). This ratio is useful for estimating the difficult-to-measure thermal conductivity of metals, when the easily measured electrical resistivity can be provided.

A rule of thumb states that, for most metals and alloys, the thermal conductivity is proportional to electrical conductivity.

This relationship is usually expressed by the Wiedemann-Franz law, which is as follows:

$$\frac{\kappa}{\sigma} = \frac{\pi^2}{3} \left(\frac{k}{l} \right) T \tag{15}$$

where σ is electrical conductivity in mhos per centimeter; κ is thermal conductivity in watts per degree Kelvin per centimeter; T is the absolute temperature; k is Boltzmann's constant; e is the electronic charge. The theoretical value of the Wiedemann-Franz ratio is 2.45 watt-ohms per degree[2]. For most metals, the ratio as observed is a little larger than that given by this formula.

A quantity called the Lorenz number is also useful in these discussions. The Lorenz number, L, is defined as:

$$L = \frac{\kappa}{\sigma T} \times 10^{-8} \tag{16}$$

Some experimental Lorenz numbers are given in Table 11 (34). Also, Powell and Hickman (35) have given consideration to this ratio for carbon, alloy, and high-alloy steels.

Resistivity in Cubic and Noncubic Crystals. In cubic crystals, the resistivity does not change with the direction of measurement.

Table 11. Lorenz Numbers of Some Elements

Metal	Lorenz number, $L \times 10^8$ watt-ohms/degree[2]	
	0 C (32 F)	100 C (212 F)
Silver	2.31	2.37
Gold	2.35	2.40
Cadmium	2.42	2.43
Copper	2.23	2.33
Iridium	2.49	2.49
Molybdenum	2.61	2.79
Lead	2.47	2.56
Platinum	2.51	2.60
Tin	2.52	2.49
Tungsten	3.04	3.20
Zinc	2.31	2.33

In noncubic crystals, the resistivity varies with the crystallographic direction. For pure tin (99.95%) of tetragonal habit, the resistivity and temperature coefficient at 20 C (68 F) along the a-axis are 14.3 microhm-cm and 0.00447 microhm-cm per °C, respectively. Along the b-axis, the resistivity is 9.90 microhm-cm; the coefficient is 0.00469 microhm-cm per °C. For hexagonal magnesium, the polycrystalline resistivity and temperature coefficient at 20 C (68 F) are 4.46 microhm-cm and 0.01784 microhm-cm per °C, respectively. The resistivity and temperature coefficient along the a-axis are 4.54 microhm-cm and 0.01889 microhm-cm per °C, and along the c-axis they are 3.77 microhm-cm and 0.01610 microhm-cm per °C, respectively.

Single crystals may have lower resistivity than polycrystalline materials. For copper, the difference is about 8%.

Single crystals of the highly anisotropic graphite (hexagonal)

**Table 12. Relative Resistance of a Single Crystal and a
Polycrystalline Titanium Sample**
[Titanium is hexagonal close-packed to 882.5 C
(1620 F) with a c/a of 1.5873.]

Temperature, K	Relative resistance, R_T/R_{273}		
	Single crystal		
	Parallel to c-axis	Perpendicular to c-axis	Poly-crystalline(a)
4.2	....	....	0.0306
19.6	....	....	0.0309
77	0.1786	0.2086	0.15
196	0.6355	0.6450	0.67
273	1.000	1.000	1.000
300	1.130	1.110	1.120
373	1.4997	1.4550	1.468
400	1.64	1.58	1.60
500	2.13	2.10	2.09
600	2.60	2.60	2.56
700	2.99	2.94	2.99
800	3.25	3.17	3.31
900	3.46	3.38	3.58
1000	3.59	3.58	3.80
1100	3.67	3.76	3.98
1200	3.43	3.61	3.705
1300	3.47	3.675	3.760
1400	3.525	3.75	3.835
1450	3.555	3.78	3.865

(a) Electrical resistivity at 273 K (0 C) is 42.67 ± 0.05 microhm-cm.

have a resistivity of 50 microhm-cm along the layers, but perpendicular to the layers (c-axis direction), the resistivity can increase by a factor of 100 to 10,000.

The variation of electrical resistivity of hexagonal titanium along and perpendicular to the c-axis is given over a wide range of temperature in Table 12; comparison with the resistivity of a polycrystalline sample is also given (36).

Electrical Resistivities of Iron, Copper and Aluminum Alloys

The electrical resistivities at 20 C (68 F) of some important iron, copper, and aluminum alloys are given to illustrate the magnitude of the resistivity of some familiar metals.

Iron Alloys. The effect of various alloying elements on the electrical resistivity of iron is shown in Fig. 7. Note how extremely effective silicon and aluminum are, in comparison with the other elements, in increasing resistivity. The increase in resistivity due

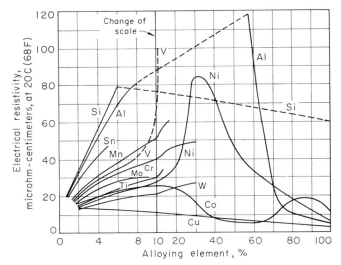

Fig. 7. Effect of alloying elements on the electrical resistivity of iron

to silicon in large part makes electrical steels useful for alternating-current magnetic purposes; the silicon reduces the eddy-current losses.

The electrical resistivities of some annealed carbon steels are given in Table 13. The resistivity of these annealed high-purity iron-carbon alloys at ambient temperatures can be expressed by the following relationship, which is valid up to 4.3% C (37):

$$\log \rho = 0.90\theta + 0.996 \tag{17}$$

where ρ is the resistivity in microhm-centimeters, and θ is the volume fraction of cementite.

Table 13. Electrical Resistivity of Some Annealed High-Purity Plain Carbon Steels

Carbon, %	Resistivity at 24 C (75 F), microhm-cm	Carbon, %	Resistivity at 24 C (75 F), microhm-cm
0.06	10.25	1.23	14.43
0.17	10.57	1.26	14.63
0.53	11.87	3.74	31.36
0.83	12.94	4.33	41.17
1.12	13.90		

Chernobrovkin (38) has investigated the resistivities of cast irons. White cast iron (3.8% C, 0.2% Si) has a resistivity of 50 microhm-cm; gray cast iron (3.9% C, 1.3% Si) has a resistivity of 80 microhm-cm; and nodular iron (3.9% C, 1.3% Si) has a resistivity of 45 microhm-cm. Electrical resistivity of cast iron depends on its graphite content. Highest values are for an iron containing a large amount of large spheroidal graphite in a pearlite-ferrite matrix.

Copper Alloys. The effect of alloying elements on the electrical resistivity of copper is shown in Fig. 8 (39). Note particularly the large influence of phosphorus and iron in increasing the resistivity and the minor influence of cadmium, zinc, and silver on

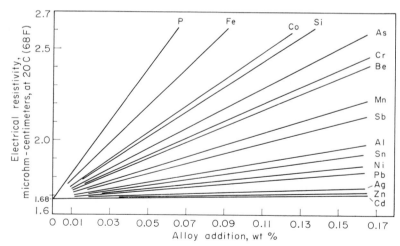

Fig. 8. Effect of alloying elements on the electrical resistivity of copper

Table 14. Electrical Resistivity of Some Annealed Copper Alloys

Alloy	Composition, %				Electrical resistivity,	
	Cu	Zn	Sn	Other	microhm-cm	ohms per cir mil-ft
Copper............	99.90+	....	....	....	1.724	10.37
Bronze...........	95	5	....	....	3.15	18.98
Bronze...........	90	10	....	....	4.21	25.36
Red brass........	85	15	....	....	4.66	28.03
Red brass........	80	20	....	....	5.31	31.95
Cartridge brass....	70	30	....	....	6.25	37.61
High brass.......	65	35	....	....	6.43	38.68
Muntz metal.....	60	40	....	....	6.04	36.25
Admiralty metal...	70	29	1	....	6.99	42.07
Phosphor bronze..	96	....	3.75	0.25 P	13.66	82.18
30% nickel silver..	47	23	....	30 Ni	48.20	290.0
5% Al bronze.....	95	....	....	5 Al	9.78	58.61
10% Al bronze....	90	....	....	10 Al	12.75	76.80
Manganese bronze	59	39	0.70	0.5 Mn,	7.00	42.15
				0.8 Fe		
Beryllium copper..	97.4	....	....	2.25 Be,	10.0(a)	60.15(a)
				0.35 Ni	6.8 to 9.8(b)	40.9 to 59.0(b)

(a) As quenched. (b) As quenched and aged.

the same property. Table 14 gives the electrical resistivities of some common alloys of copper.

Aluminum Alloys. The effect of several alloying elements on the electrical resistivity of aluminum is shown in Fig. 9 (40). Considerable variability exists in the resistivity of aluminum casting alloys in the as-cast and annealed states, as shown in Table 15 (41), where widely different compositions are compared.

Variation of Electrical Resistivity With Temperature

The resistance of most conductors and all pure metals increases more or less linearly with temperature. The thermally oscillating ions in the lattice can be regarded as elastic waves having a certain periodicity associated with them. The waves due to thermal oscillations permit a range of electron waves to be diffracted, and therefore the ordinary conduction electrons can be scattered. This scattering increases with temperature, because the amplitude of the vibrating waves increases linearly and the number of different vibrational waves also increases; it follows, therefore, that as electron paths become more frequently interrupted, the resistance increases.

At high temperatures, the electrical resistance of a pure metal is proportional to the absolute temperature, but, as the temperature decreases, the resistance decreases, and at very low temperature it is proportional to T^5. The change of resistivity with temperature of several elements is shown in Fig. 10. The temperature dependence of the relative resistivities of several metals is given in Fig. 11 (42). The decrease in resistivity with the lowering of temperature is due to the increase in the mean free path

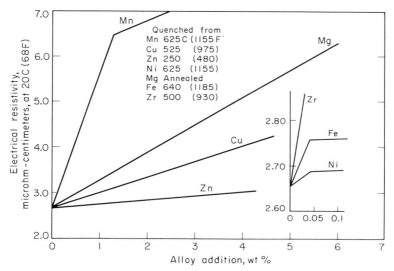

Fig. 9. Effect of alloying elements on the electrical resistivity of aluminum. Measurements were made on specimens quenched as indicated.

Table 15. Electrical Resistivity of Some Aluminum Casting Alloys

Cu	Si	Composition, % Fe	Zn	Mg	Sand cast	Electrical resistivity at 20 C (68 F), microhm-cm Sand cast, annealed	Chill cast	Chill cast, annealed
4.0	3.0	...	...	...	.....	5.62	4.57	...	...
7.0	1.5	1.2	...	...	.....	...	...	5.96	4.74
7.5	...	1.2	1.5	...	.....	5.77	4.55	5.37	...
12.0	...	...	...	...	.....	4.81	3.84	...	...
...	5.0	...	...	...	.....	4.74	4.3	4.22	3.57
...	13.0	...	...	...	.....	4.3	...	4.8	...
2.5	...	1.2	11.0	...	.....	5.2	...	...	...
10.0	...	...	...	0.2	.....	...	...	4.2	5.07
...	...	...	...	4.0	.....	4.9	...	...	...
...	...	...	...	10.0	.....	...	8.27	...	...

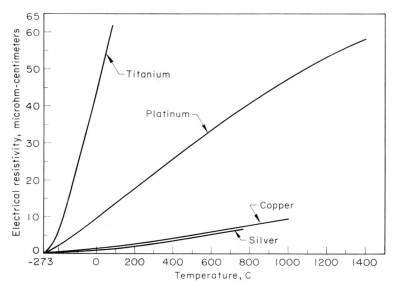

Fig. 10. *Effect of temperature on the resistivity of copper, silver, platinum and titanium*

of the electrons in the lattice. The change in resistivity of copper (as a solid and as a liquid) with temperature, from 20 to 1450 C (68 to 2650 F), is given in Fig. 12 (43). Note the approximate linear dependence on temperature and also the marked discontinuity of the resistivity at the melting point. Above the melting point, conduction is ionic.

Ames and McOwillan (44) found that the following equation held for the titanium-hydrogen and titanium-columbium systems over a wide range of temperatures:

$$\rho_T = \rho_0 + \alpha T - pe^{-q/T} \tag{18}$$

where ρ_T and ρ_0 are the resistivities at T K and 0 K, respectively, and a, p, and q are constants derived from experimental data; e is the base of natural logarithms.

Wasilewski (36) confirmed the validity of the equation for the systems Ti-Al, Ti-Sn, Ti + 1.5% O_2, Ti + 22.8% O_2, Ti-N, and annealed and cold worked titanium. Table 12 shows the variation of resistivity with temperature for a single crystal and a polycrystalline sample of titanium.

Bismuth has the greatest resistance change with temperature

of all ductile metals. At 0 C, the specific resistivity is 106.5 microhm-cm; it reaches 267 microhm-cm at 270 C (518 F); the resistivity of liquid bismuth at 271 C is 127 microhm-cm.

Certain elements (for example, gold and silver) have an anomalous minimum in resistivity at temperatures ranging from about 7 to 4 K. Some alloys also show the minimum: Solute

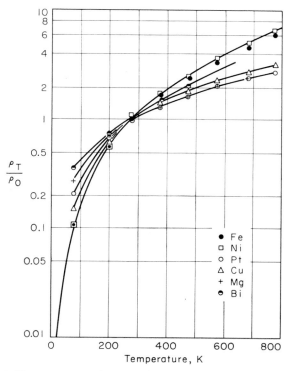

Fig. 11. Temperature dependence of the relative resistivities of several metals. The ordinate is the ratio of the resistivity at temperature T to that at 0 C (32 F). (After Seitz)

atoms of iron, tin, germanium, lead, gallium and indium in copper produce this effect. Other atoms (nickel, silver and gold) in copper produce no minimum in resistivity. The resistance of elements and alloys at low temperatures, near absolute zero, is discussed in detail by Macdonald (45).

The resistance of ferromagnetic metals rises rapidly as the

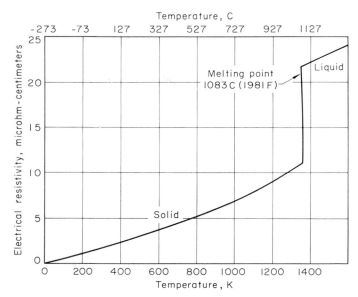

Fig. 12. Electrical resistivity of copper as a function of temperature

Curie temperature is approached, with a resulting discontinuity in the slope of the curve for resistance versus temperature occurring at the Curie temperature (46). Above this temperature the resistance behavior with temperature is normal.

Although there is a wide variation in electrical resistivities of carbon, low-alloy and high-alloy steels, ranging from 10 to 85 microhm-cm at 0 C, depending on structure, the resistivities of these steels converge at 800 C (1470 F) to values between 107.3 and 120.4 microhm-cm (35, 47).

The change in resistance of a conductor can be calculated from the temperature coefficient of resistivity. The variation of resistance with temperature can be expressed by

$$R = R_0(1 + \alpha T + \beta T^2 + \gamma T^3) \tag{19}$$

where α, β and γ are constants known as the temperature coefficients (only one, α, is normally used), and R_0 is the resistance at 0 C. For some metals, such as platinum, used in resistance thermometers, the range of temperature over which it is used is so great that it is necessary to use both α and β coefficients ($\alpha = 39.8 \times 10^{-4}$, and $\beta = -58.8 \times 10^{-8}$ at 20 C).

The variation of electrical resistance with temperature is more commonly written as:

$$R_2 = R_1(1 + \alpha(T_2 - T_1) + \ldots)$$ (20)

where R_1 is the resistance at temperature T_1 and R_2 is the resistance at temperature T_2.

The temperature coefficient of resistance, α, of a metal is defined as follows:

$$\alpha = \frac{R_2 - R_1}{R_1(T_2 - T_1)} = \frac{\rho_2 - \rho_1}{\rho_1(T_2 - T_1)}$$ (21)

where R_1 and R_2 are resistances of the material at temperatures T_1 and T_2, respectively, and ρ_1 and ρ_2 resistivities at T_1 and T_2.

For pure metallic elements, the temperature coefficient is virtually the same, being about 0.004 per °C or 0.0023 per °F. For copper, the temperature coefficient is 0.00393 when T is taken at 20 C (68 F); this is an increase of resistance of 0.4% per °C. The coefficient of an alloy is less than the average of the coefficients of its constituents. A nickel-chromium alloy (80 Ni – 20 Cr) has a coefficient of 0.00013 at 20 C. Alloys used for resistance applications will have coefficients of about 1.6×10^{-4}.

The temperature coefficient of resistance is a linear function of the conductivity (the reciprocal of resistivity) of a metal or of a binary solid solution. The coefficient increases as conductivity increases or as resistivity decreases. Small variations in minor alloying elements have a considerable effect on the temperature coefficient but not on the resistivity.

Dellinger (48) has shown that the temperature coefficient of copper is proportional to the IACS conductivity.

Polymorphic Transitions and Electrical Resistivity. The change in the curve for electrical resistivity versus temperature has sharp discontinuities at phase changes. In general, the change in resistivity is sufficiently large so that accurate measurements of resistivities can easily delineate the existence of phases. Some transformations, unfortunately, are sluggish, and hysteresis effects are noted on heating and cooling. Cobalt, for example, transforms from beta to gamma over a range of more than 100 °C on cooling. Despite these hysteresis effects, the measurement of resistivity is an excellent method of establishing the occurrence of phases and the location of phase boundaries. The Curie temperature is also readily established by resistivity methods.

The electrical resistivity and temperature coefficient of the five crystallographic phases of plutonium have been investigated by Ball and Lord (49), and their results are given in Table 16.

Phase Boundaries and Temperature Discontinuities. If there is an increase in volume at the phase boundary, an increase in slope of the curve of resistance as a function of temperature is generally found. Conversely, a decrease in volume will generally result in a decrease in the slope of the curve. Because of these effects,

Table 16. Electrical Resistivity of the Crystallographic Modifications of Plutonium

Phase	Electrical resistivity, microhm-cm	Temperature coefficient, $\times 10^5/°C$
α............	150	-22 to -40
β............	117	-5 to -11
γ............	115	-4 to -8
δ............	108	$+8$ to $+18$
ϵ............	123	....

Phase-transition temperatures
from resistivity-temperature curves

Transition	Heating	Cooling
$\alpha \rightleftarrows \beta$..........	135 C (275 F)	90 C (195 F)
$\beta \rightleftarrows \gamma$..........	220 C (430 F)	160 C (310 F)
$\gamma \rightleftarrows \delta$..........	325 C (615 F)	225 C (435 F)
$\delta \rightleftarrows \epsilon$..........	480 C (895 F)	380 C (715 F)

resistivity measurements are commonly used to supplement other procedures in establishing phases and boundaries. Saldau (50), for example, developed the iron-carbon diagram solely on the basis of electrical-resistance measurements. The Curie temperature also was easily determined by this procedure.

Anomalies in curves for electrical resistance versus temperature that are not related to phase changes are sometimes observed. In thorium and thorium-carbon alloys, Chiotti (51) has observed anomalous changes in the slope of such curves over the range from 700 to 950 C (1290 to 1740 F). In ductile titanium, Jaeger, Rosenbohm, and Fonteyne (52) noticed minor discontinuities for the same type of plot. These anomalies were ascribed to impurities in the metal they used. Presumably, they represent precipitation effects on the resistance of the material.

Discontinuities in the slope of the temperature-versus-resistance curves have been reported by Ham and co-workers that cannot be explained on the basis of phase boundaries, magnetic transformations, or precipitation of impurities. Ham and Samans (53) report anomalous discontinuities in curves for all metals of group VIII of the periodic table. The work was performed on pure metal wires and on glasses containing oxides of the metals; electrolytic conductivity was measured in the latter instance.

Resistivity of Liquid Metals (54). At the melting point, the lattice is disrupted and the resistivity changes abruptly. However, no satisfactory theory exists to explain the electrical properties of liquid-metal alloys. Electrical conductivity in liquid metals is probably similar to that in solids, except that in liquids a small fraction of the current is carried by ions (55).

Northrup (43) has measured the resistivity of copper from 20 to 1450 C (68 to 2640 F); his results can be summarized as follows:

$$\rho = 1.72 + 0.00883T \text{ at 20 C to melting point} \tag{22}$$
$$\rho = 11.3, \text{ just below the melting point (1083 C)}$$
$$\rho = 21.3, \text{ just above the melting point (1083 C)}$$
$$\rho = 21.3 + 0.00806T \text{ at 1083 to 1400 C (1980 to 2550 F)} \tag{23}$$

These data are summarized in Fig. 12.

Few data exist on the electrical resistivity of molten iron. It is reported as 131 microhm-cm by Chernobrovkin (38). On measurements of molten cast iron, Chernobrovkin states that the addition of various elements to the melt has no effect on resistance; the various molten cast irons had resistivities in the range of 145 to 155 microhm-cm.

When metals are dissolved in liquid mercury, the liquid amalgams may have either higher or lower resistance than pure mercury; solution of indium or thallium in mercury causes a large decrease in the resistivity, while solution of indium or tin in gallium causes a slight increase (56).

Effect of Alloying Elements and Impurities

One can differentiate between alloying elements and impurities on the basis of whether the foreign elements are deliberate additions or not. Alloying elements are intentionally added and may be present in relatively high concentrations. Impurities are usually undesirable elements in, or inadvertently introduced into, the base metal.

The resistance of alloys depends greatly on the presence of alloying elements and impurities. All factors that tend to disrupt the regularity of the parent lattice tend to increase the resistance. When atoms dissolve in a metal to form a random solid solution, the resistance at low and elevated temperatures is always increased. Solute atoms produce distortions in the lattice. The distortions cause scattering of conduction electrons, thereby interfering with electron flow and increasing the electrical resistivity of the metal.

Theoretically, an absolutely pure metal should have zero resistivity at absolute temperature. All metals contain some impurities, and, as the temperature of such metals is lowered to absolute zero, the resistance does not go to zero but approaches a limiting value that is due to the impurities. The same situation exists for alloys. The higher the impurity or alloy content, the higher the limiting resistance will be. Matthiessen (57) discovered the rule named after him: Namely, the increase in resistance due to a small concentration of another metal in solid solution is in general independent of temperature. As a consequence of this rule, the resistance of an alloy or an impure metal is the sum of two terms:

$$\rho = \rho_0 + \rho(T) \tag{24}$$

where ρ_0 is the residual resistance, which is proportional to the impurity and is independent of temperature, and $\rho(T)$, often called the ideal resistance, is temperature dependent.

The residual resistance is assumed to be due solely to chemical and physical imperfections. The ideal resistance arises solely from the thermal vibrations of the unperturbed lattice; that is, it is due to the ideally pure and physically perfect metal.

The effect of foreign atoms on the resistance of iron, aluminum and copper is shown in Fig. 7, 8, and 9. Electrons that are scattered by the impurity atoms in the lattice give rise to an added resistance, and, if the impurity content is small, the resistances caused by the impurities and the thermal vibrations are additive.

The scattering of electrons and the resulting increased resistance caused by impurities or alloying result from the disturbance of the lattice, but the effect may arise in several ways, as follows:

1 It may occur because of the heterovalency of the impurity atom. An atom of higher valency than the solvent atoms results in a strong "screening" of the foreign ion by the remaining conduction electrons. For instance, if divalent zinc is dissolved in a lattice of monovalent copper ions, there will be an excess unit positive charge at the site of the zinc ion. The interaction of a conduction electron with this charge results in strong screening.

2 If the solute atom is homovalent with the solvent metal (for example, potassium in sodium and silver in copper), no charge difference will exist, but scattering occurs in two ways: (a) The scattering cross section of the solute will differ from the parent metal; (b) because of the size factor of the solute atom, the matrix may be locally strained by the impurity, and this displacement of the ions will give rise to electron scattering.

3 The formation of a new phase will increase the scattering. Significant scattering would occur for either coherent or incoherent precipitation.

The measurement of the residual resistance of tungsten at low temperature is a very sensitive method for detecting impurities, vacancies, dislocations and lattice deformations (58). Because the sensitivity in detecting defects in crystals decreases with increasing temperature, most measurements are made at liquid-hydrogen temperatures (-253 C; -423 F). Plastic deformation of tungsten results in a very high residual resistance.

An atom dissolving substitutionally in the matrix will not in general scatter an electron wave of the same amplitude as the solvent atom. If the amplitudes of the waves are A and B, the increase in resistance will be proportional to $(A - B)^2$. The scattering power of an atom depends on the field within it, and the resistance should increase with the horizontal distance between the two elements in the periodic system (59). This rationalization of the resistance does not consider the possible strain introduced by solid solution. Such strain effects are assumed to be small in comparison to the scattering effect.

Linde (60) has shown that the increase in the resistivity of silver or gold due to 1 at.% of any metal to the right of them in the periodic table is proportional to $(Z - 1)^2$ where Z is the number of electrons outside a closed shell (2 for zinc, 3 for gallium, 4 for germanium, 5 for arsenic). Such behavior serves to confirm the theory of electronic conduction.

Electrical Resistivity of Alloys. The relationships between electrical resistivity and the constitution of alloys were developed

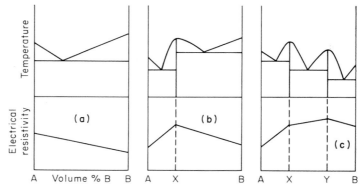

*Fig. 13. Electrical resistivity of heterogeneous mixtures —
phases immiscible in each other in the solid state. (a) Pure
metals; (b) pure metals A and B, and intermediate phase X;
(c) pure metals A and B, with intermediate phases X and Y.*

by Matthiessen (57), Le Chatelier (61), Kurnakov (62), and
Guertler (63). The generalizations developed are sometimes referred to as Le Chatelier-Guertler rules:

1 In heterogeneous mixtures of two phases, the electrical resistivity varies linearly, if the composition is given in volume per
 cent. The two phases can be two pure metals (Fig. 13,a) — for
 example, systems As-Pb, Au-Tl, Bi-Cd; pure metals and an intermediate phase (Fig. 13,b) — for example, system Mg-Si; or

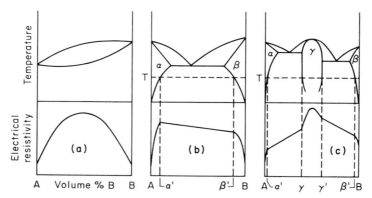

*Fig. 14. Electrical resistivity in solid solutions and mix-
tures. (a) Solid solution; (b) mixture of terminal solid solutions, alpha and beta; (c) mixture of terminal solid solutions, alpha and beta, and an intermediate phase, gamma.*

two metals and two intermediate phases (Fig. 13,c) — for example, system Na-Sb. The resistivity of intermediate phases is always higher than the value calculated using the law of mixtures.

2 In solid solutions, the electrical resistivity is always higher than that of the solvent metal and is usually higher to a considerable degree, if the composition is given in volume per cent. Increasing the amounts of solute increases resistivity, especially with the first small additions. Figure 14(a) shows the variation of resistivity of a continuous solid solution; examples are copper-nickel and silver-gold systems. The variation of resistivity in a system of terminal solid solutions is given in Fig. 14(b); systems that have a miscibility gap between solid solutions are silver-copper and lead-tin. The change of resistivity in a system that contains two solid solutions and an intermediate phase of variable composition is shown in Fig. 14(c); an example of such a system would be bismuth-tellurium.

In a continuous solid solution (silver-gold), the resistance is much greater than that of either component and reaches its maximum value at 50 at.%. In a solid solution, the electron waves are scattered from the foreign atoms present. The in-

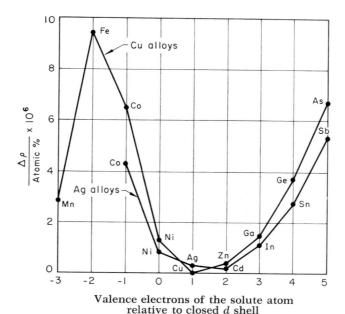

Fig. 15. *Increase in resistivity of copper and silver alloys per atomic per cent of solute (After Seitz)*

crease in resistance as a result of the solution of foreign atoms is usually very large. At room temperature, the resistivity of a metal may be doubled by the presence of 1 at.% of solute. It is because of this increase in resistance as a result of alloying that resistance measurements are used to measure the purity of a specimen. Purity of semiconductors is evaluated by this measurement.

The amount by which an alloying atom raises the resistance of a metal depends very much on the relative position of the solvent and solute in the periodic chart. The amount by which the resistance of copper and silver varies with the addition of 1 at.% of various elements is shown in Fig. 15. The residual resistance component of the total resistance changes almost quadratically with difference in valence of the solute and solvent.

In some solid solutions (for example, copper-tin), superlattice formation can occur. When ordering takes place, a decrease in resistance occurs. The influence of order-disorder phenomena on resistivity is discussed on pages 77 and 78.

Temperature Coefficient of Resistivity and Constitution. In general, Le Chatelier-Guertler's rules hold for the temperature coefficient of electrical resistivity. There is a proportionality between the electrical resistivity of binary alloys and their temperature coefficient of resistivity. The curves for temperature coefficient versus composition correspond to the resistivity-composition curves in previous illustrations. Intermediate phases always have a temperature coefficient of electrical resistivity of the same order of magnitude as that of pure metals; it is always smaller than the value calculated from the law of mixtures.

In solid solutions, there is no exception to proportionality between electrical resistivity and the temperature coefficient; both properties are controlled by Le Chatelier-Guertler rule 2; as the resistivity increases, the temperature coefficient decreases.

Alloys of zero temperature coefficient can be compounded. For example, manganin (12% Mn, 4% Ni, remainder copper) has a zero coefficient between 0 and 100 C (32 to 212 F).

Effect of Elastic and Plastic Deformation

The relationship between electrical resistance and the crystal structure is not developed sufficiently to enable prediction of the effect of strain (elastic, let alone plastic) on resistivity. However, empirical relationships exist (64).

Assume that the effect of tension on the resistivity of fine wire is required. Tension will increase the length and will reduce the cross section. The effect on resistivity occurs as a result of the changes in the cross-sectional resistance R of equation (10):

$$R = \rho \frac{l}{A} \tag{10}$$

By taking the logarithmic derivative of equation (10), the result is as follows:

$$\frac{dR}{R} = \frac{d\rho}{\rho} + \frac{dl}{l} - \frac{dA}{A} \tag{25}$$

The change in cross section is small and not readily measured. It is customary to replace A in equation (25) by Poisson's ratio, γ.[*] This can be done with the following relation:

$$2\gamma \frac{dl}{l} = -\frac{dA}{A}$$

Equation (25) can then be rewritten as follows:

$$G = \frac{dR}{R} \bigg/ \frac{dl}{l} = 1 + 2\gamma + \frac{d\rho}{\rho} \bigg/ \frac{dl}{l} \tag{25a}$$

The quantity G, which is readily measured, is called the gage factor or strain sensitivity of the material. This gage factor may vary from -12 to $+3.5$. The basis for strain gages lies in the fact that, when a wire is stretched elastically, its length and diameter change in conformity with Poisson's ratio. As demonstrated before, electrical resistance is affected by changes in length and diameter. Theoretically, elongation of a wire by 0.1%, with a corresponding change in diameter, should produce a change in resistance of 0.17%. Due to geometric factors resulting from elastic strain, any wire should have a strain sensitivity of 1.7. However, most wires have a widely different strain sensitivity for reasons poorly understood.

Within the elastic limit, the effects of deformation on the resistivity of metals are small. Plastic deformation causes the generation of new lattice defects or imperfections, such as vacancies and interstitial atoms, as well as dislocations. Hence, the resistivity increases with deformation. In alloys, the resistivity is a function of the degree of long or short-range order, and

---

[*] Poisson's ratio for the elastic range of most metals is about 0.3. If the material is deformed plastically and the volume remains constant, a value of 0.5 is used.

deformation may change the spatial arrangement of the atoms and thereby either increase or decrease the resistivity. Cold work introduces many dislocations and vacancies, as well as interstitial atoms (fewer in number than vacancies). The vacancies and interstitial atoms are responsible for virtually all additional resistance due to cold work; the effect of dislocations on resistance is small (65). When plastic deformation occurs, significant changes in resistivity occur with deformations of 10% (reduction in cross section). Nonetheless, the maximum change in resistivity by cold work is no more than that which is produced by 0.1% alloy addition.

Numerous measurements on copper plastically deformed below the boiling point of air show that the increase in resistivity, $\Delta\rho$, is a function of the mean plastic glide strain, ϵ, in per cent (65). The relation takes the form:

$$\Delta\rho = a\epsilon^p \qquad (26)$$

where p lies between 1.2 and 1.5 for polycrystalline copper and 1.8 for single crystals, and a is a coefficient of about 0.1 microhm-cm for polycrystalline material and 0.01 microhm-cm for single crystals.

Plastic strain or cold work of any variety (rolling, swaging, drawing) increases the electrical resistivity. In addition to atomic-scale imperfections, cold work produces internal strains, disturbances at boundaries between grains and grain fragments, and distortions around slip lines and precipitates, thereby further contributing to the scattering of electrons.

Guillet and Ballay (66) studied the effect of cold work on the resistivity of several metals and alloys. For pure metals, the increase in resistivity on severe working was less than 4%; for alloys, the increases were usually higher. In the copper-zinc alloys, they found that the increase in resistivity due to drawing increased with zinc content, and reported a 21.7% increase in resistance for an alloy containing 67.9% Cu. Tammann and Dreyer (67) found that cold rolling increased the resistivity of copper, gold and silver in the following manner: For copper that was cold rolled 98%, resistivity increased 1.6%; for gold cold rolled 98%, it also increased 1.6%; for silver cold rolled 90%, it increased 5%.

Bardenhauer and Schmidt (68) found that the conductivity of copper decreased by 3 to 4% when it was reduced 50% by cold

Table 17. Change in Electrical Resistivity of Armco Iron on Cold Drawing

Cold drawing, %	Electrical resistivity, microhm-cm	Cold drawing, %	Electrical resistivity, microhm-cm
0	11.2	57.2	11.27
5.6	11.17	67.9	11.3
14.0	11.15	75.9	11.27
19.2	11.19	84.2	11.30
29.5	11.24	93.8	11.32
40.7	11.24		

working. Crampton, Burghoff, and Stacy (69) reported a 4% decrease in conductivity for cold drawing copper to 84%. (The effect of cold work on the IACS conductivity of pure copper is shown in Fig. 41, Chapter 4.) They also reported that lowering of conductivity increases with alloy content and with the severity of the draw; marked changes occur in copper-zinc and copper-aluminum alloys. Balicki (70), working with Armco iron, found that the resistivity was only slightly increased, from 11.2 microhm-cm with no deformation to 11.32 microhm-cm with 93.8% reduction; this change represents a 1.07% increase (Table 17). Nickel, molybdenum, tungsten, and platinum wires drawn more than 99% show resistivity increases of 8, 18, 50, and 6%, respectively; the temperature coefficient is decreased by 5, 16, 35, and 7% for the same elements.

Plastic strain in high-resistance wire increases the resistance, primarily as a result of the change in dimensions (71). This is illustrated in Table 18.

Table 18. Effect of Plastic Strain on Electrical Properties of 45 Ni – 55 Cu (Cupron)

Strain (elongation), %	Resistance			Specific resistivity	
	Ohms per ft	Ohms per ft corrected(a)	Change, %	Ohms per cir mil-ft	Change, %
0	9.17	9.17	....	294	....
2	9.37	9.56	+4.2	294	0
5	9.63	10.11	+10.3	294	0
10	10.21	11.23	+22.5	298	+1
15	10.68	12.34	+34.0	298	+1
20	11.17	13.40	+46.0	298	+1

(a) Ohms per foot $\times$ $(1 + \epsilon)$, where ϵ is per cent elongation.

The copper-palladium system is an exception to the general behavior that plastic deformation increases resistivity. The resistivity of alloys containing 9.6 to 29% Pd was observed to decrease with plastic deformation in tension (72). Although Jaumot and Sawatzky (73) observed these anomalies in the cold working of ordered alloys, Klokholm and Hyatt were able to show that the anomaly occurred without ordering being present. According to Damask (74), the destruction of short-range order could lead to a decrease in resistivity as a result of cold work. In alloys with long-range order, cold working tends to disorder the structure, and a marked increase in resistivity occurs.

Ferromagnetic materials show unusual variations of resistivity with elastic strain. When the magnetostriction * is negative, as in the iron-nickel system containing more than 81% Ni, tension decreases the resistivity. When the magnetostriction is positive, tension increases the resistivity to a limiting value (75). For an alloy containing 89% Ni (negative magnetostriction), a stress of 6.36 kg per sq mm decreased the resistivity by about 2%. For an alloy containing 69% Ni (positive magnetostriction), a stress of 4.41 kg per sq mm increased the resistivity by 1.7%.

Change in Electrical Resistivity of Cold Worked Metals During Annealing

The annealing of cold worked metals results in the following processes, occurring in the order given: recovery, recrystallization, and grain growth (normal and exaggerated — the latter now called secondary recrystallization). The first two may occur concurrently to some extent; by definition, grain growth is considered as occurring only after recrystallization is complete. Recovery is normally associated with the relief of internal stress and is accompanied by a sharp decrease in electrical resistivity and thermal electromotive force (70), with either a slight rise or fall in mechanical properties; no change in microstructure occurs. Recrystallization, which is a nucleation and growth phenomenon, causes large changes in mechanical properties, due to the resulting strain-free structure, but is not generally held to be responsible for much change in electrical properties. No signifi-

* Ferromagnetic materials suffer minute increases or decreases in dimensions when magnetized; these changes correspond to positive and negative magnetostriction, respectively (see Chapter 5).

cant changes in electrical properties occur with grain growth. Muller (76) explains the changes in electrical properties of deformed nickel on the basis of two types of internal stress: A stress pattern of microscopic, but relatively long, periodicity, and a short-range pattern (four or five lattice parameters), whose period length is of the order of the wave length of the conduction electron. During recovery, it is postulated that the short-period stress pattern is reduced, thus causing a decrease in electrical resistivity.

Maddigan and Blank (77) have studied cold worked 70–30 brass and have attempted to explain changes in electrical and mechanical properties with respect to recovery and recrystallization. Balicki's work (70) on Armco iron shows that the resistivity decreases gradually with increasing annealing temperature for a severely cold worked (93.8%) wire. This diminution in resistivity is continuous with increasing annealing temperature up to about 550 to 650 C (1020 to 1200 F).

The higher electrical resistivity of some cold worked metals may be completely recovered to the values of the original annealed metal before hardness decreases significantly.

Copper-zinc alloys cold drawn 84% show continual recovery of electrical conductivity when annealed for 1 hr at temperatures ranging from 100 C (212 F) upward through the recrystallization range; however, the most important changes occur during recrystallization (69). The recovery of conductivity of severely cold drawn copper is shown in Fig. 41, Chapter 4.

The recovery phenomena in plastically deformed metals can be explained as diffusion processes of the lattice defects formed — vacancies, interstitial atoms, and dislocations (65). These phenomena consist of the following processes:

1 Diffusion of pairs of vacancies and dislocations, and their recombination
2 Diffusion and absorption of vacancies at dislocations to form a substructure. The remaining vacancies migrate out of the metal or into grain boundaries.
3 Complete removal of cold work by self-diffusion, polygonization, recrystallization, and grain growth. During these processes, which are mainly the result of the motion of dislocations, electrical conductivity improves and mechanical properties, such as hardness and tensile strength, decrease.

Recrystallization of cold worked (compressed) copper can be

followed by measurements of electrical resistivity. The Δ_ρ * of copper, deformed 58% and heated then at a rate of 6 °C per min decreased at about 225 C (435 F), the beginning of recrystallization, and reached zero at 300 C (570 F), the completion of recrystallization (78).

Variation of Electrical Resistivity During Precipitation, Age Hardening, Tempering of Martensitic Steels, Transformations and Strain Aging in Iron

Any solid solution in which some constituent is more soluble at a higher temperature than at a lower one is capable of experiencing the phenomenon of age hardening (79). Age hardening is revealed by supersaturated terminal or intermediate solid solutions, and by substitutional or interstitial types. The precipitating phase can be a pure metal, a terminal or intermediate solid solution, or an intermediate phase. The size and distribution of the precipitated particles and their orientation relationships to the matrix have varying effects on the properties of the metal. Ideal precipitation should always result in a decrease in resistivity, due to the depletion of solute from the matrix. The size of precipitated particles has a profound effect on resistivity.

Age Hardening. Precipitation on aging causes a gradual change in the physical properties of an alloy. Hardness usually increases with time to a maximum, after which there is a gradual decrease. Electrical and magnetic properties also change during the hardening. The resistivity of a supersaturated solid solution during aging usually shows an initial increase, followed by a gradual decrease. The maximum in resistivity usually comes before the maximum in hardness.

Because the wave length of electron waves is somewhat larger than the solute atoms, one would expect the initial stages of precipitation, in which crystals of 20 to 30 atoms are formed, to increase the resistivity. When the crystals become large compared to the electron wave length, a decrease in resistivity is to be expected. If atoms segregate into very small clusters of the order of the electron wave length (about 10 A), they are more effective in scattering the conduction electrons than if the clusters were larger or smaller. Scattering from optimum-sized clusters actually may give a higher resistivity than can be ex-

* Δ_ρ is the ratio of ρ after deformation to ρ at room temperature.

pected from a random solid solution (80). In other words, coherency hardening sets up internal strains that scatter electrons.
When incoherency occurs, there is a scattering of electrons from
the precipitated phase. In general, for the scattering of waves by
particles, the maximum value should occur when the wave
length and the particle dimensions are about the same. Because
the wave length of the conduction electrons is usually of the
order of two or three atomic distances, the precipitate should
contain between 10 and 100 atoms at the stage of maximum
resistivity.

The change of resistivity of a quenched aluminum-copper
(4% Cu) alloy on aging at room temperature is shown in Fig.

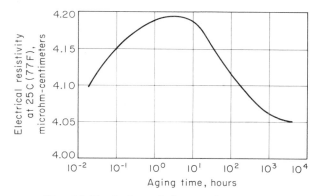

*Fig. 16. Variation of electrical resistivity
of a quenched aluminum-copper alloy
(4% Cu) on aging at room temperature*

16 (81). Note how the resistivity passes through a maximum
during the precipitation process and then drops to a value lower
than that for copper dissolved in the lattice. In alpha iron, the
precipitation of 0.01% C from solid solution causes a decrease of
2.5% in electrical resistivity (82).

Electrical resistivity can be used in studying age-hardening
systems. Alloy additions to a solid solution increase the electrical
resistivity, so that precipitation causes a decrease. However, during the early stages of precipitation of many systems, an anomalous increase in resistance has been observed. This increase has
been explained on the basis of the precipitate particles being of
the same size as the wave length of the conduction electrons

and on the basis of lattice strain caused by the precipitating particles (80).

Tempering. In the tempering of carbon and low-alloy steels, the electrical resistivity might be expected to vary with the four stages of tempering.* However, Crafts and Lamont (83) found that, on tempering, the change in resistivity was continuous and did not decrease greatly until the tempering temperatures of rapid softening were reached. The resistivity decreased as the tempering temperature was raised (Table 19).

In chromium steels, the situation appears to be different. The second, third and fourth stages of tempering in a 4.5% Cr steel

Table 19. Effect of Tempering on the Electrical Resistivity of Three Alloy Steels(a)

Tempering temperature,		Resistivity, microhm-in.(b)		
F	C	Steel 1(c)	Steel 2(d)	Steel 3(e)
As quenched		15.6	13.2	13.9
400	205	14.5	13.1	13.7
600	315	14.4	13.0	13.4
800	425	14.2	12.9	13.4
1000	540	12.8	12.4	13.1
1100	595	11.9	11.8	12.2
1200	650	11.8	11.0	11.6
1300	705	11.8	7.9	10.7

(a) Austenitized in salt at 1095 to 1260 C (2000 to 2300 F), quenched, immersed in liquid air to minimize retained austenite, tempered at indicated temperatures for 2 hr. (b) Microhm-inches $\times$ 2.54 = microhm-centimeters. (c) 0.53% C, 3.80% V. (d) 0.48% C, 5.07% Mo. (e) 0.52% C, 10.62% W.

were successfully observed (84) by resistivity measurements; the first stage was not studied. The second stage of tempering was attended by an increase in resistivity, unlike in plain carbon steels and most other alloy steels. The third and fourth stages were accompanied by successive decreases in resistivity.

Transformations in metals are readily followed by electrical-

* The four stages of tempering are as follows:

1 The original martensite decomposes into a hexagonal carbide (epsilon carbide) and another martensite containing about 0.25% C.
2 Austenite decomposes into bainite.
3 Cementite forms.
4 Alloy carbides (where alloy is available) develop.

resistivity measurements. Colner and Zmeskal (85), in studying a precipitation-hardenable austenitic steel, found that during the austenite-to-ferrite transformation resistivity increased, while for the ferrite-to-austenite transformation it decreased. Resistivity changes in martensite and pearlite reactions are opposite to those observed in stainless steel (86) — the electrical resistivity decreases when the austenite transforms to martensite and pearlite.

Strain Aging. In strain aging of iron — the precipitation of carbon and nitrogen as influenced by cold working — the electrical resistivity decreases a small amount. Carbon and nitrogen atoms in solution scatter electrons very effectively, but at dislocations the scattering is less effective. The resistivity is, therefore, highly sensitive to the amounts of these elements in solution. It has been shown that a decrease of 0.01 wt % in solution causes a decrease in resistivity of 2.5% for carbon and 3.5% for nitrogen (82). Although the transfer of these atoms from random solution to dislocation sites cannot be as effective in reducing resistivity as would removing them completely, it is reasonable to expect an effect. Cottrell and Churchman (87) found such a change in resistivity to vary from 0.18 to 0.24% when the strain or degree of cold work varied from 8 to 42%. The amount of cold work has little effect on the time of aging; at 31 C (88 F), the change in resistivity reduces to zero in about two or three days, regardless of the degree of deformation.

Electrical Resistivity and Pressure

Most metals show a reduction of electrical resistivity under pressure, but the rate of change decreases as the pressure increases. However, some metals show an increase in resistivity under pressure and for these (for example, lithium and bismuth) the rate of increase of resistance becomes greater as the pressure increases. In general, the changes in resistivity are greater for the softer metals with low melting points. For example, under pressure of 30,000 kg per sq cm, strontium has its resistivity increased by nearly 3.5 times its normal value.

The zone theory of metals, which takes into account the energy structure of the electrons, provides the basis for an explanation of the effect of pressure on electrical resistivity. The average behavior of the electrons in a band will be a mean between the behavior of those that are free and those that are not. This mean behavior will depend on the structure of the band and also on the pressure. Unfortunately, the theory is not developed sufficiently to explain many anomalies — for example, increase in resistivity with pressure and single-crystal behavior.

Ordinarily, the resistance of bismuth increases with pressure. At 25,000 kg per sq cm, the phase changes and the resistivity

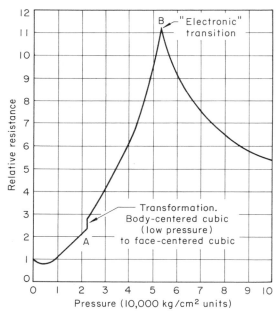

Fig. 17. Effect of pressure up to 100,000 kg per sq cm on the relative resistance of cesium

drops by a factor of six. The resistivity of the high-pressure modification then decreases with increasing pressure. At a second transition point at about 27,000 kg per sq cm, the resistance rises again by a factor of 2.6.

The explanation of the pressure effect used before the development of wave mechanics is still useful in visualizing the mechanism responsible for the pressure effect. As the pressure increases, the natural frequency of vibration of the atoms increases (because of the greater intensity of the restoring forces at small volumes) and the amplitude decreases. This explains qualitatively why the resistivity of most metals decreases under pressure.

Bridgman (88) has measured the effect of pressure on 52 elements, 47 of which were metals. Of the metals, 31 exhibited the expected behavior — that is, the resistivity decreased with pressure along a curve that was convex toward the pressure axis. The resistivity of the remaining elements is still somewhat anomalous, although some explanation of the increased resistivity in

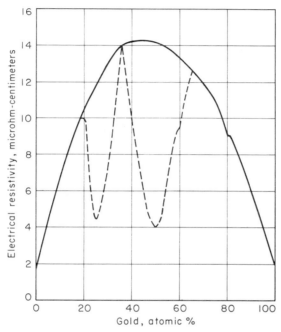

Fig. 18. Effect of order-disorder transformation on electrical resistivity of gold-copper alloys at 0 C (32 F). Dashed lines are for the ordered condition, and the solid line is for the disordered condition.

lithium and cerium has been achieved by band-theory considerations. For cesium, the variation of resistivity with pressure can be explained in the following manner (see Fig. 17): The discontinuity at A is the phase transformation from body-centered to face-centered cubic. The cusp at B is the electronic transition, due to the shift of the valence electron from the 6s orbit to the empty 5d orbit as the orbits are compressed.

Single crystals of noncubic metals under pressure show large variations in resistivity. Zinc decreases in resistivity in all crystal-lographic directions, but exhibits a curious dissymmetry of the pressure effects in the different directions, so that at high pressures the relative resistivities along the principal directions are reversed. The resistivity of single-crystal antimony in certain directions first increases with pressure, then passes through a maximum, and then decreases. At high pressures, tellurium has a positive temperature coefficient of resistivity; ordinarily, it has a negative coefficient.

Electrical Resistivity and Superlattice Formation

A well-ordered superlattice has lower electrical resistivity than a disordered lattice. In some alloys, the difference in resistivity between ordered and disordered lattices is large, as in the copper-gold, copper-platinum and copper-palladium alloys. In other alloys, the difference in resistivity is small, as in beta brass, iron-cobalt, and Ni_3Mn. Lattice irregularities that occur as a result of disorder increase the scattering of electrons. Figure 18 shows the effect of order-disorder on the resistivity of gold-copper alloys (89). The dashed curves are for the ordered condition, and the solid curve is for the disordered situation.

When a disordered solid solution is retained at room temperature by quenching from above a critical temperature, T_c, strains from the irregularity of atomic distribution are superimposed on those from thermal vibration. By annealing below T_c, order begins to appear and the resistivity is lowered. The influence of order on the electrical properties has been discussed by Muto and Takagi (90). Bozorth (75) has shown that the electrical resistivity decreases with ordering in iron-nickel alloys at compositions near $FeNi_3$.

Ordering has a considerable influence on the temperature coefficients of resistivity. For example, in iron-platinum alloys near the Fe_3Pt composition, alpha is 35×10^{-4} per °C below the ordering temperature, but it is only 3×10^{-4} per °C above the ordering temperature (91).

Because neutron irradiation enhances diffusion, it is possible to cause the disordered alloy of Cu_3Au to assume the ordered condition at much lower temperatures when it is subjected to neutron bombardment.

Magnetoresistance

The change of the resistivity of the normal metallic elements (excluding bismuth, antimony, arsenic and the ferromagnetic metals) when placed in a magnetic field has been investigated up to 300,000 oersteds (92, 93). A magnetic field always increases the resistivity. If the resistance of a metal in no field is R and the change in resistance caused by an increase in magnetic field, H, is ΔR, the ratio $\Delta R/R$ has been shown to increase in proportion to H^2 for comparatively low field strengths and to H for high field strengths. For most metallic elements, the electrical resistivity is increased on the order of 0.01% by a field of 10,000 gausses. The effect of a magnetic field was first noted in iron by Thomson (94).

The outstanding example of the increase in resistivity by magnetization is diamagnetic bismuth. The effect is so large that calibrated bismuth wires are used for measuring high magnetic fields. The resistance change at -192 C (-324 F) is 88-fold that at room temperature, and, at 18 C (64 F), it increases threefold when the magnetic field is increased from zero to 35,000 oersteds. The increase in resistance with field is linear in the range of 2000 to 35,000 oersteds.

Justi (95) has suggested that the magnetoresistance of odd-valent metallic groups in the periodic table (Table 1) tends toward a saturation value, while that of even-valent groups continues to increase quadratically with a certain parameter of the field H. The magnetoresistance of some single crystals varies remarkably with angle of rotation.

The magnetoresistance of ferromagnetic materials is greater than for nonmagnetic substances. The increase in resistivity of a nickel-iron alloy with 78% Ni was found by Bozorth (75) to be 2% at a field of 25 oersteds; an alloy with 89% Ni showed a change of 3.5% at the same field.

When magnetostriction is negative, as in alloys of iron and nickel containing over 81% Ni, the magnetic field increases resistivity. When the magnetostriction is positive (40 to 80% Ni), the resistivity also increases with the field, but the limiting values of resistivity are found to be different because of the variation of magnetostriction with crystallographic direction.

The temperature coefficient of resistivity of a ferromagnetic material consists of the normal temperature coefficient and a coefficient proportional to the rate of change of the energy of spontaneous magnetization.

The resistivity change due to a magnetic field is proportional to the square of the carrier mobility in a semiconductor material. Because intermetallic semiconductors have very high electron mobilities, it is now possible to make practical use of the magnetoresistance effect. For instance, resistances of a 0.1 ohm can be increased to 2.5 to 5.0 ohms by the application of a field of 10,000 gausses. In the semiconductor indium antimonide, resistivity changes of up to 90 to 1 at $H = 30,000$ have been obtained. Such large changes in resistivity can be used for the measurement of magnetic effects.

Resistivity and High-Energy Radiation

In general, the changes in properties produced by irradiation seem to be less harmful or to disappear more rapidly in metals than in nonmetals. Metals and alloys exposed to high-energy radiation (neutrons, protons, deuterons, electrons, alpha particles) will experience an increase in electrical resistivity. The bombardment of metals with alpha particles, neutrons, or deuterons creates a large number of vacancies and interstitial atoms by knocking atoms out of position in the lattice (96, 97, 98). Probably only a few dislocation-type structures are produced by irradiation.

The resistivity of a pure metal is usually increased by irradiation and this change then provides a measure of the alteration of the lattice. The change in resistivity of gold with 1% vacant lattice sites is calculated to be about $\Delta\rho = 1.5 \times 10^{-6}$ ohm-cm, and, for a concentration of 1% of vacancy-interstitial pairs, the change in resistivity is about $\Delta\rho = 3.0 \times 10^{-6}$ ohm-cm. Ordered alloys disorder under bombardment with nucleons.

Irradiation experiments on metals must be performed at very low temperatures, because much of the damage anneals out at room temperature or below. It has been found necessary to go to liquid-helium temperatures (-253 C; -423 F) to preserve irradiation defects. The conductivity of copper is reduced 90% at 4 K under neutron bombardment. Warming of the irradiated metal restores most of its conductivity, and not much heat is needed. Copper, gold and silver bombarded with electrons at 11 K show no annealing; the annealing effect sets in at 17 K. The recovery of metals after bombardment results from the diffusion processes of the induced lattice defects. These processes are the diffusion of interstitial atoms, the diffusion of vacancy pairs and their recombination, the diffusion of vacancies, and the self-diffusion of ions in the metal.

It has been inferred that mobile lattice defects produced by cold work are not identical with those produced by irradiation. Meechan and Sosin (99), in an effort to explain the recovery of metals after electron, deuteron, and neutron irradiation, made comparative studies of the recovery of electrical resistivity of high-purity copper, gold, and nickel following cold working (by tension) at 4 K. The total amount of resistivity recovery, relative to the amount of cold work, was about 2%, varying slightly with the degree of cold work. The resistivity recovery was an order of magnitude smaller than that which follows particle radiation.

Increase in Electrical Resistivity as a Result of Quenching

Lattice defects can be generated in a metal as a result of quenching from temperatures near the melting point. Because of the relatively small energy (about 0.9 ev) required for the formation of vacancies, this is the only type of defect that remains in considerable concentration in the metal after quenching; few or no dislocations form and no interstitial atoms are produced. The recovery of metals from the increased-resistivity condition caused by quenching results from the diffusion of vacancies and their recombination.

It is possible to measure quench vacancies in metals and then to observe their disappearance on annealing by electrical-resistivity measurements. Kauffman and Koehler (100) have made such resistivity measurements on gold, and Panseri, Gatto and Federighi, on aluminum (101). In the latter work, quenching high-purity aluminum wires from 504 C (939 F) into water resulted in an increase of resistivity of 0.18%. The vacancies are annealed out at room temperature in about 25 min. A concentration as small as 0.13 at.% Mg in aluminum is sufficient both to trap vacancies and to suppress their annealing-out at room temperature (102). The resistivity increase can be annealed out at 80 to 120 C (176 to 248 F). Additional experiments with cold worked aluminum-magnesium alloys confirm the view that cold working generates vacancies.

Thin Films

The results of studies of the electrical resistivity and aging of thin films made since the work of Faraday (103) are summarized in part by Belser (104). Thin metal films (from about 100 to 5000 A) may undergo resistivity changes with natural aging or by heating, and these changes reflect certain structural changes in the film. The changes on prolonged or excessive heating may proceed to the destruction of the film and the attainment of infinite resistance.

Films are prepared by evaporation, sputtering and electroplating. Belser has shown that thin metal films appear to be in a state of strain and that heating of the deposit assists in the removal of these strains, the removal of absorbed or occluded gas, and the growth of crystallites in the film.

The resistivity of a film is the product of its thickness in centimeters and its resistance per square.* For evaporated films of gold, silver, aluminum and copper near 1000 A in thickness (10^{-5} cm), a resistivity of about twice the bulk density (ρ_b) is obtained initially. This resistivity is reduced to about 1.3 ρ_b after aging. Sputtered films had initial values of 3 to 10 ρ_b, which on aging were reduced to 1.5 to 1.8 ρ_b. Table 20 gives some resistance values of evaporated films. Films of iron-nickel alloys (45 Fe – 55 Ni and 85 Ni – 15 Fe) of thicknesses ranging from 500 to 5000 A have the same resistivity as does the bulk material.

Semiconductors

Semiconductors are unique materials (105 to 107) with some characteristics of conductors, some of insulators, and some peculiar to themselves; they are literally half conductor and half insulator. Actually, they are electronic conductors whose conductivity depends in a large measure on impurities, lattice defects, and temperature. Their conductivities lie between those of conductors and insulators; although the resistivity range is not sharply defined, semiconductors generally have resistivities between 10^{-2} and 10^6 ohm-cm. A semiconductor is not merely a

---

* This unit (resistance per square) is the resistance of a coated area of a centimeter square of specified thickness. When the resistance per square is multiplied by the film thickness in centimeters, a microhm-centimeter resistivity value is obtained.

Table 20. Resistance Measurements of Evaporated Films Before and After Aging

Film	Thickness, angstroms	Before aging		After aging		Per cent of original resistance (after aging)
		Ohms/sq	ρ/ρ_b	Ohms/sq	ρ/ρ_b	
Silver......1515		0.191	1.82	0.146	1.39	77
Gold........1930		0.249	1.97	0.176	1.39	70.7
Aluminum...2040		0.317	2.28	0.196	1.42	61.3

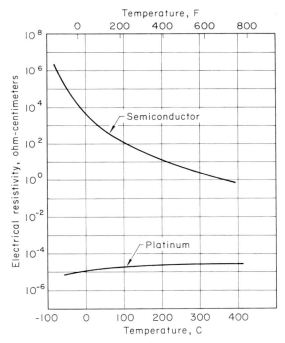

Fig. 19. Variation of resistivity of a typical semiconductor and a typical metal (platinum) with temperature

poor conductor — mixtures of graphite and clay (as in some resistors) are poor conductors, but they are not semiconductors.

The importance of semiconductors in electronics is increasing at a very rapid pace. Devices built with semiconductors can perform many of the functions of vacuum tubes, and they can perform them more efficiently and in smaller space. Semiconductor devices, for example, can amplify, rectify, oscillate, limit, count, and do other operations. The earlier semiconductor devices (transistors) had limited frequency response; the newer devices circumvent this difficulty, and the new tunnel diodes (108) appear most attractive for very high frequencies; successful operation of the tunnel diodes at five billion cycles has been reported. Semiconductors are also used for thermoelectric cooling as well as generation of electricity.

The most definite characteristic of a semiconductor is its

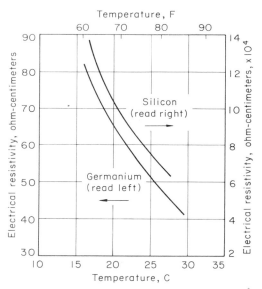

Fig. 20. *Variation of resistivity of intrinsic semiconductors (germanium and silicon) with temperature (after Evans)*

anomalous change in resistivity with temperature. In most conductors, the resistivity increases with temperature. With semiconductors the resistivity generally decreases, and these materials have a negative temperature coefficient of resistivity (Fig. 19 and 20).

Very pure germanium has a specific resistivity of about 60 microhm-cm. The presence of 0.0001% As can reduce the resistivity of germanium to less than 0.1 microhm-cm. Arsenic influences the resistivity of germanium in this way because it has five valence electrons and germanium has four. Four of the arsenic electrons are required in the lattice, but the remaining electron becomes free for conductive purposes. Because germanium has only a few conduction electrons at room temperature, the addition of even a few extra ones from arsenic causes a marked change in its conductivity. Other elements having five valence electrons behave like arsenic when placed in the germanium structure; these are phosphorus, antimony and bismuth. These elements are called "donors"; the doped material is referred to as an *n*-type conductor (see Fig. 21, c).

Elements having three valence electrons form holes when

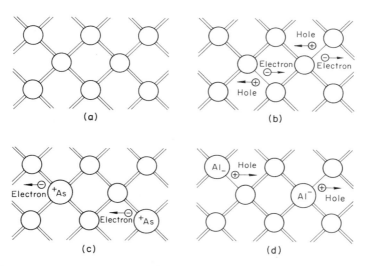

(a) Germanium as an intrinsic semiconductor. Germanium has four valence electrons and each atom forms a covalent bond with four other atoms in a three-dimensional lattice. At absolute zero, there are no thermally excited electrons or holes.

(b) At an elevated temperature, thermal agitation gives rise to mobile electron–hole pairs in the intrinsic germanium semiconductor.

(c) Germanium doped with a donor impurity, such as arsenic, provides mobile electrons. The positively charged arsenic is not

free to move. Four of the arsenic electrons are required to satisfy the covalent bonds of the neighboring germanium ions; only the fifth is mobile. This is an *n*-type conductor.

(d) Germanium doped with an acceptor impurity, such as aluminum, provides mobile, positively charged holes. The negatively charged atoms of aluminum are not free to move. Note that the aluminum, because of its valence of three, does not satisfy the requirement of four covalent bonds. This is a *p*-type conductor.

Fig. 21. Germanium as an intrinsic semiconductor and as n and p-type conductors (after Chapin, Fuller and Pearson)

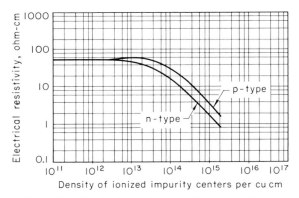

Fig. 22. Variation of electrical resistivity
of germanium with impurity concentration; at room temperature (After Evans)

present as impurities in germanium; these are aluminum, indium, and gallium. These elements are known as "acceptors";
the doped material is referred to as a p-type conductor. This situation is shown in Fig. 21(d).

Minute changes in the quantity of impurity may change the
mode of conduction from n to p-type, or vice versa. In any semiconductor, both types of carriers are present. In an n-type semiconductor, the electrons are called the majority carrier and the
holes are called the minority carrier. The reverse is true for the
p-type conductor. The effect of impurities on germanium is illustrated in Fig. 22.

When impurities are introduced into the semiconductor crystal, disturbances are caused in the energy levels. This effect provides extra energy levels in the forbidden zone. The energy
bands can be redrawn as shown in Fig. 23. The n-type impurities
produce levels near the conduction band, and the donated electron obtains sufficient thermal energy to jump into the conduction band. In a like manner, the p-type impurities provide energy
levels in the forbidden zone but just above the valence band. In
this instance, the electrons from the valence band can generally
jump, as a result of thermal excitation, into the impurity levels.
Ionization of the p-type impurity provides a hole.

Although electrons and holes can coexist, there is a definite,
appreciable probability of recombination. The average time that
an electron can exist before combining with a hole is called its

lifetime. In many instances, the lifetime of the minority carrier should be as long as possible (several hundred microseconds, if feasible); changes in the minority carrier density alter the conductivity of the semiconductor. The lifetime of the minority carrier is an inverse measure of the rate of recombination, and also a measure of the rate of generation of electron-hole pairs. Thus, if the lifetime of the minority carrier is low, the generation of pairs is high.

Internal crystal imperfections on the atomic scale favor the recombination of holes and should be avoided. Grain boundaries, as imperfections, cannot be tolerated. Hence, semiconductors are produced as single crystals.

Electrons can also be injected into a semiconductor by the simple expedient of applying a negative voltage. Holes can be injected into a semiconductor by applying a positive potential. A positive electrode possesses great affinity for electrons and at-

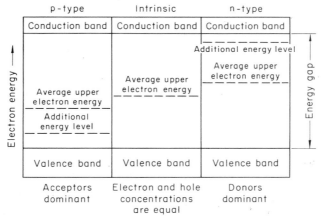

Fig. 23. Schematic diagrams for p and n-type semiconductors. The intrinsic or high-purity material is shown in the center.

tracts electrons in the vicinity of the electrode from their normal positions in the lattice. The ability to add or subtract holes from semiconductors explains much of their usefulness in practical devices, such as rectifiers. Holes and electrons can, and normally do, coexist in a semiconductor. Dynamic equilibrium exists in the material, with electron-hole pairs being continuously created by thermal agitation and destroyed by recombination.

As the characteristic mobility of carriers increases in a given semiconductor, the energy gap between the valence and conduction bands tends to decrease. The energy gap also increases with melting point, but decreases with the increase in the mean atomic weight. The mobility of carriers also increases with atomic weight. Table 21 lists some semiconductors with their electron and hole mobilities.

Certain semiconductors exposed to nuclear radiation show marked changes in electrical conductivity, because interstitial atoms may ionize, thereby increasing the number of electrons that are free to move in an applied electric field. The extra electrons interfere with the motion of holes. The net effect is a significant increase in resistivity.

Classes of Semiconductors. Semiconductors can be divided into two groups:

1 Valence crystals whose bonding comes from s-shell and p-shell electrons. Examples of valence crystals are as follows:

n-type (excess electron) . . ZnO, PbO_2, SnO_2, CdS, $CdSe$
p-type (hole) . . . . CuO, Cu_2O, Se, CuI
Both n and p types . . . . Si, Ge, Te, PbS, $PbTe$, SiC
Intermetallic compounds . . . . Mg_2Sn, $InSb$, Cs_3Sb, ZnS

2 Crystals whose atoms have incomplete d shells (mostly oxides of transition metals). Examples are not differentiated according to types because the crystals may be either n or p-type, depending upon impurities:

$$NiO, Fe_2O_3, Fe_3O_4, CuO, MnO$$

The d-shell semiconductors are used primarily for thermistors (thermally sensitive resistors).

Group III elements of the periodic table have one valence electron less than group IV, and group V elements have one electron more. The elements of groups III and V influence the semiconducting characteristics of the group IV crystals (germanium, silicon, diamond, and gray tin).

The semiconductor compounds can be classified by their position in the periodic table (100). In the III–V compounds (GaAs, InAs, and InSb) the elements come from the third and fifth columns of the periodic system. Other classes are as follows: II–VI (CdS, ZnS), II–IV (Mg_2Si, Mg_2Ge), IV–VI (PbS, $PbSe$), and I–II–V (chalcopyrites).

Valence-type conductors are used as single crystals of extreme

d SOLIDS

Table 21. Some Semiconductor Materials and Their Characteristics (a)

	Semiconductor	Energy gap at 300 K, ev	Mobility at 300 K, cm/v-sec Electrons	Holes	Melting point, F
1	Germanium (Ge)	0.72	3,900	1900	1708
2	Gallium antimonide (GaSb)	0.68	4,000	700	1295
3	Silicon (Si)	1.12	1,500	500	2588
4	Indium phosphide (InP)	1.27	4,000	650	1922
5	Gallium arsenide (GaAs)	1.4	5,000	400	2262
6	Cadmium telluride (CdTe)	1.45	1,000	100	1913
7	Aluminum antimonide (AlSb)	1.6	400	400	1922
8	Cadmium sulfide (CdS)	2.4	250	..	..
9	Silicon carbide (SiC)	2.8	(about 200)	..	..
10	Diamond (C)	6.0	1,800	1200	..
11	Gallium phosphide (GaP)	2.25	100	65	..
12	Gold-doped germanium	0.72	3,900	1900	1708
13	Mercury telluride (HgTe)	0.06	17,000	..	1238
14	Indium antimonide (InSb)	0.16	75,000	800	972
15	Indium arsenide (InAs)	0.33	40,000	600	1727
16	Lead telluride (PbTe)	0.3	2,000	1100	1688
17	Lead selenide (PbSe)	0.26	1,200	600	1976
18	Lead sulfide (PbS)	0.4	800	400	2048
19	Bismuth telluride (Bi_2Te)	0.16	570	400	1076
20	Cadmium antimonide (CdSb)	0.5	....	400	852

(a) Semiconductors 1 and 2 are used for rectifiers and transistors. Those numbered 3 through 11 are used for high-temperature rectifiers, transistors, solar batteries, infrared optics and photocells. Those numbered 12 through 15 are used for infrared detectors, radiation filters, magnetoresistance devices, Hall-effect devices and thermistors. Those numbered 16 through 20 are used for infrared detectors and thermoelectric devices.

purity; 99.99999% purity in germanium is sometimes required. Semiconductors owe their unique electrical properties to minute impurity contents, the method of preparation, and heat treatment. Absolutely pure silicon has a resistivity of 300,000 ohm-cm. By doping with boron, a *p*-type crystal with a minimum resistivity of 1000 ohm-cm is produced.

In the preparation of semiconductors, the materials are first purified to the highest degree possible by repeated zone-melting techniques (105). The single crystals are an important byproduct of zone melting. The high-purity semiconductor is referred to as an intrinsic material. A measured amount of impurity is introduced to produce the desired resistivity and the proper conductivity type. The degree of purity is extremely high, and the electrical resistivity is the only means of estimating it.

Semiconductor Theory. The valence and conduction bands in the intrinsic or high-purity semiconductor material at absolute zero are shown schematically in Fig. 3(b). At this temperature, a vacant conduction band exists that is separated by an energy gap, E_g, from a filled valence band. With an increase of temperature, electrons are thermally excited from the valence band to the conduction band, where they become mobile. Then the electrons in the conduction band and the vacant states or holes left behind in the valence band contribute to electrical conductivity. The variation of electrical resistivity with temperature of high-purity germanium and silicon (intrinsic semiconductors) is shown in Fig. 20 (109). The situation at absolute zero and at higher temperatures is indicated in Fig. 21(a) and (b).

For the intrinsic semiconductor, the number of electrons in the conduction band is equal to the number of holes in the valence band. Excitation depends exponentially on $E_g/2KT$, where E_g is the width of the forbidden or energy gap. The values for this gap or band separation are given in Table 21.

The theoretically pure semiconductor does not exist; and all practical semiconductors contain controlled amounts of special impurities or carriers, generally in concentrations of the order of one part in one hundred million. When the impurities are greater than 0.001%, the semiconductor loses its unusual properties and behaves more like a metal. The quantity and identity of the impurity determine in a large part the properties of a semiconductor. The germanium transistor is made from a material with an electrical resistivity of about 5 ohm-cm. This resistivity corresponds to an impurity concentration of 3.5×10^{14} per cu cm for the n-type and 7×10^{14} per cu cm for the p-type. Because the number of germanium atoms per cubic centimeter is 5×10^{22}, the impurity densities correspond to a ratio of 1 to 10^8 (109).

Electrical current flow occurs in a semiconductor in two modes, each of which is distinguished by the sign of the carrier. Conduction is by electrons and holes. There are excess or conduction (valence) electrons in energy bands that do not participate in the chemical or metallic bonds of the lattice. These electrons move freely through the lattice.

A hole corresponds to an electron that is missing from a chemical or metallic bond in the lattice. Existence of the hole corresponds to a positive charge equal in magnitude to that of the missing electron. Under some conditions, an electron from an adjacent bond may fall into this hole, and a positive hole then appears in the space formerly occupied by the electron. These holes or defects can therefore move freely through the crystal and contribute to conduction.*

The question naturally arises as to the source of the electrons and holes. At sufficiently low temperatures, each electron in the semiconductor is bound to an atom and the material is an insulator. At higher temperatures, a few of the electrons are released from the parent atom by thermal agitation. Conduction of this kind is referred to as intrinsic. With the introduction of impurities, the electrical conductivity of a semiconductor is profoundly affected. Depending on the nature of the impurity, electrons or holes can be added to a lattice with relative ease.

In a real crystal, the thermal generation of electrons and holes is going on continuously, regardless of impurity content. Only when the impurities exceed the concentration of the thermally excited carriers will the impurities exert their unique effects.

* Current semiconductor theory now refers to "light" and "heavy" holes, as in p-type germanium, in which the holes are fractions of the mass of the electron.

Chapter 3

Electrical Phenomena Associated with Metals

SEVERAL IMPORTANT phenomena that are attributes of metals will be discussed here.* These phenomena include electron emission (thermionic, photoelectric, secondary, and field emission), thermoelectricity (Seebeck, Peltier, Thomson effects), Hall effect, the somewhat-related Ettingshausen, Nernst, and Righi-Leduc effects, and superconductivity.

Electron Emission

Although electrons in a metal are considered to be free, they are always under the influence of the attractive field of the lattice and hence cannot escape from the metal into air, nor can they be pumped off by a vacuum. Additional energy must be given to the electrons to enable them to leave the metal.

Electrons can be accelerated so that they can leave metals in the following ways: (a) heating (thermionic emission); (b) light (photoelectric emission); (c) electron bombardment (secondary emission); (d) application of an intense electric field (field emission).

Heating. If the temperature of the metal is increased, the kinetic energy of some electrons increases so that they can surmount the potential barrier at the surface and escape. This process is called thermionic emission. Thermionic emission from a pure metal becomes appreciable only at temperatures of about 2500 K. In 1883, Thomas Edison discovered the emission of elec-

---

* Electrode potentials, corrosion, batteries and related phenomena, material transfer in arcs (welding), and catalytic behavior are not discussed here, as extensive treatments are to be found in appropriate texts.

trons from metals in vacuum during his work with the incandescent lamp, but he engaged in little further study of the phenomenon.

Light. Electrons in a metal can also secure the additional energy required for liberation by photons of light impinging on the surface. This characteristic is called photoelectric emission.

Electron Bombardment. Secondary emission occurs when electrons in a metal are bombarded with electrons and ions and acquire sufficient energy to escape the barrier.

Field Emission. A basically different mechanism exists in field emission. An intense surface electric field produced by an adjacent positively charged electrode is used to modify the confining potential-energy barrier to such an extent that electrons with an energy near the energy of the work-function level penetrate the barrier and escape.

Thermionic Emission

When a metal that has been heated in vacuum is made electrically negative (cathode) with respect to another metal (anode), an electric current flows between the two metals. This current increases as the anode potential increases. If the anode potential becomes sufficiently high with respect to the cathode, a saturation current flows, the value of which depends ideally only on the temperature of the cathode and the metal that is used.

There is a certain minimum energy, different for various metals, that an electron must have to be able to escape from the metal. This minimum energy (usually measured in electron-volts) is called the work function, ϕ. The condition of the metal surface has extremely great effect on the work function.*

The value of the current, I, can be related to temperature according to the Richardson-Dushman equation:

$$I = AT^2 e^{-\phi/kT} \text{ amp per sq cm} \tag{27}$$

where T is the absolute temperature of the cathode, A is a con-

---

* Much of the thermionic and photoelectric data for ϕ are given in volts. The relation between the potential difference (volts) and electron-volts (a unit of energy) should be kept in mind and is as follows:

$$\begin{aligned} \text{ev} &= 1.602 \times 10^{-19} \times \text{volts} &&\text{(in joules)} \\ &= 1.602 \times 10^{-12} \times \text{volts} &&\text{(in ergs)} \end{aligned}$$

stant, ϕ is the work function of the metal, e is the base of natural logarithms, and k is Boltzmann's constant.

Not all electrons have sufficient energy to escape the metal; some are reflected at the surface. If R is the reflection coefficient,* the formula known as the revised Richardson equation holds:

$$I = (1 - R)A_0T^2e^{-\phi/kT} \tag{28}$$

The exponential term of either equation dominates the T^2 term; hence, the current, I, is very dependent on both the work func-

Table 22. Thermionic Constants of Some Elements

Element	A, amp/sq cm/°K²	ϕ, volts
Barium	60	2.11, 2.52
Calcium	60	2.24, 3.20
Carbon	15	4.4
Cesium	160, 162	1.81
Chromium	48	4.6
Cobalt	41	4.41
Columbium	37	4.01
Hafnium	14	3.53
Iron (alpha)	26	4.48
Iron (gamma)	1.5	4.21
Molybdenum	55	4.15
Nickel	30	4.61
Palladium	60	4.99
Platinum	32	5.32, 5.40
Rhenium	200	5.1
Rhodium	33	4.8
Silicon	8	3.6
Tantalum	60, 55	4.12, 4.2
Thorium	70, 60	3.38, 3.35
Tungsten	60, 100, $\sim$ 75	4.54
Uranium	6	3.27
Zirconium	330	4.12

tion, ϕ, and temperature, T. Obviously, any change in the work function produces a large change in thermionic current.

The properties of the emitting metal are often specified in terms of the experimental values of A in amperes per square centimeter per °K², and of the work function, ϕ, in volts. The work function is determined from the slope of the experimental curve obtained by plotting $\log I/T^2$ against $1/T$. Theoretically, A

* Since it is less than 10%, R is usually neglected.

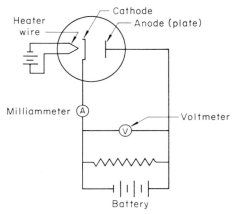

Fig. 24. Schematic representation of a typical
circuit for demonstrating thermionic emission

can be expressed as follows:

$$A = \frac{4\pi mek^2}{h^3} = 120 \text{ amp per sq cm per } °K^2 \tag{29}$$

where m is the mass of the electron, e is the charge on the electron, k is Boltzmann's constant, and h is Planck's constant. For most metals, actual values of A are somewhat lower than the theoretical one.

It is not possible to calculate the work function reliably. Observed values of A and ϕ for some elements are given in Table 22.

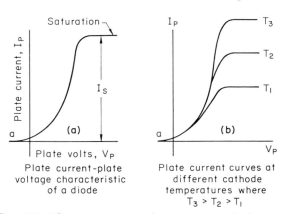

Fig. 25. Characteristics of a vacuum diode, and
the effect of temperature on thermionic emission

A typical circuit for demonstrating thermionic emission is given in Fig. 24. The cathode is often in the form of a hollow cylinder that is heated by a fine resistance wire within it. Electrons are emitted from the outer surface of the cathode and are attracted to the anode or plate. The electron current is of the order of milliamperes. The potential difference between the plate and cathode can be controlled by the rheostat and can be read on the voltmeter. When the potential between the cathode and anode is small (few volts), only a few electrons reach the plate. As the plate potential is increased and with about 100 v, all of the emitted electrons arrive at the plate. A further increase in voltage does not increase the current, for at that potential the current has reached a saturation value.

Figure 25 shows the typical plate voltage–plate current characteristics of a diode.* The characteristics are determined by the electron emission from the cathode. At any temperature, saturation occurs. Note saturation current, I_s, in Fig. 25(a). If the temperature is increased, the thermionic emission increases as shown in Fig. 25(b). Note that the plate current, I_p, is not zero (at point a), even when the plate voltage, V_p, is zero. This effect is the result of electrons that leave the hot cathode with an initial velocity, the more rapidly moving ones penetrating the cloud of space charge** and reaching the plate even with no accelerating field.

The work function is usually between 1 and 7 v, varying with material and surface preparation (Fig. 26). The height of the potential barrier existing at the surface of the metal is E_0 in volts above the zero energy level in the metal. The work function, ϕ, represents the minimum energy that electrons have to acquire to take them from the energy level E_f to outside the metal. High

---

* In its widest meaning, a diode is a two-electrode electronic device having an anode and a cathode, and having marked unidirectional characteristics. In the instance above, the diode is an electron tube. There are also crystal and semiconductor diodes.

** Streams of electrons or of positive ions may occupy sizable regions about an electrode to the virtual exclusion of carriers of opposite sign. The localization of electrons or positive ions in these regions is called a space charge, and may exert a marked influence on the performance of such tubes as thermionic rectifiers. An electron leaving a cathode finds itself in the company of a swarm of other electrons, all similarly charged, from which it is repelled. This swarm of electrons or space charge will drive most of the electrons back into the cathode, preventing their migration to the anode. Space charge can be eliminated by introducing positive ions to neutralize the space charge; cesium has been used for this purpose.

emission efficiency is obviously favored by a low work function.

The work function, ϕ, is a periodic function of the atomic number (112). The progressive rise and fall of work-function values throughout the periodic table is regular enough to permit approximations to be made for the metallic and semimetallic elements on which no data are as yet available. The theory of thermionic emission for a clean metal surface is satisfactory; it is not well developed for coated, nonuniform emitters (113).

Adsorbed Layers. At the surfaces of clean metals, residual forces exist that can tenaciously hold a monomolecular adsorbed

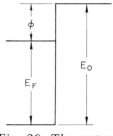

Fig. 26. The nature
of the work function

layer of foreign atoms. These forces are short ranged, and, although the first layer is tightly bonded, the second is only loosely held. Most commercial electron tubes have oxide-coated or thoriated cathodes, because the electropositive layers decrease the potential barrier and the work function, whereas an electronegative layer increases both. Some values of electropositive layers on tungsten are given in Table 23. The common commercial electropositive layer is thorium on tungsten. Thoria, ThO_2, is processed into tungsten by powder metallurgy, and, at high temperatures, the thoria dissociates and diffuses to the surface to form an adsorbed layer of thorium, which is reasonably stable at temperatures used in vacuum tubes. Carburization of thoriated tungsten reduces the evaporation of the thorium and allows the filament to be operated at higher temperatures.

Other cathodes of practical importance are made with coatings of metallic oxides, which are applied to a metal base. Many commercial cathodes are coated with mixtures of barium and strontium oxide on nickel or nickel alloy, which, after suitable

Table 23. Thermionic Constants of Tungsten
with Adsorbed Electropositive Layers

Material	A, amp/sq cm/°K^2	ϕ, volts
Pure tungsten...................	60	4.54
Barium on tungsten............	1.5, 1.6	1.56, 2.00
Thorium on tungsten...........	3.0, 2.6	2.63, 3.00
Cerium on tungsten............	8.0	2.71
Cesium on tungsten............	3.2	1.36

activation (heat treatment), have a low, although indefinite, work function of about 1.0 v (A is about 0.01). Such cathodes are capable of giving very large currents for short times and are used in tubes for pulse transmission, as in radar.

For clean metal surfaces, such as tungsten, tantalum, and molybdenum, the emission current is given by the Richardson-Dushman equation. For the clean refractory metals, the plate current reaches a temperature-limited or saturation value of the current, as shown in Fig. 25(a). Tubes having oxide-coated cathodes exhibit a marked failure to saturate with increasing plate voltage. This failure to saturate indicates that either A or ϕ, or both, in the Richardson-Dushman equation is not obeyed. Wright (114) gives an excellent summary of the knowledge on thermionic emitters as of 1953.

The work function of a metal single crystal depends on the crystallographic plane that forms the surface.

In all metals, nonmetals, and oxides, emission increases as the temperature is raised. The maximum operating temperature for a cathode is determined by the rate at which material evapo-

Table 24. Operating Temperature and Emission of Some Typical Cathodes

Material	Temperature, K	Emission, amp per sq cm	Watts radiated per sq cm
Tungsten..................	2500	0.1 to 0.5	55 to 80
Tantalum..................	2500	0.1 to 0.5	50 to 75
Carbonized thoriated tungsten..................	2050	0.5 to 2.0	15
Barium/strontium oxide on nickel................	1000 to 1100	0.1 to 0.5	2 to 5
Barium on tungsten.........	2050	1.0 to 10.0	20
Thorium on tungsten........	2050	0.5 to 2.0	15
Thorium oxide only.........	1900 to 2000	0.2 to 1.0	40

rates from it. Table 24 gives a few common cathodes and their optimum operating temperatures.

In alloys, ordering affects electron emission; a discontinuity in emission is observed at the ordering temperature, T_c, and there is a departure from the Richardson-Dushman equation. Similar discontinuities in emission occur at the melting point of an element.

Photoelectric Emission

Photoelectric emission (115) occurs in metals and compounds when the absorption of electromagnetic radiation, from ultraviolet to infrared, causes any of the following phenomena:

1 Electrons are liberated from a surface (photoemission or external photoeffect).
2 A change occurs in the electrical conductivity (photoconductive or internal photoeffect).
3 An electromotive force is set up between two electrodes when either of them or the intervening medium is illuminated (photovoltaic effect).

Photoemission. The photoemissive effect is observed on the surface of metals or metal compounds. It was first observed by H. Hertz (116) in 1887, but he did not study it further. The effect was thoroughly studied by Hallwachs (117) and is sometimes called the Hallwachs effect. A typical circuit for demonstrating the effect is shown in Fig. 27. A photocell is a device based on the principle of photoemission; the cell can be used in a circuit as shown. In principle, the effect can be demonstrated as follows: A light beam falls on a photosensitive surface, and electrons emitted from this surface are attracted to a collector. The collector is customarily maintained at positive potential with reference to the emitter. Both electrodes are maintained in a vacuum. The photoelectric current, a few microamperes per lumen of light flux, is read on an ammeter.

When light of sufficiently high frequency falls on a metal, electrons are emitted. In order that electrons shall be emitted with zero velocity at absolute zero, the energy of light must equal the energy corresponding to the thermionic work function. The energy of emitted electrons depends only on the frequency of the incident radiation, but the number of electrons emitted is proportional to the intensity of the radiation. Classical theory was unable to explain the effect. The facts were first rationalized by Einstein (118) in 1905.

Light consists of quanta or photons that are absorbed in a quantized manner, with the energy of each photon being completely transformed into the kinetic energy of an electron in the metal.

The energy of a photon can be expressed as

$$E = h\nu \tag{30}$$

where h is Planck's constant and ν is the frequency in cycles per second.

The electron in the metal absorbs energy from the photon and acquires sufficient energy to overcome the potential barrier and hence escapes:

$$E = h\nu - e\phi \tag{31}$$

where E is emission energy of the photoelectron, e is the charge on the electron, and ϕ is the work function (in volts).

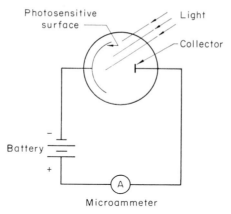

Fig. 27. *Photocell circuit utilizing the photoelectric effect*

Substituting for h, e and ν, where ν is equal to c/λ, the emission energy of the photoelectron is as follows:

$$E = \frac{12.3 \times 10^3}{\lambda} - \phi \tag{32}$$

where E becomes the voltage (corresponding to the emission energy), λ is the wave length in angstroms, ϕ is the work function of cathode material in volts, and c is the velocity of light.

Emission cannot occur unless the radiation (electron-volts per photon) is equal to or greater than the work function. The energy, E, of emitted electrons is given by

$$E = h(\nu - \nu_0) \tag{33}$$

where h is Planck's constant, ν is the frequency of the incident radiation, and ν_0 is the threshold frequency, below which no emission takes place. There is a threshold frequency, ν_0, where

$$h\nu_0 = e\phi \tag{34}$$

If the frequency of the light is ν, where ν is greater than ν_0, the maximum energy of the emitted electrons has the value $h\nu - h\nu_0$. The lower the work function, the further the threshold frequency shifts toward higher wave lengths. Above absolute zero, the threshold is not sharp, because light of frequency less than ν_0 can liberate only a small number of electrons.

The number of electrons emitted when the frequency is greater than ν_0 is proportional to the intensity of the light. The emission cannot be predicted theoretically as yet.

Table 25 shows the photoelectric work functions for some elements and for two typical photocell surfaces.

When the energy per photon of the incident light exceeds the work function, the electrons can escape at a substantial rate. The energy distribution of the emitted electrons is approximately

Table 25. Photoelectric Work Functions

Surface	ϕ, volts	Surface	ϕ, volts
Aluminum	2.26	Molybdenum	4.15
Beryllium	3.2	Nickel	5.0
Bismuth	4.6	Palladium	4.97
Calcium	3.2	Potassium	2.24
Cesium	1.9	Rhenium	4.98
Cobalt	4.3	Rubidium	2.18
Copper	4.1	Silver	4.75
Gold	4.9	Sodium	2.25
Iron	4.8	Tantalum	4.11
Lead	4.15	Tin	4.3
Lithium	2.28	Tungsten	4.54
Magnesium	2.42	Cesium/cesium oxide on silver	0.9
Mercury	4.5	Cesium/antimony	1.8

symmetrical about the median between zero and the maximum possible value.

The intensity of the incoming light (watts per unit area) has no effect whatever on the electron after escape, nor on the energy distribution among the escaping electrons. These quantities are controlled entirely by the light frequency. The number of electrons ejected per second is directly proportional to the intensity of the incident light, provided the wave length, angle of incidence, and polarization of the light remain unchanged.

The response or sensitivity of a photoelectric tube as a whole, or unit area of a sensitive surface, may be expressed variously: (a) quantum yield in per cent (the number of electrons emitted per hundred incident photons), (b) photoelectric yield in amperes per watt of light energy input, and (c) amperes per lumen. The photoelectric yield is very sensitive to the nature of surface preparation.

As the frequency of the light rises above the threshold value, the sensitivity increases rather rapidly; it is believed to increase indefinitely, but at a decreasing rate.

In a semiconductor, light photons may increase the conductivity by giving energy to electrons in filled levels or in donor impurity levels, thereby lifting these electrons either into conduction levels or into acceptor impurity levels and producing mobile electrons and holes.

Photoelectric emission is not materially affected by variations in temperature, unless such variations are so extreme as to modify the structure of the emitting surface. Minor effects resulting from pronounced temperature changes are accounted for by an increase in the energy of the conduction electrons.

If λ_0 is the threshold wave length and c is the velocity of light,

$$c = \lambda_0 \nu_0 \tag{35}$$

The photoelectric thresholds for pure metals (119) are given in Table 26. As can be seen, the thresholds for all pure metals are in the ultraviolet region. The addition of electropositive layers moves the photoelectric threshold from the ultraviolet to longer and longer wave lengths; the type of radiation and its corresponding wave length are given in Table 27.

The photoemissive effect is virtually instantaneous; the time between absorption of light and emission of a photoelectron is about 3×10^{-9} sec.

The facts regarding photoemission are not reconcilable with classical physics. Current ideas on photoelectric emission are discussed by Fan (120). The photoemissive layer is neither highly reflective nor highly transparent. However, the cathode material must give up electrons easily. Elements in the first column of the

Table 26. Photoelectric Thresholds of Some Pure Metals

Metal	λ_0, angstroms	Metal	λ_0, angstroms
Bismuth	2870	Molybdenum	2850
Cerium	4300	Nickel	2550
Chromium	2840	Platinum	2000
Gold	2650	Silver	2610
Iron	2680	Tantalum	3010
Lead	1960	Tungsten	2700
Mercury	2735	Uranium	3400

Table 27. Type of Radiation and Its Corresponding Wave Length

Radiation	Wave length, angstroms
Cosmic	0.0005
Gamma	0.01 to 1.4
X-rays	10 to 150
Ultraviolet	<4000
Visible	4000 to 7000
Infrared	>7000

periodic table have the least tightly bound valency electrons; hence, the photoelectric effect is strongest in the alkali metals, lithium, sodium, potassium, rubidium and cesium.

Photoconductive Effect. Photoconductivity occurs when a semiconductor material is illuminated with light of the appropriate wave length and an electric current results. Actually, the illumination causes a decrease of electrical resistance. The effect occurs when a photon is absorbed and causes an electron to move from a localized energy state to a conduction state. The energy of the photon must correspond to the difference in energy between the bound state and the conduction state.

The photoconductive cell requires current from an external circuit to flow along a very thin layer of light-sensitive semiconducting material. Figure 28 shows schematically a photoconductive cell in a circuit.

Photoconductivity was discovered by Smith (121), who observed that selenium increased in conductivity upon illumination. The selenium photoconductive cell played a dominant role in the field of photoelectricity for many decades, but it has been superseded by photoemissive cells and photovoltaic cells. During the Second World War, the photoconductive cells attained renewed importance as high-sensitivity infrared detectors. Today,

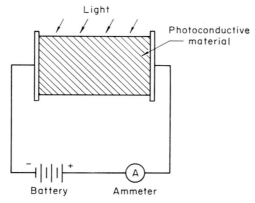

Fig. 28. A photoconductive cell

the photoconductive effect finds practical application in television cameras and light meters, and indirectly in the photographic process.

Many substances, particularly sulfides, selenides, tellurides, oxides, halides, and transition elements between metals and nonmetals, exhibit photoconductivity. Some of the more useful materials, in addition to selenium, are thallous sulfide, lead sulfide, silicon, and cadmium sulfide. However, the discussion of photoconductivity in semiconductors generally refers to lead compounds, such as lead sulfide, lead selenide, and lead telluride. The light-sensitive material is generally an evaporated layer and not a single crystal.

When a semiconductor is exposed to light, the direct effect is to increase the number of mobile charge carriers in the crystal. Conduction then may be initiated by the photoexcitation of an impurity or of an electron in the top filled band. The threshold wave length, λ_0, will be determined by the energy difference between the original state of the electron and the excited state, which may give rise to a mobile electron or a mobile hole. The absorption of the photon excites an electron in the valence band. In this situation, both the hole in the valence band and the electron in the conduction band may contribute to the conductivity. Unfortunately, this process does not account fully for the continuous current observed under constant illumination. The hole

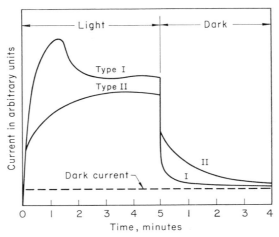

Fig. 29. Photoconductive response of two selenium cells

and electron eventually recombine with each other, but in the interim each may spend finite times trapped on impurities and imperfections in the crystal. Traps are of considerable importance in photoconductive response.

The photoconductive effect consists of two components: the primary current, which is proportional to light intensity (no time lag), and the secondary current, which has a time lag. The secondary current frequently exceeds the primary current. The primary current occurs when the photon excites the electron in the valence band. The secondary current occurs by release of trapped electrons or holes by thermal excitation and the drawing of additional electrons from the cathode and holes from the anode; these processes imply a time delay.

Figure 29 shows the response of two selenium cells to light.

Note that an appreciable secondary (dark) current flows even after illumination has been removed.

A photovoltaic effect occurs when a semiconductor or a *p-n* junction absorbs radiation and converts it into an electrical signal that is related to the intensity of the incident radiation. Figure 30 illustrates the nature of the effect. Perhaps the most com-

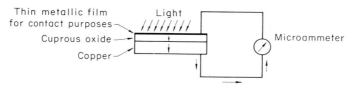

Fig. 30. A photovoltaic cell. Small arrows indicate directions of current flow

mon use of the photovoltaic effect is in photographic exposure meters. The effect depends to some extent on wave length. There is also a cutoff point, beyond which longer wave lengths do not activate the crystal. The cutoff wave length is inversely proportional to the band separation in the semiconductor. Semiconductors are available as detectors of radiation, ranging from gamma rays, through the visible, and out to the intermediate infrared spectrum.

The important semiconductor detectors for the infrared region are lead sulfide, lead selenide, indium antimonide, germanium and silicon. The military establishment is currently interested in the use of infrared devices for guidance, detection, and control of missiles.

The silicon photovoltaic cell developed in 1954 by Chapin, Fuller and Pearson (122) is a *p-n* junction device. For solar batteries, conversion efficiency is, of course, important. Cells with *p-n* junctions in silicon have a maximum theoretical efficiency of energy conversion of 20 to 25%; however, operating efficiency at present is about 10 to 15%. Cells operating at this efficiency generate about 100 w per sq yd of cell surface area on a bright day.

The photovoltaic effect was observed by E. Becquerel (123) in 1839. He allowed light to fall on one of two halide-coated silver electrodes in dilute sulfuric acid and observed current flow. With pure metals, the effect is small. An electrode coated with a semiconductor, such as copper oxide or a silver halide, and immersed in an electrolyte can develop a voltage of 0.1 v, on open circuit. Cells with a fluorescent electrolyte will develop open-circuit voltages of 0.25 v.

Grondahl (124), who discovered the rectifying action of the copper – cuprous oxide rectifier in 1920, observed a few years later (with P. H. Geiger) that illumination of the cuprous oxide caused a current to flow in an external circuit without an auxiliary power supply. Lange (125) rediscovered this photovoltaic effect in 1930.

The important cuprous oxide barrier-layer cell consists of a sandwich of copper, cuprous oxide (formed on the copper), and a lead electrode. If the copper electrode is made a few volts negative with respect to the lead electrode, a current will flow through the cell. If the polarity is reversed, virtually no current flows. If the cuprous oxide is illuminated (for example, if the lead electrode is a flat spiral), current will flow in an external circuit. The rectifying and photovoltaic effects take place at the junction of the cuprous oxide and copper. This barrier layer is about 1 micron thick. Under illumination, the photoelectrons travel from the cuprous oxide to the copper, in the high-resistance direction.

The theory of the barrier layer rectifiers has been treated by Schottky (126, 127), who established that both the photoelectrons and the rectifying action took place at the junction of the cuprous oxide and copper.

Cuprous oxide containing oxygen is a defect conductor: It conducts current by virtue of holes present in its uppermost, filled energy band. These holes are formed when electrons are thermally excited from this band, filling impurity levels provided by the excess oxygen atoms.

If electrons are raised by photoexcitation from the filled band to the empty conduction band in the semiconductor, the electrons will drop quickly into one of the many impurity levels and will not contribute to conduction. On the other hand, if excitation takes place in the barrier layer, the lifetime of the holes will be relatively long, because there are no empty levels. The field across the barrier layer will accelerate the electrons toward the metal and will give a photocurrent in the observed direction.

Theory indicates that the open-circuit voltage should approach saturation for strong illumination — that is, it should be the difference in the work function of the metal and semiconductor; this is close to the observed voltage of 0.2 v.

The photoelectric effect has been observed in natural silver sulfide, zinc sulfide, molybdenum sulfide, selenium, and lead sulfide.

A semiconductor is transparent to light of a wave length longer than the cutoff wave length of the material. When a semiconductor is operating in the photovoltaic region, it is opaque to the incident radiation. Hence, semiconductors can serve as windows or filters for selected regions of the spectrum and, in some instances, can be used for lenses. Semiconductors used for selective light transmission are germanium, silicon, indium antimonide, indium arsenide, and cadmium telluride.

Secondary Electron Emission

If the surface of any solid is bombarded by electrons with velocities greater than a critical value, electrons may acquire enough energy to overcome the potential barrier and escape from the solid (128). The secondary electrons leave the surface in the direction from which the primary arrive. The total flow of electrons in this direction consists of the following: (a) electrons elastically reflected, (b) electrons reflected inelastically after an energy loss of some tens of electron-volts, and (c) true secondary electrons with energy independent of the primary energy, and with a mean energy of the order of 10 ev.

The number of true secondary electrons increases as the primary energy increases, reaches a maximum, and then falls. The total flow leaving the surface involves flows (a), (b), and (c) above, and the ratio of this flow to the primary current, I, is defined as the secondary emission coefficient, δ:

$$\delta = \frac{a + b + c}{I} \tag{36}$$

It is common to quote the maximum value, δ_{max}, and the primary energy at which the maximum occurs in volts.

The number of secondary electrons, δ, per incidence of primary electrons varies considerably with the nature of the surface and with the energy and the angle of incidence of the primary electrons. In electron tubes, δ should be as small as possible, but it should be as large as possible for applications such as secondary-electron multipliers.

The variation of the number of secondary electrons with primary energy is of great importance. The value, δ, reaches a maximum at about 200 to 600 v. As the primary energy increases, more electrons in the solid gain sufficient energy to permit them to escape, but, at high velocities, the primary electrons penetrate too far into the solid for all the secondary electrons to reach the surface before being scattered in the solid.

Table 28. Secondary Emission from Various Materials

Element	Secondary emission, δ_{max}	Primary energy at δ_{max}, volts
Metals Outgassed by Heating in Vacuum		
Bismuth	1.35	500
Columbium	1.18	400
Copper	1.35	500
Gold	1.47	700
Iron	1.32	400
Lead	1.08	500
Molybdenum	1.23	400
Nickel	1.27	500
Platinum	1.78	700
Silver	1.47	800
Tantalum	1.35	600
Titanium	0.9	300
Tungsten	1.43	700
Zirconium	1.1	300
Carbon	1.0	300
Films Formed by Evaporation in High Vacuum		
Aluminum	0.97	300
Barium	0.90	400
Beryllium	0.90	200
Cesium	0.90	400
Lithium	0.55	100
Magnesium	0.95	300
Potassium	0.69	300
Rubidium	0.85	400

In general, when the work function is low, the secondary emission is low. Pure metals have rather low secondary emission.

At low primary energy, the secondary emission from the metals with low density and low work function is greater than that from more dense metals. The reverse is true of δ_{max} and of the secondary emission at high primary energies; a crossover occurs at primary energies between 50 and 100 v.

The behavior is dependent on the condition of the surface of the substance. The emission for elements that can be thoroughly cleaned by heating in a vacuum is given in Table 28. With metals of low density and low work function, it is possible to obtain films with clean surfaces by evaporation in high vacuum. The secondary emission of some of these elements is also shown in Table 28. There is no indication that the secondary emission from thin films is different from that of the bulk metal.

The ratio of the electron current leaving the target to the electron current incident in the target is called the secondary emission yield. This yield increases with the accelerating voltage of the primary beam, passing the value of unity at about 40 v and reaching a maximum at about 500 v.

Compounds, such as the oxides, also possess the characteristic of secondary emission. Alkali halides and magnesium oxide have high secondary emission. Semiconductors, such as cuprous oxide (Cu_2O), silver oxide (Ag_2O), and molybdenum sulfide (MoS_2), have yields around unity. Silver-cesium, oxide-cesium, and silver-antimony-cesium photosurfaces have yield ratios of about eight at 500 to 700 v.

For gas-contaminated or oxidized metals, secondary emission ranges as high as six. If surfaces are rough, or covered with particles of metal or carbon, secondary electrons released from the solid may be trapped and the effective secondary emission will be low. Anodes in electronic tubes are often covered with a black deposit of sputtered metal or deposited carbon to minimize secondary emission.

Field Emission

Thermionic emission occurs only at high temperatures and is negligible even for oxide-coated cathodes at less than 800 K. In field emission, the application of a high positive field in the vicinity of the cathode can produce considerable emission, even at room temperature. Under special conditions, the emission can be greater than the maximum thermionic emission. Field emission occurs under conditions of highest vacuum.

The action of the field is to lower the potential barrier at the metal surface so that the work function, ϕ, is reduced. Because the work function enters exponentially into the Richardson-Dushman equation (27) for emission current density, a small reduction in it results in an increased emission, if the temperature is not too low. At the same time, the lowering of the potential barrier allows the tunnel effect to become operative (see below). This effect can give rise to a large emission, whatever the temperature may be.

Field emission theory plays a very important part in the explanation of the large emission current densities observed at the cathode spot of an arc between metallic welding electrodes.

Schottky Effect. If the potential barrier, normally of magnitude E_0, is placed in the influence of an electric field, the barrier is reduced to a value E_0'. This difference in potential barriers represents a decrease of work function for an emitted electron:

$$E_0' - E_0 = \Delta\phi \tag{37}$$

A new work function, ϕ', is given by the following expression (compare with Fig. 26):

$$E_0' - E_F = \phi' \tag{38}$$

The insertion of this value of ϕ' in Richardson-Dushman equation (27) will give a higher value for the current density. If i_s is the current density calculated in absence of a positive field, E, the new value of i_s' at temperature T is given as follows:

$$\frac{i_s'}{i_s} = e^{4.403\sqrt{E/T}} \tag{39}$$

This equation was derived by Schottky (129).

Because i_s' is also governed by the Richardson-Dushman equation, the increase in emission will only be appreciable for large values of temperature. The equation holds for clean surfaces of pure metals but does not hold for contaminated surfaces.

In an illustration given by Cosslett (130), a vacuum diode with a tungsten filament, operated at an anode potential of 44 v (versus about 4.4 v for normal thermionic emission) and 2000 K, has an increase in emission of about 10%, but, at an anode potential of 4400 v and at the same temperature, the emission is increased 8000-fold over simple thermionic emission. In the electron microscope, field emission makes an important contribution to the beam current. The Schottky effect, which is easily measured, is not of great importance at low voltages.

Tunnel Effect (Autoelectronic Emission). In quantum theory, the tunnel effect depends on the finite probability that an electron on one side of the surface potential barrier may pass across it, if there is no occupied state of the same energy on the other side. Obviously, on a metal surface there is no other side to the potential barrier, but within the metal the barrier potential in the presence of an external field will fall below the energy level of the topmost band of valency electrons. A finite probability always exists that the electrons will jump the barrier; also, the higher the applied field, the greater the probability of tunnel emission. Fowler and Nordheim (131) have shown that the tunnel or autoelectronic current is given by an equation similar to that of Richardson-Dushman:

$$i_s = A_f E^2 e^{-b_f/E} \qquad (40)$$

where E is the field strength at the surface. A_f and b_f are constants that depend on the work function, ϕ. The equation is good for pure metals with carefully cleaned surfaces, but it is not obeyed if surfaces are contaminated.

The effect is independent of temperature and increases rapidly with field strength. The rate of arrival of free electrons at the surface limits the current, which is large and equivalent to a current density of about 10^{13} amp per sq cm. Surface contamination with certain metals lowers the work function. By using coated filaments, high fields, and high temperatures, current densities of 1000 amp per sq cm have been obtained (132). The field emission microscope, or "point projector microscope," represents a simple application of the principle of field emission; magnifications of 10^5 and higher are possible (133).

Thermoelectricity

Thermoelectricity is electricity produced at a heated junction of two dissimilar conductors. The observation that two dissimilar metals that are joined and heated at the junction give rise to a small voltage is known as the thermoelectric effect. The effect has long been used for measuring temperatures above and below room temperature. Today, through thermoelectricity, the direct conversion of heat into electricity, with reasonable efficiencies, and the development of a refrigeration effect from a flow of electricity through a junction are approaching reality. Thermoelectricity can be generated with metallic conductors, semiconductors, and valence compounds of metals of the transition series.

The subject of thermoelectricity covers three thermoelectric phenomena: the Seebeck effect, the Peltier effect, and the Thomson effect. Of these, the Seebeck effect is most familiar, being used in thermocouples for temperature measurement.

Seebeck Effect. In 1823, Seebeck (134) discovered that, if in a loop or closed circuit that incorporated two dissimilar conductors, the two junctions were maintained at different temperatures, a steady voltage was produced. Such an electromotive force is called a thermoelectric force. The electromotive force causing current was found to be proportional to the temperature difference between the two junctions and the materials making up the circuit. This arrangement has become known as a thermocouple, and it is widely used in the field of temperature measurement.

Since Seebeck's discovery, there have been many attempts to generate electricity directly from heat. In the past, these attempts have failed because of the very small currents produced and the low efficiencies obtained — less than 1%. With the advances in solid-state physics, semiconductor compounds can attain efficiencies as high as 10%.

The thermoelectric force between two metals is the actual voltage generated by the Seebeck effect in a loop of the two metals whose junctions are at different temperatures. The thermoelectric power is the voltage per degree of the temperature difference between the junctions. The thermoelectric power of a single

Table 29. Thermoelectric Force of Some Elements Relative to Platinum

Element	Thermoelectric force, millivolts at temperature of hot junction (cold junction, 0 C)			
	−200 C	−100 C	+100 C	+200 C
Aluminum	+0.45	−0.06	+0.42	+1.06
Bismuth	+12.39	+7.54	−7.34	−13.57
Cadmium	−0.04	−0.31	+0.91	+2.32
Copper	−0.19	−0.37	+0.76	+1.83
Germanium	−46.00	−26.62	+33.9	+72.4
Gold	−0.21	−0.39	+0.74	+1.77
Iron	−3.10	−1.94	+1.98	+3.69
Lead	+0.24	−0.13	+0.44	+1.09
Magnesium	+0.31	−0.09	+0.44	+1.10
Nickel	+2.28	+1.22	−1.48	−3.10
Palladium	+0.81	+0.48	−0.57	−1.23
Silicon	+63.13	+37.17	−41.56	−80.58
Silver	−0.21	−0.39	+0.74	+1.77
Tungsten	+0.43	−0.15	+1.12	+2.62

metal may be measured on an absolute scale, so that the thermo-electric power between two metals is the algebraic sum of their absolute thermoelectric powers.

A given metal is said to be thermoelectrically positive with respect to another metal if the current flows from the first metal to the second at the cold junction. Table 29 gives the thermoelectric force of several elements with respect to platinum. A positive sign in Table 29 signifies that the current in the thermocouple circuit flows from the element to platinum at the reference junction at 0 C. The thermal electromotive force generated by any two elements, A and B, can also be found from the table. The electromotive force of any two elements is the algebraic difference, $A_e - B_e$, between values for the electromotive force generated by each relative to platinum. A positive sign indicates that current flows from A to B at the reference junction, and a negative sign that it flows from B to A.

A thermoelectric circuit used for the measurement of temperature is shown in Fig. 31. There are three junctions: (a) The

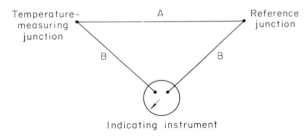

Fig. 31. Simple thermocouple circuit

junction of the two dissimilar wires at an elevated temperature is commonly called the hot, temperature measuring, or thermocouple junction; (b) the junction of the two dissimilar metals at a constant, cold, or reference temperature is known as the reference junction; and (c) the junction where the wires meet at a millivoltmeter is called the measuring junction.

The thermoelectric power generated in the circuit, as given in Fig. 32, depends on the temperatures of all the junctions of dissimilar metals. If all the junctions are maintained constant except one, which is the hot junction, the resultant voltage, as measured by the voltmeter, varies only with the temperature of the hot junction.

The thermoelectric power of a thermocouple is influenced by many factors: elastic strain, cold work, chemical composition, structural change, and magnetization (135). Thermoelectric power is set up by an elastic strain (in similar metals, where one is strained and one is not) and is proportional to it both in tension and compression. Values are about 10^{-5} v per °C per unit strain. Cold work increases thermoelectric power; values range about 10^{-7} v per °C. Unmagnetized ferromagnetic materials show

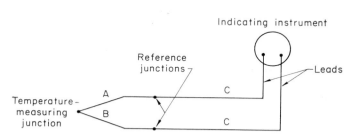

Fig. 32. Thermocouple connections

a variation with time after cold working. Annealing reduces the thermoelectric power due to cold work but does not destroy it entirely. Recovery occurs over a wide annealing-temperature range but proceeds more rapidly at higher temperatures. The largest thermoelectric powers, around 10^{-5} v per °C, are developed between two metals. Alloying elements affect the thermoelectric power. If the alloying element is from a lower group of the periodic table than the solvent, it increases the thermal electromotive force; if it is from a higher group, it decreases it. A concentration of 0.1% of alloying element changes the thermoelectric power by about 10^{-7} v per °C. Phase changes alter the thermoelectric power. In iron, the alpha-gamma and gamma-delta transformations cause discontinuous changes in the electromotive force of about 10^{-6} v per °C. At the melting point, the electromotive force changes to about the same degree. At the Curie point, there is a sudden change in the slope of thermoelectric power versus temperature. Magnetizing a wire of a ferromagnetic material gives rise to a thermoelectric power that changes by 10% or so within 100 hr of magnetization. Nickel shows an increase in the electromotive force with time, while iron and cobalt show a decrease; the effect is about 10^{-7} v per °C.

Peltier Effect. The inverse of the Seebeck effect is the Peltier effect: That is, when a current flows around a loop formed by two dissimilar metals, heat is taken in at one junction and given off at the other. Ordinarily, the effect is small — less than a 1 °C change. In 1950, a temperature drop of 10 °C (18 °F) was obtained with bismuth alloys. The effect becomes pronounced with the use of semiconductors. For example, junctions of p and n-type semiconductors (Bi_2Te_3 or PbTe) give drops of 40 to 50 °C (70 to 90 °F).

Peltier (136) found that, if a current is passed across the junction of two dissimilar metals in one direction, heat is absorbed and the junction is cooled; when the current is passed in the opposite direction, the junction is heated. For a given current, the rate of heat absorption or liberation at the junction of two dis-

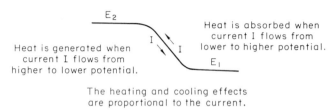

E_2

Heat is generated when current I flows from higher to lower potential.

Heat is absorbed when current I flows from lower to higher potential.

E_1

The heating and cooling effects are proportional to the current.

Fig. 33. Schematic representation of the Peltier effect

similar metals depends on the thermoelectric power, dE/dT, of the metals and is independent of the form and dimensions of the metals at the junction. Icilius (137) showed that the rate at which heat is absorbed and evolved is proportional to the current. The Peltier effect is not to be confused with the Joule heating effect, which is proportional to the electrical resistivity and to the square of the currents, as well as the dimensions of the conductor, and, furthermore, does not change sign when the current is reversed.

With the Peltier effect, the evidence is simply that, when a current "flows up" a potential gradient, heat is absorbed, and, when a current "flows down," heat is generated (Fig. 33).

The Peltier coefficient, or electromotive force, is defined as follows: If P is the rate at which heat (in joules per sec or watts) is absorbed or evolved when a current of 1 amp flows across the junction of two dissimilar metals, then P is the Peltier coefficient of the junction (in watts per amp) or simply the Peltier voltage.

The direction and magnitude of the Peltier electromotive force depend on the metals and the temperature of the junction.

Thomson Effect. In 1851, W. T. Thomson (later Lord Kelvin) concluded that the reversible absorption of heat at the junctions of dissimilar metals was not the only reversible heat effect in the thermoelectric circuit. His reasoning led him to believe that there must be a reversible absorption of heat due to the flow of current through those parts of the conductors in which a temperature gradient exists. In 1854, Thomson (138) was able to prove that such an effect existed. He showed that, in some metals, heat is absorbed when current flows from colder to hotter parts of the metal and heat is generated when current flows from the hotter to the colder parts (Fig. 34). For other metals, the effect is reversed, and, in still others, the effect is too small to be easily measured. Because the Thomson effect is so small, it is generally disregarded in thermoelectric considerations.

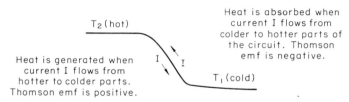

Fig. 34. Schematic representation of the Thomson effect

Table 30. Thermoelectric Materials and Some of Their Characteristics

Thermoelectric material	Junction temperature, C	Seebeck coefficient, $\mu v/°K$	Electrical resistivity, ρ, ohm-cm	Thermal conductivity, κ, watts/cm °K
ZnSb	200	+220	0.0023	0.016
InSb	500	−130	0.00045	0.075
InAs-S	750	−123	0.00045	0.075
Bi-Te	127	−250	0.0019	0.015
$Li_{0.05}Ni_{0.95}O$	1100	+225	0.008	0.035
TiO_2	727	−200	0.0148	0.034
$Mg_2Si_{0.7}Sn_{0.3}$	500	−200	0.0098	0.01
$CrSi_2$	500	+120	0.01	0.03
$MnSi_2$	700	+175	0.0149	0.022
$Li_{0.03}Mn_{0.97}Se$	300	+170	0.0075	0.017
Ge	700	−210	0.00145	0.2
$MnTe_{0.95}As_{0.05}$	400	+300	0.04	0.006
$Bi_2(Te,Se)_3$	100	−210	0.00105	0.016
$(Bi,Sb_2)Te_3$	25	+195	0.0009	0.0147

Generation of Electricity — Thermoelectric Cooling (139). Semiconductors function well in devices that use the Seebeck effect for the generation of power and in devices that use the Peltier effect for heating or cooling. Under Russia's first five-year plan, a kerosine-powered generator operated radio equipment.

For generation of power, lead telluride is outstanding; equally promising is indium arsenic phosphide. Efficiencies of 7% have been attained. For generation of power, hot junctions must operate at 595 C (1100 F) or higher. At about 1100 C (2010 F), efficiencies of 10% have been reported. Mixed-valence compounds of the transition metals (for example, lithium-doped nickel oxide) can be operated at high temperatures; samarium sulfide can be operated to 1100 C (2010 F).

A germanium-silicon alloy, operable to about 1000 C (1830 F), promises efficiencies to about 15%. A cube ¼ in. on the side can produce 2.4 w with an efficiency of 9% when heated to 900 C (1650 F). The average figure of merit for n-type material was 0.9×10^{-3} per °C from 350 to 900 C; for the p-type 0.6×10^{-3}.

In thermoelectric cooling, temperature drops of 22 to 28 °C (40 to 50 °F) have been attained. One element is ZnSb, CdSb, or Bi_2Te_3, and the other is a metal alloy. With p and n-type semiconductors (Bi_2Te_3 or PbTe), temperature drops of 40 to 50 °C (70 to 90 °F) have been reported. For cooling, the hot junction would probably not exceed 85 C (185 F). Requirements for efficient Seebeck power generators and for Peltier cooling are similar.

The thermoelectric value, expressed as a "figure of merit," is defined by three physical properties:

1 The Seebeck coefficient, S, (also called thermoelectric power) expressed in volts per °K. This coefficient should be high.
2 The specific electrical resistivity, ρ, in ohm-centimeters. This resistivity should be low.
3 The specific thermal conductivity, κ, expressed in watts per centimeter °K. This conductivity should be low.

The figure of merit, Z, is then defined as follows:

$$Z = \frac{S^2}{\rho \kappa} \tag{41}$$

A high value of Z is considered necessary for high efficiency.

Table 30, from Celent (139), gives Seebeck coefficient, resistivity, and thermal conductivity of thermoelectric materials.

The maximum temperature difference attainable with a single-stage Peltier thermocouple is:

$$\Delta T = \frac{S^2 T_c^2}{2\rho\kappa} \tag{42}$$

where T_c is the temperature of the cold junction in °K.

Liquid-metal arrangements show thermoelectric phenomena. Stoneburner, Yang, and Derge (140) have demonstrated that molten iron sulfide – solid tungsten thermocouples can give approximately 55 microvolts per °C in a temperature range of 1200 to 1400 C (2190 to 2550 F).

Hall Effect

In 1879, Hall (141) discovered that, if a magnetic field is applied at right angles to a current flowing in any conductor, the moving charges, which constitute the current, are deflected sidewise, and a potential difference is built up between the two sides of the conductor. The creation of the transverse electric field, which is perpendicular to both the magnetic field and the current flow, is called the Hall effect or voltage. Reversing either the current or the field reverses the direction of the voltage. In Fig. 35, the Hall voltage is expressed by the following equation:

$$V_H = \frac{RIH}{t} \tag{43}$$

where R is the Hall coefficient, I is the current in amperes, H is the magnetic field, and t is the thickness of the sample.

In metals, the effect is small, but in semiconductors, considerable Hall voltages can be developed and are being put to use in numerous Hall-effect devices. In copper, for instance, 0.024 mv per kilogauss at an 0.2-watt input can be obtained, but 110 mv per kilogauss at the same input is possible in semiconductors.

This galvanomagnetic effect represents the best experimental evidence for the concept of positive current carriers or holes in crystals. The effect is an important tool in semiconductor research, because it provides a direct estimate of the concentration of charge carriers in certain instances. The Hall coefficient, R, is:

$$R = \frac{1}{Nec} \tag{44}$$

where N is the carrier concentration, e is the electronic charge, and c is the velocity of light. If the carriers are electrons, R is negative; if carriers are holes (positive charges), the constant is positive.

The Hall constant for several metals is given in Table 31; values calculated from the concentration of valence electrons are also given. Agreement with theory and experiment for monova-

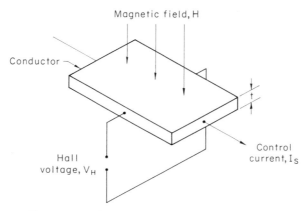

Fig. 35. *Schematic representation of the Hall effect. The control current,* I_s, *is at right angles to the magnetic field,* H, *and produces a voltage,* V_H, *in the conductor.*

Table 31. Hall Coefficients of Metals at Room Temperature

Metal	Hall coefficient, v-cm/amp-oersted Observed	Calculated
Aluminum	−4	....
Beryllium	+24.4	−2.5
Bismuth	∼−1000	−4.1
Cadmium	+6.0	−6.5
Cesium	−78	−73
Copper	−5.5	−7.4
Gold	−7.2	−10.5
Lithium	−17.0	−13.1
Potassium	−42	−47
Silver	−8.4	−10.4
Sodium	−25.0	−24.4
Zinc	+3.3	−4.6

lent metals is good. For divalent metals, the agreement is poor and the sign of the effect is opposite to that predicted. The situation is rationalized by consideration of band theory. Bismuth has the highest Hall coefficient of the ductile metals. Its anomalous value is explained by band theory as caused by electrons in low concentration outside nearly filled bands. The Hall effect in ferromagnetic materials is not directly proportional to the applied magnetic field; an extra term related to the spontaneous magnetization must be added (142, 143).

Ordering affects the Hall coefficient. In Cu_3Au (144), the disordered Cu_3Au has a negative Hall coefficient (about -640×10^{-6} emu), while the ordered Cu_3Au has a positive Hall coefficient (about $+172 \times 10^{-6}$ emu). The change in sign is due to a change in band structure. Conduction is also changed in Ni_3Mn (145). Disordered Ni_3Mn has positive hole conduction, while ordered Ni_3Mn has negative electron conduction.

Ettingshausen, Nernst, and Righi-Leduc effects (146, 147) are phenomena of minor importance and are slight in normal metals, but they are much greater in elements, such as antimony and

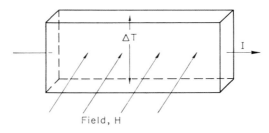

Fig. 36. Schematic representation of the Ettingshausen effect

bismuth, in which nonmetallic properties begin to appear, and they are relatively large in semiconductors.

If an electric current flows through a plate, heat effects will be produced and all edges of the plate will be at the same temperature. On the application of a magnetic field perpendicular to the plate, the equipotential lines of electric current flow will be rotated, and the plate undergoes an unequal change in temperature at its lateral edges (148), as shown in Fig. 36. The magnitude of the Ettingshausen galvanomagnetic effect varies directly with the current and magnetic field, and inversely with the thickness; the effect is reversed with a reversal of the current or field. In a copper ribbon 0.01 in. thick carrying 1 amp in a field of 12,000 gausses, the change in temperature is only 0.000075 °C. For bismuth the effect is positive, and for iron it is negative.

The magnitude of the temperature difference, ΔT, developed is given by the following equation:

$$\Delta T = \frac{EI - \frac{1}{2}\rho I^2}{b\kappa} \tag{45}$$

where κ is thermal conductivity, I is the current, ρ is electrical resistivity, E is volts ($E = eH$), e is the Ettingshausen coefficient, H is the magnetic field, and b is a constant.

The Ettingshausen effect has been considered for refrigeration possibilities by O'Brien and Wallace (149). The effect is not large, and preliminary experiments with bismuth alloys have given cooling effects of about 0.25 °C.

The Nernst thermomagnetic effect occurs when a conductor is placed in a magnetic field and in a temperature gradient along the strip. A voltage is detected between the edges; reversal of the field or temperature gradient reverses the voltage. A bismuth strip in a field of 9000 gausses in a gradient of 100 °C per inch develops 0.0012 v per inch of separation (between the edges).

In the Righi-Leduc thermomagnetic effect, a magnetic field produces a temperature difference across the width of a metal strip in which a current flows longitudinally.

Underlying the galvanomagnetic and thermomagnetic phenomena is the Lorentz force. This is a fundamental interaction between electric charges (in this case, electrons) and magnetic fields. Any charged particle moving through a field experiences a force that is perpendicular to both its direction of motion and direction of field.

Superconductivity (150)

The experiments of Onnes (151) on the liquefaction and solidification of helium led to his discovery of the phenomenon of superconductivity. His initial discovery was that the electrical resistance of purified mercury suddenly became zero (immeasurably small)* at the boiling point of liquid helium, 4.2 K (-269 C),

* The resistance of a superconductor below its transition temperature is no more than 1×10^{-15} of its value at room temperature.

as shown in Fig. 37. The effect is reversible: On reheating, the material regains its normal resistivity at the same temperature — the transition temperature. This bizarre phenomenon still defies satisfactory explanation. The current creates a magnetic field around the superconductor, which stays constant indefinitely.

Numerous elements are superconducting at low temperatures (Table 32). The superconducting property is found in those elements that have 2 to 5 valence electrons outside the closed shells. Metals that are poor conductors at normal temperatures are most likely to be superconductors. Monovalent metals, ferromagnetic (with a few exceptions), and antiferromagnetic materials are not superconductors.

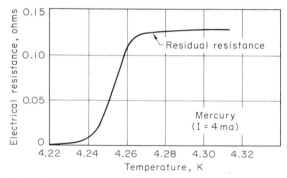

Fig. 37. Onnes's curve for superconducting mercury

Table 32. Superconducting Elements

Element	Critical temperature, T_c, K	Element	Critical temperature, T_c, K
Aluminum	1.14	Rhenium	1.7
Cadmium	0.54	Ruthenium	0.5
Columbium	9.22	Tantalum	4.38
Gallium	1.07	Technetium	11.2
Hafnium	0.35	Thallium	2.38
Indium	3.37	Thorium	1.32
Iridium (a)	0.14	Tin	3.69
Lanthanum	4.71	Titanium	0.53
Lead	7.26	Uranium	0.8
Mercury	4.12	Vanadium	5.1
Molybdenum(a)	1.0	Zinc	0.79
Osmium	0.7	Zirconium	0.70

(a) Iron content must be less than 10 to 20 ppm.

Many alloys and intermetallic phases are superconducting. In alloys, the resistance falls to zero gradually over one or two degrees; in metallic elements, the transition is sharp in a very small part of a degree. Most superconducting alloys have one or more components that are superconducting. Some semiconductors are superconducting, and in most instances they contain a superconducting element. Table 33 lists superconducting alloys and intermetallic phases. Superconductivity often occurs in elements or alloys having an average of 3, 5, or 7 valence electrons per atom; a cubic structure also favors superconductivity.

Onnes found that the transition temperatures depended on the current used to measure the resistance. At first he was inclined to identify the effect with current density, but later it was demonstrated that the effect was due to the magnetic field of the measuring current (Fig. 38). Meissner (152) discovered that metals in the superconducting state were impervious to a magnetic field

Table 33. Some Superconducting Alloys and Intermetallic Phases

Phase	Transition temperature, K	Alloy	Transition temperature, K
One or More Elements Superconducting			
Bi_6Tl_3	6.5	Sn-Bi	3.79
$SbTl_7$	5.5	Sn-Zn	3.66
Na_2Pb_5	7.2	Sn_3Sb_2	4.0
Hg_5Tl_2	3.8	Sn-Cd	3.62
VN	2.4	Sn-Ca	3.6
TiN	1.4	Sn-As	4.0
TiC	1.1	Tl-Ag	2.65
TaC	9.4	Tl-Cd	2.41
CbC	10.3	Tl-Au	1.8
ZrB	3.0		
TaSi	4.2	Pb-Sn	6.6
PbS	4.1	Pb-Cd	7.2
CbH	15.0	97 Pb – 3 As	8.4
VSi	17.2	Pb-P	7.8
Mo-Ru (50:50)	10.6	Pb-Ca	7.0
Cb-Sn	18.0	Pb-Li	7.2
Cb-N	14.7	Pb-Sn-Bi	8.5
		Pb-As-Bi	9.0
Components Nonsuperconducting		Pb-Bi-Sb	8.9
Au_2Bi	1.7	Pb-Bi-Sb-As	9.0
CuS	1.6	Pb-Bi-Sn-Cd	8.5
WC	3.8	Ti-Zr	1.3
W_2C	2.7	57 Pb – 43 Bi	8.8
$CoSi_2$	1.27		

— the superconductor expelled the magnetic field; up to a certain strength, a magnetic field cannot penetrate a superconductor.

Superconductivity is controlled by temperature and magnetic field. A transition temperature, T_c, is one below which the material is superconductive.

If a metal in the superconducting state is subjected to a magnetic field of increasing intensity, a field strength is eventually

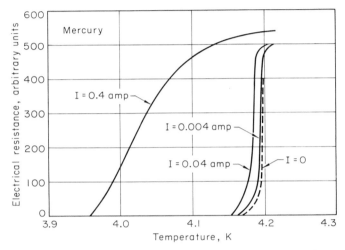

Fig. 38. Temperature-resistance characteristics of mercury, showing effects of variation in current (after Onnes)

reached at which the normal resistance suddenly reappears. At any temperature below the normal transition temperature (for zero field), the magnetic field intensity that brings the resistance back to its normal value is called the critical field strength or threshold field, H_T, for that temperature. The farther the temperature is decreased below the transition temperature, the greater becomes the threshold field (Fig. 39). For every temperature below the transition temperature, there is a value of the magnetic field that destroys superconductivity. Superconductors that are exposed to alternating currents of frequencies above 10 mc exhibit some electrical resistance. Superconductors are classified as ideal or "soft," or nonideal or "hard." In a soft superconductor, the current is carried only in a thin surface layer. In the hard type (for example, columbium-zirconium), the current appears to be carried by filaments inside the wire. The number of filaments is increased by cold working the superconductor.

In any study at low temperatures, it is appropriate to ask how the temperature is measured. Down to about 1 K, the gas (helium) thermometer can be used, but, in the range below 1 K, such an instrument is useless. The method used below 1 K is based on measurements of the magnetic properties of paramagnetic samples, because the lower the temperature, the greater the magnetic moment that can be induced in a sample by a small magnetic field. In ideal paramagnetic substances, Curie's law, that the sus-

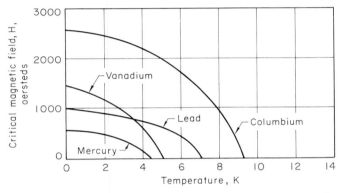

Fig. 39. Critical magnetic fields of four superconducting elements

ceptibility is proportional to the reciprocal of the absolute temperature, holds. Even though no ideal paramagnetic exists, the principle has been investigated, so that a magnetic temperature scale has been established (141).

In one of the more recent theories of superconductivity, Bardeen (142) has postulated that, at low temperatures, the vibrating ions in a crystal lattice no longer impeded the electron flow but began to conduct the electron flow in a wavelike way. Lattice vibration becomes the agent that makes the metal superconducting as a result of interactions between ions and electrons: The electrons reduce their energy and ride along with the lattice vibration as a wave. In this way, resistance to the flow of electrons is said to disappear. In spite of the advances in the fundamental theory, it is still impossible to predict the transition temperature of any material from its lattice or electronic properties.

New research not only sheds more light on superconductivity

but will make a comprehensive theory more difficult to develop. Matthias (155) has shown that the magnetic moments of some elements dissolved in superconducting metals will raise their transition temperature. Bozorth and Davis (156) report that ferromagnetism and superconductivity can coexist in separate domains of some alloys of rare earth and second-transition-series elements ($Gd_{0.08}Ce_{0.92}Ru_2$).

Giaever (157) found that tunneling occurred in devices consisting of two metal thin films that were separated by a thin insulating layer, when one or both films was in the superconducting state. The tunneling occurs through the charge-depletion region of a p-n junction. The films used were all superconductors, aluminum, lead, indium and tin, and the insulating layers were Al_2O_3, TaO, CbO and NiO.

Technetium has the highest transition temperature of any element — 11 K; an intermetallic phase of columbium and tin has the highest (18 K) transition temperature of any compound. Superconductivity at reasonably high temperatures is hoped for.

The transition temperature of 18 K of the tin-columbium alloy brings superconductors into a temperature range where this effect can be put to practical use. Cooling such conductors to this temperature with cold helium gas or liquid hydrogen is practical. Considering that the threshold field of a superconductor increases with decreasing temperature (Fig. 39), an alloy with a transition temperature of 18 K has a very high critical field.

The compound Cb_3Sn remains superconducting in pulsed fields up to 185 kilogausses. By extrapolating to zero current, the critical field at about 1.6 K is 188 kilogausses. The compound V_3Ga holds out the most promise of attaining the highest continuous magnetic fields ever achieved by man. The vanadium-gallium material has a critical field in excess of 400,000 gausses.

Potential uses for superconductors are for sensitive electrical instruments, switches, and computer memory devices, making it possible to handle extremely small currents or signals without loss of energy. Operating transformers (iron-core or air-core) at low temperature would obviously save much electrical power. Relatively inexpensive superconducting magnets of 100,000 gausses or more are in sight. Attainment of such fields at ambient temperature with more conventional techniques is expensive, because of the megawatts of power and thousands of gallons of cooling water required.

Chapter 4

Conductors, Resistors and Other Circuit Elements

CONDUCTION in solids and various electrical phenomena associated with metals were discussed in Chapters 2 and 3. This chapter is an extension of that discussion, with an emphasis on applications. These applications are treated in a descriptive outline form; at no time are they spelled out in any appreciable detail.

Electrical circuits or apparatus are composed of one or more of the following building blocks of electrical engineering: conductors, magnetic materials, inductors, resistors and capacitors. The use of inductors has permitted the building of transformers, electromagnets, motors, and generators. The use of resistors has allowed the development of electric lights, electric heaters, and controls. The use of capacitors has made possible communications circuits.

In addition to the circuit elements mentioned above, synoptic discussions are included on electron tubes, photocells, rectifiers, transistors, Hall-effect devices, contacts, transducers, relays, fuses, and strain gages. These components are circuit elements in the broadest sense of the expression.

In the past decade, a new science of materials, popularly known as solid-state electronics, has evolved. Starting with the examination of crystals for dislocations and vacancies, this science has developed into an astounding technology that was nonexistent before the Second World War. This new technology deals mainly with semiconductors, but to some degree with magnetic materials (essentially films) and ceramics (ferrites and ferroelectrics). The progress in semiconductor development is largely the result of refinement of processing and the impurity-control techniques used in the preparation of ultra-high-purity

129

semiconducting elements such as germanium and silicon. The aims of solid-state electronics are to have the device microsize, virtually weightless, supersensitive, of high-power output with microwatt consumption, thoroughly reliable, and operating indefinitely. Some of these goals are within reach.

Some of the circuit functions of vacuum tubes that were developed over a 40-year period are already being usurped by solid-state electronics. Noble (158) lists 30 functions that are threatened by the new technology.

Conductors

A conductor is so constructed from conducting materials that it may be used as a carrier of electricity. Generally, a conductor is made of a material of relatively high electrical conductivity, and consists of a solid wire or a multiplicity of wires stranded together, either bare or insulated. The conductor is usually copper or aluminum, but, for applications requiring strength (such as overhead transmission lines), bronze, steel, and composites are used. Conductors may be wires, cables,* flat straps, square or rectangular bars, angles, channels, tubes, and special designs.

There is no clear-cut distinction between bus conductors and metallic electrical conductors. The term bus has been applied to bars, channels, and tubular shapes used for sections of the main circuits in power stations that carry considerable electrical power. In addition to power stations, bus conductors are used for lines supplying current to electrolytic cells in metallurgical and chemical plants and in power switchgear ** assemblies. In assemblies of electronic equipment, usage assumes the wires to be metallic conductors. Figure 40 shows the tubular bus structure that carries 6500 amp at 20 kv from the generator to the power transformers at the Astoria station of the Consolidated Edison Co., Astoria, Long Island; the copper bus is 13½ in. OD and has a 0.406-in. wall.

Next to silver, copper is the best electrical conductor. For electrical purposes, copper is usually required to have the highest

* A cable may be a stranded conductor (single conductor cable) or a combination of conductors insulated from one another (multiple conductor cable).

** The term switchgear covers switching and interrupting devices and asemblies of those devices, with control, metering, protective and regulating equipment and associated interconnections and supporting structures.

Fig. 40. Tubular bus conductor structure at the Astoria station of the Consolidated Edison Co., Astoria, L. I. The copper bus, 13½-in. OD and a wall thickness of 0.406 in., can carry 6500 amp at 20 kv. (Courtesy, Anaconda Co.)

possible electrical conductivity. Unfortunately, copper is relatively heavy and has low mechanical strength; it has a density of 8.9 g per cu in. and a tensile strength of about 32,000 psi in the annealed condition.

Aluminum is competitive with copper for power transmission. It is low in density (2.7 g per cu in.), and its tensile strength (13,000 psi) is lower than that of annealed copper. Its resistivity is 17.1 ohms per cir mil-ft compared with 10.4 for copper, but its weight is only one third that of copper. Therefore, for equal resistance, the weight of aluminum is only about 54% that of copper. For a given cross section, aluminum has about 61% of the conductivity of copper. Aluminum conductors, which are 30% larger in diameter than copper conductors, offer greater wind resistance and have a greater ice load, necessitating strong supports.

Modern bronzes, copper and tin with phosphorus, silicon, manganese, zinc, aluminum, and cadmium, are also used for conductors. For better conductivity, the tin and other alloy additions are kept low.

Iron and steel are used principally for telephone and telegraph lines. Iron has a resistivity of 60.2 ohms per cir mil-ft, while soft steel has a resistivity of about 71 and hard steel of about 271 ohms per cir mil-ft. Steel wire is used for comparatively short taps on power distribution lines and for long conductor spans where high tensile strength is required. Iron wires are protected from corrosion by zinc (galvanized) coatings. High-strength low-resistance galvanized steel telephone and telegraph wires have been perfected. To provide added strength, copper or aluminum is sometimes wrapped over a steel core. Copper or aluminum may also be bonded to a steel core.

The construction of a modern telephone cable involves the gathering together of 2121 pairs of fine copper wire, binding the multiple-stranded conductor with strong paper tape, covering the conductor with an aluminum foil for electrical shielding and lightning protection, and finally wrapping the cable with a protective ribbon of tin plate.

Work hardening, by cold rolling or by drawing through dies, increases electrical resistivity. If annealed copper of 101.1% IACS is very severely cold worked to full hardness, the conductivity will decrease to about 98.0%. The work-hardened high-purity copper softens at about 175 C (350 F) on heating for about ½ hr.

Table 34 gives resistances of solid-wire conductors.

IACS Conductivity. The conductivity of a conductor is often rated in terms of its ratio to the conductivity of the chemically

Table 34. Comparative Resistances of Solid-Wire Conductors of Various Sizes

Metal	D-C resistance at 20 C (68 F), ohms per 1000 ft			
	No. 4 gage (0.2043- in. diam)	No. 6 gage (0.1620– in. diam)	No. 8 gage (0.1285- in. diam)	No. 10 gage (0.1019– in. diam)
Copper (hard) (a)	0.2485	0.4108	0.6533	1.039
Copper (medium) (a)	0.2570	0.4087	0.6499	1.033
Copper (soft) (a)	0.2485	0.3951	0.6282	0.9989
Bronze (b)	1.656	2.634	4.188	6.659
Copperweld (40% IACS)	0.6337	1.008	1.602	2.547
Copperweld (30% IACS)	0.8447	1.343	2.136	3.396
Aluminum	0.408	0.648	1.03	1.64
Pure iron	1.409	2.241	3.563	5.666

(a) Hard drawn wire is wire finished from rod by cold working (drawing) and with no intermediate annealing. Soft wire is cold reduced wire that has been annealed. Medium or medium-hard drawn wire is annealed wire that has been drawn to a slightly smaller diameter. (b) ASTM B105–47, grade 15.

pure corresponding metal or in terms of its ratio to the conductivity of the International Annealed Copper Standard. The ratio can be expressed either as the volume-conductivity ratio, where the cross sections are equal, or as the mass-conductivity ratio, where the masses are equal.

The per cent conductivity of copper, for instance, is calculated by dividing the resistivity of the International Annealed Copper Standard (IACS) at 20 C (68 F) by the resistivity of the sample at 20 C. Either mass or volume resistivity may be used.

In North American usage, the International Annealed Copper Standard is the accepted value for the resistivity of annealed copper of 100% conductivity. This standard is expressed in terms of mass resistivity of 0.15328 ohm (meter, gram) — that is, the resistance of a uniform round wire, 1 m long, weighing 1 g at 20 C. Extremely pure copper has a higher conductivity than 100%. The usual conductivity of American commercial electrolytically refined copper in the annealed condition is about 101.0% IACS. Spectroscopically pure copper (99.999%) has a IACS conductivity of 102.32% (159). Conductivities of other grades are:

Electrolytic tough-pitch ....102.1% IACS
Oxygen-free high-conductivity (OFHC) 101.4%
Tough-pitch lake (0.015% Ag) 100.5%

The conductivity of common conductor materials is given in Table 35. The conductivity of pure silver is 105% IACS.

Table 35. Conductivity and Resistivity of Some Common Conductors

Metal	Condition	Conductivity at 20 C (68 F), % IACS	Mass, ohms (m, g)	Resistivity	
				Volume, ohms per mil-ft	microhm-cm
Copper	Low-resistance lake wirebar, electrolytic wirebar, oxygen-free wirebar	100	0.15328	10.371	1.7241
	Hard bus bar.........	98.4	0.15577	10.540	1.7522
Copper alloy	ASTM B105–47, gr 85	85.0	0.18039	12.206	2.0291
	ASTM B105–47, gr 55	55.0	0.27864	18.854	3.1343
	ASTM B105–47, gr 20	20.0	0.76638	51.856	8.6207
Aluminum	Hard.................	60.97	0.076441	17.011	2.828
Copperweld	Hard.................	29.41	0.47773	35.26	5.8617
Iron	Armco ingot..........	16.1	0.840	64.3	10.7
	Galvanized...........	16.0	0.849	65.0	10.8
	Telegraph wire........	14.6	0.928	71.0	11.8

Table 36. Effect of Temperature on Conductivity of 100% IACS Copper

Temperature, C	F		IACS conductivity, %	Temperature, C	F		IACS conductivity, %
20	68	....	100	70	158	....	83.5
40	104	....	92.7	80	176	....	80.9
50	122	....	89.4	85	190	....	79.6

The effect of temperature on the conductivity of 100% IACS copper is given in Table 36.

The effect of cold work on the conductivity of copper is given in Fig. 41 (69, 159). The recovery on annealing is also shown.

Wire Gages. Wires for electrical conductors are made in many diameters and are usually identified by gage numbers or circular mils. The most common gage used in America for electrical wires is the Brown & Sharpe or American Wire Gage (AWG). The American Wire Gage is used from No. 40 to 0000 AWG, while the circular mil is used for sizes in excess of No. 0000 AWG. The commonly used gage for steel wires is the Birmingham Wire Gage. There is a tendency to specify wire sizes by the diameter in mils (thousandths of an inch) rather than by gage.

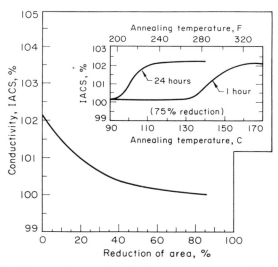

Fig. 41. Change in conductivity of spectrographically pure copper with cold deformation and its recovery on annealing

Table 37. Wire Table, Standard Annealed Copper
(American Wire Gage (Brown and Sharpe) and English units)

Gage, AWG	Diameter at 20 C, mils	Cross section at 20 C, cir mils	Cross section at 20 C, sq in	Ohms per 1000 ft at 20 C	Pounds per 1000 ft	Feet per pound	Feet per ohm at 20 C	Ohms per pound at 20 C	Pounds per ohm at 20 C
0000	460.0	211,600	0.1662	0.0490	640.5	1.561	20,400	0.000076	13,070
000	409.6	167,800	0.1318	0.0618	507.9	1.968	16,180	0.00012	8,219
00	364.8	133,100	0.1045	0.0779	402.8	2.482	12,830	0.00019	5,169
0	324.9	105,500	0.0829	0.0983	319.5	3.130	10,180	0.00031	3,251
1	289.3	83,690	0.0657	0.1239	253.3	3.947	8,070	0.00049	2,044
2	257.6	66,370	0.0521	0.1563	200.9	4.977	6,400	0.00078	1,286
3	229.4	52,640	0.0413	0.1970	159.3	6.276	5,075	0.00124	808.6
4	204.3	41,740	0.0328	0.2485	126.4	7.914	4,025	0.00197	508.5
5	181.9	33,100	0.0260	0.3133	100.2	9.980	3,192	0.00312	319.8
6	162	26,250	0.0206	0.3951	79.46	12.58	2,531	0.00497	201.1
7	144.3	20,820	0.0163	0.4982	63.02	15.87	2,007	0.00791	126.5
8	128.5	16,510	0.0130	0.6282	49.98	20.01	1,592	0.01257	79.55
10	101.9	10,380	0.0082	0.9989	31.43	31.82	1,001	0.03178	31.47
15	57.07	3,257	0.0326	3.184	9.858	101.4	314.0	0.3230	3.096
20	31.96	1,022	0.0008	10.15	3.092	323.4	98.5	3.283	0.3046
25	17.90	320.4	0.00025	32.37	0.970	1,031	30.90	33.37	0.0299
30	10.03	100.5	0.000079	103.2	0.3042	3,287	9.69	339.2	0.0029
35	5.61	31.52	0.000025	329.0	0.0954	10,480	3.04	3448	0.00029

In American and English wire tables, the circular mil is the standard unit of wire cross section. A square mil is the area of a square each side of which is 1 mil (0.001 in.), and it is equal to 0.000001 sq in. A circular mil is the area of a circle whose diameter is 1 mil (0.001 in.), and it is equal to 0.000000785 sq in. $[\pi/4(0.001)^2]$.* A convenient unit of resistivity is the resistance

Fig. 42. *Use of copper in motors. Note the compensating windings of rectangular copper bars (the nested U-shaped conductors in edge view) that run through the stator of an Elliott 800-hp d-c motor. (Courtesy, Anaconda Co.)*

of a circular mil-foot — the resistance of wire that has a cross section of 1 circular mil and the length of 1 ft.

Some selected data from wire tables for annealed copper of standard resistivity are given in Table 37. In order to use the wire table for copper of another resistivity, a factor must be used. For example, hard-drawn copper has about 2.7% higher resistivity than the annealed form.

Copper Conductors. Copper is preferred for electrical conductors because of its low electrical resistivity, slow rate of corrosion and oxidation, high heat conductivity, relatively high softening

---

* To obtain the number of circular mils in a solid wire, express the diameter in mils and square it. To obtain the diameter of a wire having an area of so many circular mils, take the square root of the circular mils, and the result will be the diameter of the wire in mils.

temperature of the cold worked metal, high melting point, satis-factory strength, good ductility and workshop workability, ability to be "tinned" with silver, tin or solders, and ease of soldering and brazing. Figure 42, which shows sets of compensating wind-ings of copper conductors, illustrates an application requiring the enumerated characteristics to varying degrees. For the physi-cal metallurgy and mechanical properties of copper and copper alloys, Brace (160) should be consulted.

The electrochemical properties of copper are such that it can be readily deposited as cathode copper, to the virtual exclusion of most impurities existing in the crude anodes. The deposited copper is then melted (control of oxygen content is important) and cast into various shapes preparatory to subsequent rolling, forging, wiredrawing, or other metal-working operations.

The heat developed by the I^2R loss * is the limiting factor on the amount of current density a conductor can tolerate. Safety requirements impose a limit on the current to be carried by con-ductors, because, when I^2R losses produce more heat than can be radiated, the conductor temperature will rise, and the insulation may be harmed; this creates a fire hazard. For copper bus bars, the accepted value of current density is 1000 amp per sq in.**

The design of apparatus or its installation and the choice of conductors are usually based on a maximum temperature rise of 30 °C (54 °F) over a 40 C (108 F) ambient temperature under a continuous, full load. Factors to be considered in an installation are whether the site is warm or cold, ventilated or not, and the probability of overloading, with the incidental mechanical stresses developed. The passage of excessively large currents through wires causes them to explode.

In 1914, the Bureau of Standards measured a large number of copper samples and established standard values of resistivity and temperature coefficients that have subsequently been adopted by the International Electrotechnical Committee and the American Institute of Electrical Engineers. The established rules are:

1 At 20 C (68 F), the resistance of a wire of standard annealed cop-per 1 m in length and of a uniform section of 1 sq in. is ⅟₅₈ ohm or 0.017241 ohm.

* In a circuit containing a conductor (or resistor, for that matter) of resistance R, the flow of electrical energy will generate heat, and the rate of development of heat is proportional to the square of the current, I.

** The National Electrical Code provides tables for allowable current-carrying capacities of bare and insulated wires.

2 At 20 C (68 F), the density of standard annealed copper is 8.89 g per cu cm.

3 At 20 C (68 F), the constant mass temperature coefficient of resistance of standard annealed copper, measured between two potential points rigidly fixed to the wire, is 0.00393 or $\frac{1}{254.45}$ per °C.

4 At 20 C (68 F), the resistance of a wire of standard annealed copper of uniform section, 1 m in length and weighing 1 g is $\frac{1}{58} \times 8.89$ or 0.15328 ohm.

Four types of electrolytic high-conductivity copper are commercially available: (a) tough-pitch copper, (b) deoxidized copper, (c) oxygen-free copper, and (d) free-machining copper.

The purity of these coppers must be carefully controlled. With the exception of lead, silver, and oxygen, small amounts (a few tenths of a per cent) of impurities rapidly decrease conductivity.

Tough-Pitch Copper. The greatest proportion of refinery production is tough-pitch copper. This copper generally contains about 0.04% O, precipitated as Cu_2O or a Cu-Cu_2O eutectic. If it is lake copper, it may also have about 0.025% Ag in solid solution. Neither this oxygen nor silver content appreciably affect the electrical conductivity. Values of 101% IACS are readily attained. The mechanical properties of tough-pitch copper fall somewhat below those of the oxygen-free types; the reduction in area is particularly decreased by the presence of copper oxide.

The most serious difficulty encountered with oxygen-bearing coppers is their tendency toward embrittlement above 400 C (750 F) when exposed to reducing gases, particularly hydrogen.

Deoxidized High-Conductivity Copper. When copper is properly deoxidized with such agents as phosphorus, calcium or lithium, the oxygen content can be reduced to very small percentages and very little of the deoxidizer is retained. Deoxidation with phosphorus is carefully carried out in order to recover a residual phosphorus of 0.01% or less. Conductivities of 101% IACS are readily obtained.

Oxygen-Free High-Conductivity Copper (OFHC). If the melting and casting of copper is performed in such manner that oxygen is not absorbed, the product is called oxygen-free high-conductivity copper (OFHC); it may have a conductivity of 102% IACS. The material shows no tendency toward hydrogen embrittlement when annealed in a reducing atmosphere.

Free-Machining Copper. Pure copper is difficult to machine; hence, lead is sometimes added to improve machinability. Alloys containing 1% Pb have a conductivity of 99% IACS and a machinability of about 80% of free-machining brass, which is an ideal material from the standpoint of machinability. There is little sacrifice of strength, although the ductility is somewhat reduced. Up to 1% S, 1.5% Se, and 2.5% Te can also be added to improve machinability.

The effect of various elements, as alloys or impurities, on the conductivity of copper is shown in Fig. 43. Note the harmful ef-

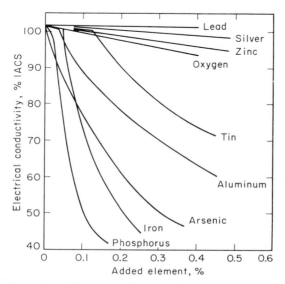

Fig. 43. Effect of alloying elements on electrical conductivity (per cent IACS) of copper

fect of phosphorus, iron, and arsenic and the slight effect of silver, zinc, and oxygen (161); see Fig. 8 also.

Aluminum Conductors. Aluminum is one of the lightest of the structural metals. It is made by the electrolysis of aluminum oxide dissolved in molten cryolite. Aluminum has a higher strength-weight ratio than copper and good electrical conductivity. For this reason, it is used for wide spans. Owing to its high strength-weight ratio, steel-cored aluminum and aluminum alloy conductors have been more susceptible to vibration, leading in several instances to breakage of binders and conductors. The problem has been solved by reducing conductor tension.

The cost of constructing aluminum conductors is less than for copper conductors. Common difficulties encountered in their use include: conductors burned down at connections, loose connections (causing lights to flicker), and high-resistance connections caused by corrosion of material. These problems have been solved in large part by welding and improved fasteners.

The most important single application of aluminum has been in ACSR (Aluminum Cable Steel Reinforced) cable. This cable is used for more than 90% of the overhead, high-voltage power transmission, because of the low corona loss,* due to greater diameter for the same conductance. Aluminum is also taking over a large share of the overhead distribution and service drop business. It is used as a sheath in coaxial cables and as braid in Navy and coaxial cables. It is also used for magnet wire and electrical conduit. In substations, welded aluminum is used in bus construction for switchboards and transmission of power. It withstands high short circuits successfully. Aluminum has been used for rotor windings of induction motors, field windings of some motors, and high-speed turbogenerators.

The electrical conductivity of annealed aluminum (99.97%) is 64.6% IACS, and of hard-drawn aluminum, it is 61% IACS.

Copper Alloy and Composite Conductors. High-strength high-conductivity copper alloys are required for certain applications. For trolley wires, where abrasion resistance must be considered, a beryllium-copper alloy is frequently used. A 0.4% Be alloy has a conductivity of 48% IACS and a tensile strength of 86,000 psi, and a 0.9% Be alloy has a conductivity of 28% IACS and a strength of 122,000 psi.

Copper containing 4 to 7% Ag (6½% optimum) has a conductivity of 70% IACS and a tensile strength of 160,000 psi. Electrolytic tough-pitch high-conductivity copper has been used for commutators of rotating machines since the first of these machines was made. With increasing power requirements, which result in higher operating temperatures, the heavy duties have been met with either copper containing 25 to 30 troy ounces of silver per ton or copper containing about 0.85% Cr. Copper-chromium and copper-silver alloys, in which the chromium and

---

* Corona loss occurs as a result of a discharge brought about as a result of the ionization of gas surrounding a conductor. The corona discharge occurs when the potential gradient exceeds a certain value but is not sufficient to cause sparking.

silver contents may be in ranges between 0.3 to 1% Cr and 0 to 0.1% Ag, have valuable electrical and mechanical properties. Leaded copper of 98% IACS has a relative machinability index of 80, compared with 20 for tough-pitch copper of 101% IACS.

Cables of concentric strandings and of three-wire construction for smaller sizes are available as composites. Three-wire construction, consisting of one high-strength and two high-conductivity (for example, copper-copper alloy, copper-steel) wires are used particularly for rural electrification. Steel reinforced copper or aluminum cable, in various combinations of conductor and steel, is used for overhead transmission lines. Corrosion due to galvanic action of the combination is negligible except in areas about three miles from salt water. During the Second World War, field wire for telephone communications with advanced troops was made with a combination of fine steel (for strength) and copper strands, encased in plastic insulation.

Copper-covered steel wires are a compromise between copper and steel; they are inferior to copper and superior to steel in conductivity, but are of greater strength than copper. Commercial copper-covered steel manufactured by a special casting process is marketed under the trade name of Copperweld. High-strength, 40% IACS Copperweld wire has a tensile strength of 80,000 to 138,000 psi. Aluminum-coated steel, Alumoweld, has one third the conductivity of aluminum and eight times its strength.

For overhead applications, copper wire is used in the range of No. 10 to 4 AWG. Copperweld for signal and communications is used in AWG sizes No. 17 to 10. Some typical uses and characteristics of conductor wires are given in Table 38.

Copper must be protected from progressive oxidation at high temperatures. Electroplating with nickel and silver is often satisfactory, but sometimes Inconel, chromium, and stainless steel have been used as bonded sheaths on the copper. The latter coatings, 5 to 10% by weight, reduce the conductivity to about 90% IACS. Although such coatings reduce oxidation, diffusion as a result of high-temperature exposure can give brittle diffusion interfaces of high resistance. A thin nickel layer between the silver and the copper prevents formation of the highly resistive copper-silver alloy. Nickel-clad copper wire insulated with a flexible vitreous enamel has good heat resistance to 650 C (1200 F).

Printed circuits are insulating plates carrying a pattern of con-

Table 38. Typical Applications of Electrical Conductors

Uses	Materials and required characteristics
Contact (trolley) wires	Hard-drawn copper wire or bronze alloy must have current-carrying and abrasion-resistance characteristics. Wire is often grooved to facilitate support.
Bus conductors	Copper and aluminum must have current-carrying capacity and requisite mechanical strength.
Power conductors	Bare, solid or stranded copper or copper alloy. For specific applications, Copperweld, aluminum, and steel. For overhead lines, hard-drawn or medium-hard tempers. Insulated, soft or annealed grounding or bonding, weatherproof cables with copper or aluminum wires reinforced with steel wire.
Signal or communications	Copperweld, weatherproofed or insulated.
Telephone and telegraph	Galvanized iron and steel.
High-voltage transmission	Hollow copper. Large outside diameter reduces corona loss. Current-carrying capacity greater when used for alternating current.

ductors or resistors (metallic lines), which replace some of the wiring in mass-produced electronic equipment. Almost any form of wiring on an insulating support is called a printed circuit, regardless of whether printing, as such, was used in construction.

In the most common current technique, printed circuits are made from insulators covered with metal foil, although Eisler (162) lists 26 other methods of producing printed circuits.

In principle, a foil (copper) is bonded with some cement to an insulating panel (Bakelite or plastic). An acid-resistant image is made in the foil in one of two ways: (a) *Printing:* An acid-proof ink is used. On placing in acid, the uninked portion is dissolved away, while the acid-resistant areas remain. (b) *Photomechanical:* Metal foil is covered with a light-sensitive coating. A transparent negative in contact with the light-sensitive coating is exposed to illumination. Light reaching the sensitive coating through clear areas of the negative hardens the coating and makes it insoluble in a developer. Opaque areas on the film keep light from the sensitive layer and these areas are soluble in the developer.

Conductors can be deposited as thin films in a vacuum (163). Sputtering is preferred to evaporation, because sputtering results in less contamination.

Electrical Connectors. For power lines, bus bars, and the like, bolting, brazing, and welding are used. For bus bars, the contacting faces, almost always silver plated, are bolted. Silver alloy brazing, phosphor copper brazing, and welding are used to a lesser extent.

Electrical connections, for example, light switches, wall plugs, telephone dials, and extension-cord connectors, are necessary for transferring electricity from one discrete body of metal to another. A big problem with switches is the formation of oxide, which is a nonconductor.

The first choice of metal for terminals is copper, because of its conductivity and good formability. For corrosive situations, special finishes, organic or metallic, are provided on the conductor. The simplest and oldest type of wire connection is probably the twisting together of clean wires and looping them under a screwhead. Application of solder to twisted wires was an early improvement. Another early development was the small spade stamping to which the wire was soldered. In recent years, the mechanically joined, pressure, or solderless, terminals have been winning considerable acceptance.

Permanent electrical connections are made by four basic methods: soldering, brazing, welding, and mechanical pressure. The first three methods require heat; the fourth does not. The first two require a third metal; the others do not.

In soldering, with either lead-base or tin-base alloys, the heat is high enough — 205 to 370 C (440 to 700 F) — to damage insulation, if precautions are not exercised. Much research has been conducted on solders, soldering temperatures, wettability of the solder, oxide films and fluxes, and corrosion problems. Pure tin is used to solder coil leads to commutator risers and banding wire on large direct-current generators. With increased operating temperature, tin-antimony solders (93 Sn – 7 Sb or 95 Sn – 5 Sb) have found usefulness; however, neither the tin nor tin-antimony solders should be used above 120 C (250 F), as diffusion of copper into the solders embrittles the joints, which may fail under impact.

Brazing and welding provide higher strength than soldering and are used for large conductors for heavy currents, where high mechanical strength is required. The much higher temperatures used in brazing and welding — above 425 C (800 F) — as compared with soldering make preservation of insulation more difficult.

Pressure connectors must be so designed that the contact between terminal and conductor is not affected by springback * or subsequent relaxation of the compressive stress.

Solderless wrapped connections are made by wrapping a solid wire tightly in coil fashion around a terminal, and the connection thus made is held together by elastic stresses in the two members. A minimum of five turns of wire is used for No. 22 gage wire and a minimum of six turns for No. 24 wire. The solderless connection has been used since 1952 by the Bell system, during which time several hundred million connections have been made (164).

Gallium alloys (66 Cu − 34 Ga or 82 Au − 18 Ga) offer promise for fastening wires to heat-sensitive materials (semiconductors), and to cold solder ceramic and metallic surfaces (165). Like mercury, gallium combines with many metals to form dental-type alloys, which harden after from 2 to 24 hr. While the alloys are soft when mixed, they harden so that they have excellent strength.

Resistors (166)

Every resistor introduces resistance into an electrical circuit, but the functions of the resistor may differ. As circuit elements, they introduce a fixed amount of resistance into an electronic circuit to develop signal or operating voltages of a desired amplitude. Resistors are used to convert electrical energy into heat for stoves, toasters, irons, ovens and furnaces.

As electronic circuit elements, resistors are of three types: fixed, adjustable, and variable. Fixed resistors are generally color coded. Adjustable resistors, sometimes called rheostats, have connections on each end and to a movable tap. A voltage-dropping resistor is one whose function is to reduce the voltage to particular values. A voltage-divider resistor provides voltages to various circuits, when each one is drawing a predetermined current through the divider. Although the variable resistor with an easily movable tap is often called a potentiometer, the term is reserved in the instrument field for a device that measures

---

* Springback is the tendency of a metal to return to the unstressed state when an applied stress is removed. Springback is indicative of plastic stresses. It is measured as the increase in diameter of a curved strip after removing it from a mandrel about which it was held.

potential; the terms voltage-dividing resistor and potentiometer-rheostat are also used in this connection. In the discharge of stored energy, it is advisable to pass the energy through a resistor to prevent damage to the circuit from a voltage surge.

The three most important characteristics of resistors are their resistivity, temperature coefficient of resistivity, and operating stability. Other properties are also examined before a combination of metals is selected for a specific type of resistor: Mechanical strength, maximum working temperature, corrosion and oxidation resistance, aging, and temperature coefficient of expansion are some. Manufacturers offer resistors in a wide variety of size, power rating, tolerance, temperature coefficient, and reliability under various conditions.

Composition resistors * are cheap and widely used but do not have as good stability as the more expensive, precision, ** wire-wound types. Power-carrying resistors are wire wound. The composition, carbon-film, and metal-film resistors have better high-frequency characteristics than wire-wound resistors, because the wire types will have an inductance. However, some wire-wound types have noninductive windings. Alloy wire, insulated with silk or cotton, is generally wound on spools.

Wire-wound resistors fall into the following classes:

High ohmage — 675 to 815 ohms per cir mil-ft
   1 Nickel-chromium alloys
   2 Nickel-chromium-aluminum alloys
   3 Modified nickel-chromium alloys
Low ohmage — 30 to 300 ohms per cir mil-ft
   4 Copper-base alloys (copper-nickel and copper-nickel-manganese)
   5 Noble metals (platinum and palladium-base alloys)

Compositions are given in Table 39. The noble metal resistors are used primarily in potentiometers, because the absence of surface oxide permits good contact at low pressures.

The demand for stable resistances for high-quality electrical apparatus, such as decade boxes, potentiometers, and standard resistors, has encouraged development of alloys having small

---

* These resistors are compounded of carbon or graphite with talc and cement.

** A precision resistor is defined as one with an electrical-resistance tolerance of 1% or less — that is, the rating must be within 1% of the specified value. Some resistors have tolerances of 0.01% or less.

Table 39. Properties of

Material	Ni	Cr	Fe	Mn	Cu	Other
Kanthal A-1	...	23	rem	...	...	5.7 Al, 2 Co
Radiohm	...	12 to 13	rem	...	...	4 to 5 Al
Karma	76	20	2	...	...	2 Al
Chromel C	61	16	23	...	...	...
Nichrome	65	11 to 18	22 to 36	0.70	...	0.26 Si
Nichrome V	80	20	...	...	...	...
Chromax	35	20	rem	...	...	...
Comet	30	5	65	...	...	...
Nirex (Inconel)	rem	13	8	...	...	...
Nilvar	36	...	rem	...	...	...
Type 304 stainless	8	18	rem	...	...	...
42 alloy	42	...	rem	...	...	...
Advance	44 to 46	...	...	54 to 55	...	...
Manganin	4	...	...	12	84	...
Lucero	70	...	...	...	30	...
52 alloy	52	...	rem	...	...	...
Monel	67	...	1.4	1.0	30	...
Midohm	22 to 23	...	...	...	rem	...
R-63 alloy	rem	...	...	4	...	1 Si
Hytemco	70	...	rem	...	...	...
Magno	rem	...	...	4.5	...	...
Manganese nickel	rem	...	...	2.0	...	...
Platinum	...	...	...	...	...	...
Tungsten	...	...	...	...	...	...
Molybdenum	...	...	...	...	...	...

temperature coefficients of resistance at room temperature. Manganin and copper-nickel alloys are the most common types of materials used for small precision resistance elements. Manganin (4 Ni – 12 Mn – 84 Cu) is used extensively by electrical instrument manufacturers because it has high specific resistance (290 ohms per cir mil-ft, 49 microhm-cm), the thermal electromotive force against copper is very small, and the resistance is highest at 25 C (77 F), decreasing above and below this value in the room-temperature range.

Several copper-nickel alloys are used for applications at moderate temperatures and for cold resistance applications, such as resistors for electrical apparatus, rheostats, and so on. Some commercial compositions are Midohm (22 to 23% Ni, remainder copper) and constantan (44 to 46% Ni, remainder copper). Constantan is also known as Advance, Copel, and Cupron. Constantan

Electrical Resistance Alloys

Resistivity 20 C (68 F), ohms per cir mil-ft	Temperature coefficient, per °C	Temperature range, C	Linear temperature coefficient, per °C, ×10⁻⁶	Expansion temperature range, C	Melting point, C
872	0.000015	20 to 500	17.4	20 to 1000	1505
800	0.0007	20 to 500	15.5	20 to 1000	1480
800	0.0005	−65 to 250	13.3	−65 to 250	. . . .
675	0.00015	20 to 500	17.0	20 to 1000	1350
675	0.00017	20 to 500	17	20 to 1000	1350
650	0.00013	20 to 500	17	20 to 1000	1400
600	0.00031	20 to 500	15.8	20 to 500	1380
570	0.00088	20 to 500	15.0	20 to 500	1480
590	0.000125	20 to 500	16.1	20 to 750	1395
484	0.00135	20 to 100	10	20 to 100	1425
438	0.00094	20 to 500	20	0 to 1000	1399
400	0.0012	20 to 500	5.3	20 to 400	1425
294	±0.00002	20 to 100	14.9	20 to 100	1210
290	±0.000015	15 to 35	18.7	15 to 35	1020
290	0.001	20 to 250	12.5	20 to 100	1350
260	0.0029	20 to 500	9.5	20 to 500	1425
256	0.00145	20 to 500	14.0	0 to 100	1360
180	0.00018	20 to 100	17.5	20 to 500	1160
150	0.0027	20 to 250	15.2	20 to 500	1425
120	0.0045	20 to 100	15.0	20 to 1000	1425
120	0.0036	20 to 100	14.3	20 to 500	1435
85	0.0045	20 to 100	14.6	20 to 500	1435
72	0.00393	0 to 1000	8.9	20 to 100	1773
30	0.0048	0 to 1000	4.45	20 to 100	3370
33.3	0.00367	0 to 1000	4.9	20 to 100	2625

may be used for thermocouples and heating elements up to 425 C (800 F); it has virtually a constant resistance in the range of 20 to 480 C (68 to 900 F). Constantan has a resistance change of only about ±0.1% from −60 to +100 C (−76 to 212 F). Most of the compositions are usable to about 570 F (300 C) without deterioration.

Other resistance alloys are used for less exacting applications. The nickel-chromium alloys have high electrical resistivity, low temperature coefficient, and high resistance to oxidation and alteration at high temperatures. Iron-nickel alloys have lower resistivity and resistance to oxidation. Copper-nickel-zinc alloys or nickel silvers (for example, 18 Ni − 17 Zn − 65 Cu) are the oldest of electrical-resistance materials, but they have been largely replaced by nickel-chromium alloys.

Film resistors for low power dissipation were originally made of carbon. In Germany, this type was used almost exclusively during the Second World War. Resistance was obtained by varying the thickness. Carbon has a large negative temperature coefficient. The widely used metallic-film resistors, made from tin oxide, nickel-chromium alloys, secret alloys, and mixtures, are deposited on a glass or ceramic substrate in the form of flats, tubes and rods. Tin oxide films can be made with resistances of 5000 ohms per square, and Nichrome films with resistances of 500 ohms per square.* These types of resistors are protected by varnish, sealing in ceramic tubes, or encapsulation in plastic to protect them, mainly from moisture, the most common enemy of resistor stability. Sputtered thin-film resistors of tantalum and titanium show promise for microminiature electronics; they are produced on glass or ceramic in lines as narrow as 1 mil spaced 1 mil apart. Through the use of masks, patterns can be made to produce multiple resistors in one evaporation. In some instances, resistors, conductors, and insulators can be deposited to form laminar circuits (163). Normal aging and electrical overloads will alter film characteristics.

Metallic Heating Elements. Although heating elements can be correctly called circuit elements, it is more common to refer to them as heaters. Electrical heating, as exemplified by toasters, grills, coffee pots, flatirons, Calrod stove elements, and water heaters, is indeed commonplace and has been widely extended into the field of industrial heating, examples of which are metallurgical heat treating furnaces and industrial ovens. At the high temperatures used in heating appliances and industrial furnaces, the popular chromium-nickel alloys are outstanding and outlast the copper-nickel alloys used at the beginning of the century about 500-fold.

The most useful of the metallic heating elements are the austenitic nickel-chromium alloys with and without iron, and, to a lesser degree, the ferritic iron-chromium-aluminum alloys. The iron-free nickel-chromium alloys contain 80% Ni and 20% Cr, while in the iron-bearing alloys the nickel varies between 18 and 62% and the chromium between 14 and 25%. The ferritic alloys contain 7 to 30% Cr and about 5% Al.

Austenitic types, which have better high-temperature strength than the ferritic types, are not used above 1200 C (2190 F), but

* For an explanation of this terminology, see the section on thin films, page 82.

the ferritic types can be used to 1350 C (2460 F). The ferritic alloys show a greater (undesirable) propensity to grain growth than the austenitic alloys.

The primary requirements of resistance elements (167) are as follows: (a) moderately high resistivity, (b) stability of resistance at operating temperature, (c) good corrosion (oxidation) resistance, and (d) good mechanical properties.

Resistance elements should have moderately high resistivity, because the heat developed is directly proportional to the resistance of the material.* Of course, the heating effect should remain constant during the period of operation; precipitation effects should be absent, and phenomena of volatilization and oxidation should be as small as possible. Uniform oxidation, while destroying the element, reduces the cross section of the resistor; grain-boundary oxide penetration is more dangerous, and can decrease the resistor cross section more severely and gives rise to stress concentrations. High-temperature strength (low creep or flow) is necessary to avoid changes in shape or cross section.

Life of a resistance element is a complex property. It is defined as the ability to withstand exposure at elevated temperatures in air under either cycles or steady-state conditions for prolonged periods of time.

The following requirements must be met in high-temperature electrical resistance alloys:

Melting Point. Although the melting point of the metal must be above the safe operating temperature when new, it sometimes happens that, after prolonged service, contamination with carbon, zinc, tin, or lead may lower the melting point. The presence of 1.97% C in an 80 Ni – 20 Cr alloy lowers the melting point from 1400 C (2550 F) to about 1290 C (2350 F).

Thermal Stresses. Stresses caused by nonuniform distribution of temperature can lead to failure by (a) thermal shock, if the stresses exceed the rupture strength of the alloy, or (b) thermal stress fatigue, if the stresses are of a lower magnitude and the material has been cycled. The iron-chromium-aluminum alloys are more susceptible to these kinds of failure than the nickel-chromium alloys, particularly at 1260 C (2300 F) and above.

---

* This is a consequence of Joule's law:

$$H = 0.24RI^2t \tag{46}$$

where H is the heat measured in calories, I is the current in amperes, R is the resistance in ohms, and t is the time in seconds.

Mechanical Properties. A good resistance alloy must have a high creep strength above 1150 C (2100 F), low modulus of elasticity (to minimize thermal stresses), and good ductility during lifetime. Even though resistor elements carry no mechanical load, they may creep from their own weight. If creep should lead to nonuniform sections, such as reduced cross-sectional area, hot spots may develop and failure often follows quickly.

Volatilization. Preferential loss of elements, such as chromium in nickel-chromium alloys, will occur above 1105 C (2000 F), and depletion of chromium leads to faster oxidation rates.

Oxidation. The alloys must have good oxidation resistance. There is no strict correlation between rate of oxidation and life of an alloy as a resistor. For example, about 6% Cr added to nickel decreases the rate of oxidation and increases the life; addition of silicon to 80 Ni – 20 Cr increases the rate of oxidation and increases the life. Minor additions of strong deoxidizers (copper, zirconium, mischmetal) markedly improve the life of electrical-resistance alloys.

Resistor Materials. Nearly all resistance alloys contain iron, nickel, or chromium as major constituents and copper, aluminum, cobalt, manganese, and silicon as minor additions. Table 39 gives the compositions and characteristics of some common resistance elements. Resistivities cover a range of 10 to 150 microhm-cm (60 to 900 ohms per cir mil-ft). Two types of alloys are most commonly used: nickel-chromium and nickel-iron-chromium.

Nickel-Chromium Alloys. The simplest and most effective alloy for electrical resistance is the 80 Ni – 20 Cr alloy, known as Chromel A, Tophet A, or Nichrome V. The alloy is a nickel-rich solid solution. For workability and deoxidation, 2% Mn and 0.1% Si are often added. The electrical resistivity of 80 Ni – 20 Cr is 108 microhm-cm (650 ohms per cir mil-ft). The change in resistance with temperature is nonlinear, and hence a temperature coefficient is difficult to define. The alloy resists most furnace gases satisfactorily, except the reducing sulfur-bearing gases. It is useful to about 1200 C (2190 F).

Nickel-iron-chromium alloys, containing 60 to 62% Ni, 12 to 15% Cr, and up to 2% Mn, with the remainder essentially iron, are also used extensively for resistance purposes. They are known commercially as Chromel C, Tophet C, or Nichrome. Their specific resistivity is 112 microhm-cm (675 ohms per cir mil-ft). They are useful to 900 C (1650 F). The alloys are solid-solution types.

Iron-Chromium-Aluminum Alloys. The Kanthal series (168) of alloys, of which 25% Cr, 5% Al, 3% Co, remainder iron is an example, have excellent electrical and oxidation-resistance characteristics, and can be used at temperatures above those safe for Nichrome V. Like most metals, these alloys become brittle at elevated temperatures, which is in part due to the very large grains developed. The alloys also have low strength at elevated temperatures. These aluminum-containing alloys have excellent resistance to oxidation at elevated temperatures, because an aluminum oxide film forms on the surface. The alloys can be used in a range from 1150 to 1425 C (2100 to 2600 F).

Molybdenum, Tungsten, and Platinum Heating Units. For temperatures to about 1600 C (2910 F), molybdenum or tungsten can be used, but they must be used with a protective atmosphere, such as hydrogen. The resistivities of molybdenum and tungsten are 5 microhm-cm (30 ohms per cir mil-ft) and 5.51 microhm-cm (33.3 ohms per cir mil-ft), respectively. Platinum can be used in air, and is useful to temperatures of about 1600 C (2910 F). It has a resistivity of 10.5 microhm-cm (72 ohms per cir mil-ft) at room temperature.

Metal Filament (Incandescent) Lamp. The improvement in the incandescent lamp has been mainly an improvement in the filament. The first lamps of T. A. Edison and J. W. Swan (1878 to 1880) had filaments of carbon. In 1898, an osmium wire was introduced; tantalum filaments followed in 1903. By 1904, the superiority of tungsten had been demonstrated, and it is still in use today.

The metal filament lamp consists essentially of a fine tungsten wire heated by the passage of a current in an evacuated or gas-filled glass envelope. Energy, supplied to the wire, is transformed to heat and light. The proportion of the energy radiated as light increases with temperature. Hence, the filament is operated at as high a temperature as is consistent with a reasonable life (750 to 1000 hr). The normal operating temperature for a 40-watt lamp is 2650 K, and for a 2000-watt projector lamp, about 3000 K. These temperatures are still considerably below the melting point of tungsten, 3410 ± 20 C (6170 ± 36 F), the highest of the metals.

In the early lamps, tungsten filaments were placed in evacuated bulbs to prevent oxidation of the wire. These evacuated lamps subsequently blackened, due to the evaporation of the tungsten. Blackening was minimized by operating at a lower temperature (2400 K), but there was a loss of light. Blackening was significantly minimized by using nitrogen and argon mixtures in the bulbs. The use of gas, however, increased the loss of heat, due to convection. This loss was found to be least with a short, thick filament. The modern lamp has the filament in a close spiral. The latest development is the recoiling of the filament spiral into a helix — the coiled coil filament.

The luminous output of a filament is as follows for a given temperature and material:

$$\text{Luminous output} = kld \tag{47}$$

where l is the filament length, d is the diameter of the wire, and k is a constant.

The light from a filament lamp is affected considerably by a change in applied voltage. A 10% drop in voltage results in a 30% drop of luminous output. The color changes with variations in voltage. At normal voltage, the light is essentially white, but, as the voltage is decreased, the light becomes more red, until at the point of extinction it is dull red.

Tungsten filaments range in size from 0.0005 to 0.060 in. Tungsten wire is made from powder by hydrogen sintering, followed by treating — that is, heating the sintered bar by its own resistance — then hot swaging, and finally warm wiredrawing.

The purest tungsten is the most satisfactory for service. Addition of small quantities of partly vaporizable alkali silicates and inert oxides, such as silica, alumina, lime or thoria, to tungsten during powder metallurgy production inhibits undesirable grain growth, which formerly resulted in premature filament failure, due to fracture and offsetting (movement of entire grains along a grain boundary and across the diameter of the filament). Sagging or separation of adjacent turns on coiled filaments was also solved by additions to the tungsten.

Heat-Sensitive Resistors (Thermistors) (169). Thermistors are thermally sensitive ohmic resistors made of semiconducting crystals possessing a high negative temperature coefficient. Thermistors have extreme sensitivity to relatively minute temperature changes (ambient and self-heating). Figure 19 shows the effect of temperature on a thermistor (semiconductor) and a metal (platinum). Note the wide variation in resistivity with temperature for the thermistors. Thermistors can be metallic oxides and sulfides, germanium, selenium, silicon and indium alloys.

Semiconductors with either negative or positive temperature coefficients are known (Fig. 44). Thermistor behavior results from the effect of temperature on the electrons of a pure semiconductor material. The number of electrons (positive carriers) free to carry the electric current in oxide-type semiconductors (copper oxide, selenium oxide) increases with increasing temperature. In the newer materials (indium antimonide and indium arsenide), proper doping (type and amount of impurities) will give elements comparable to currently available thermistors,

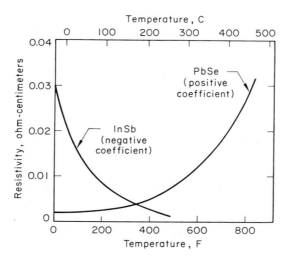

Fig. 44. *Variation of resistivity with temperature for low-resistivity semiconductors having positive (lead selenide) and negative (indium antimonide) temperature coefficients*

whose negative temperature coefficients are 2 to 3% per °F. The new semiconductor materials have low resistivities. This low resistivity is useful in fabrication of thermistors in a much lower impedance range (0.001 to 100 ohms) than was possible with oxide types.

The variation of voltage and current is rather unique in thermistors (Fig. 45).

Thermistors can be used as thermal switches when bimetallic elements are impractical. For instance, they can be used for over-temperature protection of hermetic motors in large air conditioning and refrigerating systems. They can be placed in motor windings to operate an external relay. This relay de-energizes the motor or gives a signal when overheating occurs. Thermistor thermometers are commercially available for ranges of −8 to +125 C (18 to 257 F). In addition to temperature sensing,

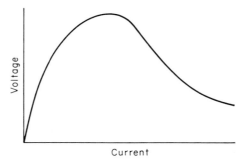

Fig. 45. Characteristic shape of a thermistor curve (linear scale)

thermistors are used for temperature compensation, measuring and control devices.

In thermistors, resistance increases abruptly when a specified temperature is reached. This is important in positive-temperature-coefficient thermistors, as opposed to the conventional type. The positive-coefficient thermistors have greater sensitivity, and they have more sharply defined and controllable temperature ranges within which the resistance increases abruptly.

Semiconductors such as lead selenide have large positive temperature coefficients (Fig. 44). The positive coefficient is caused by a decrease in the mobility of current-carrying electrons with increasing temperature. The increase in resistivity is approximately proportional to the cube of the absolute temperature.

Inductors

When there is a current in a circuit, this current sets up a magnetic field that is linked with the circuit and that varies with the variation of current. Hence, any circuit in which there is a varying current has an electromotive force (called self-induced electromotive force) induced in it, because of the variation in its own magnetic field. This property of the electric circuit is known as inductance. Straight conductors have relatively little inductance, but coils, especially those having iron cores, may have very large inductances.

A circuit or a part of a circuit that has inductance is called an inductor. A conductor wound in the shape of a coil is considered an inductor; it is also called a reactor or a choke. A magnetic core will increase the inductance of a coil, because the iron causes a magnetic field to be increased near the coil.

In an air-core coil, as the current increases, the magnetic field or flux density increases linearly. When a magnetic core is used, the flux density increases manyfold, although in a complex nonlinear manner, with increase in current. At high currents, the magnetic core becomes saturated and the iron no longer contributes to the flux density. Core saturation is a useful property in constant-voltage transformers and magnetic amplifiers.

Inductance, L, is expressed in henrys, in honor of Joseph Henry. A circuit element has an inductance of 1 henry, if a uniform current change of 1 amp per sec through the element causes a counter electromotive force of 1 v to be induced in the element. Because a henry is such a large unit, it is more common to consider millihenrys and microhenrys.

Thin films can also be used as inductors. A 82 Ni − 18 Fe alloy, 1000 to 4000 A thick, is used as a low-frequency inductor. Deposited thin-film ferrites (magnesium-manganese, manganese-zinc, and nickel-zinc ferrites) have useful high-frequency characteristics (163).

Transformers (170) are excellent examples of inductors. A transformer is an alternating-current device, without moving parts, that allows an incoming voltage, called the primary, to be delivered at a higher or lower voltage, called the secondary. In electronic circuits, transformers are used when it is necessary to couple a signal from one circuit to another. In power applications, transformers are used to increase the voltage for transmission, and then are used again to decrease the voltage, in order that it can be used safely.

An air-core transformer is a practical realization of the principle of mutual induction. The simplest transformer consists of two neighboring coils, as shown in Fig. 46. If an alternating current flows in A, it sets up an alternating magnetic flux. Some of the flux then links coil B. As a consequence, an alternating electromotive force is induced in B.

One of the most useful features of alternating current is the ease and efficiency with which voltages and currents are increased or decreased by means of transformers. For efficiency, electrical power is transmitted at high voltage and low currents to reduce the I^2R heating of a transmission line. To generate and utilize electric power, low voltages are used.

Basically, a transformer consists of two coils, electrically in-

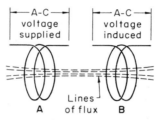

Fig. 46. Mutual inductance. Diagram of simplest transformer.

sulated from each other but wound on the same iron core. Application of alternating current to one winding creates an alternating flux in the magnetic core. This induced flux in the core links the second winding and, in so doing, induces an alternating voltage in the second coil.

The coil winding to which power is supplied is called the primary. The winding from which power is delivered is called the secondary. Either winding may be used as the primary. Usually, the two coils will have a different number of turns, so that the transformer can either step up or step down the voltage. The ratio of the primary to the secondary electromotive force is equal to the ratio of the primary to secondary turns according to the following equation:

$$\frac{E_2}{E_1} = \frac{N_2}{N_1} \tag{48}$$

By choosing the turn ratio N_2/N_1, any desired voltage may be obtained from the primary voltage. If E_2 is greater than E_1, a step-up transformer results; if E_1 is greater than E_2, a step-down transformer results (Fig. 47).

The power output of a transformer is slightly less than the input, because of unavoidable heat losses. These losses consist of the I^2R heating in the copper of the primary and secondary windings (copper losses), and the core loss of the iron path. The core loss (discussed in Chapter 5) consists of hysteresis loss and eddy-current loss. Despite these losses, transformer efficiencies are high, generally over 90%, and in large installations up to 99%.

In the transformer, the flux lines are not completely confined to the iron core, but some leak through the air, as shown in Fig. 47. The flux that links both the primary and secondary wind-

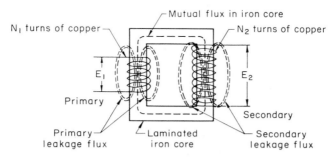

Fig. 47. Schematic representation of a transformer, showing arrangement of copper windings on the iron core

ings is called the mutual flux. The flux that takes an air path at the primary winding is called the primary leakage flux, and the part linking the secondary is called the secondary leakage flux (Fig. 47).

The reactance, X_L,* of an inductor depends on a change of flux. However, when the magnetic core is saturated, the flux does not change, even though the current through the inductor changes. For this reason, the reactance of an inductor with a saturated core falls to zero. Because the reactance increases with frequency, an inductor can be considered a frequency-sensitive element. An inductor in series with a signal can pass direct current or low-frequency alternating current and block high-frequency alternating current. This action is opposite to that of a capacitor, which passes alternating current and filters out direct current.

Inductors are used in five basic ways: as frequency-responsive elements, as voltage-changing devices, as coupling devices, as

---

* $X_L = 2\pi fL$, where X_L is the inductive reactance, f is frequency in cycles per sec and L is the inductance in henrys. Because the current, I, is equal to E divided by the inductive reactance, reactance is expressed in ohms.

elements in resonant circuits, and as saturable reactors and magnetic amplifiers.

A magnetic amplifier (170, 171) is an inductor whose reactance is controlled by the magnetic permeability of the core. The most common magnetic amplifier controls the reactance of the main winding by controlling the saturation of the core; core saturation is controlled by a small direct current in one winding on the core

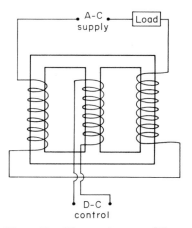

Fig. 48. Magnetic amplifier; three-legged saturable reactor

(Fig. 48). As a result, a secondary winding on the same core can pass large or small alternating currents, depending on the reactance of the inductor.

When the core is saturated, only the direct-current resistance of the coil wire impedes the current, and the maximum current flows. When the core is not saturated, the reactance of the load or main winding is high, and a small current flows.

Because a large current can be controlled by a relatively weak current in the control winding, the device is an amplifier. For magnetic amplifiers, a core that saturates easily is required. A good core material for a magnetic amplifier should have a sharply rectangular loop with small area (low hysteresis loss). Applications include: amplifiers for alternating or direct current, voltage or power, including amplification of thermocouple and photocell outputs; regulators of voltage, current and power supplies, and of generators; saturable reactors; and computer compo-

nents, including impulse-storing, memory-device, adder, subtrac-
tor, multiplier, divider, differentiator, and integrator.

The advantages of magnetic amplifiers are that they have
no moving parts or hot filaments; their power gain, which is
comparable to vacuum tubes, can be cascaded to any value; their
efficiency is greater than that of vacuum tubes; they require no
warm-up time; they can amplify signals too weak for vacuum
tubes to handle; they are stable direct-current amplifiers when
used in conjunction with rectifiers; and they are rugged and relatively shock resistant. Magnetic amplifiers also have some disadvantages; for instance, their speed of response is lower than that
of vacuum tubes, but still shorter than electromechanical devices; their upper frequency response is 500 kc, and the 60-cycle
units are larger than competitive electronic amplifying units, although the size decreases as the frequency increases.

Capacitors (172 to 174)

A capacitor (or condenser) has the ability to store electrostatic
energy and to release it under controlled conditions.

The capacitor (the Leyden jar) was invented in 1746 by Deen
Van Kleist. The Leyden-jar-form condenser remained unchanged
for more than 200 years! Leyden jars were used for communications up to the eve of the First World War; it was the American-
invented mica condenser that broke the German Leyden-jar
monopoly.

The simplest capacitor consists of two conductors, called
plates, separated by an insulator or dielectric, which can be air,
mica, glass, wax paper, oil, or almost any nonconductor (Fig.
49, a). To increase capacitance, a plurality of plates or foils
interleaved with layers of dielectric can be stacked into a pile;
every second plate is connected to one terminal and the alternate
plates are connected to the other terminal.

Capacitance is the property of a capacitor to allow current to
flow when the voltage across it changes. Capacitance is measured in farads, in honor of M. Faraday. A capacitor is said to
have a capacitance of 1 farad when a charge of 1 v across it
produces a current of 1 amp through it. A farad is too large a
unit for practical purposes, so it is more common to discuss
microfarads or micromicrofarads. (A microfarad is one millionth
of a farad and a micromicrofarad is one millionth of a micro-

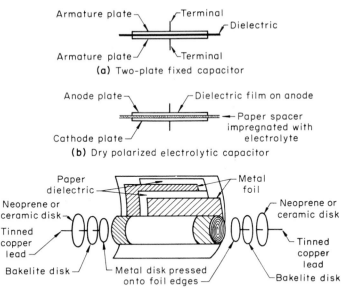

(a) Two-plate fixed capacitor

(b) Dry polarized electrolytic capacitor

(c) Paper capacitors

(d) Tantalum electrolytic capacitor

Fig. 49. Schematic representation of four types of capacitors: (a) two-plate fixed capacitor; (b) dry, polarized, electrolytic capacitor; (c) paper capacitors; (d) tantalum electrolytic capacitor

farad.) Capacitors are rated by two characteristics: capacitance and voltage. Capacitance is the charge that a capacitor can carry at a certain voltage; this depends on the surface area of the conductors, and on the thickness and insulating value of the dielectric. The voltage rating is the maximum potential at which the capacitor operates without unacceptable direct-current leakage through the dielectric.

In electronics, capacitors are used in two basic ways: In one instance, they are used as a storage device, and, in the other, they are used as a circuit-coupling device. In the electrical power industry, capacitors are used to improve the power factor of the system.*

As a storage device, one plate accumulates an excess of electrons and the other plate a deficiency. By utilizing the storage ability of a capacitor, it is possible to charge it from any direct-current source, hold the charge for a time interval, and regulate the charging and discharging time. Capacitors are used as triggering and timing devices by releasing the accumulated charge when it reaches a certain value. The storage characteristic allows the capacitor to be used as an integrating device. The charging and discharging feature is useful in shaping signals in instruments as counters. In automobiles, the capacitor permits an increase in current in an induction coil, and the spark is strengthened as a result.

Capacitors are used as filters where a direct current must be removed to allow alternating current to pass. In amplifier circuits, capacitors are used to couple stages of amplification. In a power system, capacitors reduce power costs, raise voltage levels, release the capacity of the electrical system, and, in some instances, improve voltage regulation.

Depending on construction, the five most common types of capacitors are variable, paper, mica, ceramic, and electrolytic.

Variable capacitors, generally the air-dielectric type, are used in circuits where capacitance must be continuously variable, as in tuning controls in radio receivers and signal generators. A simple variable capacitor consists of two sets of brass or aluminum plates insulated from one another and arranged so that one set rotates with respect to the other set.

Paper capacitors consist of two electrode foils, wound with insulating separators and rolled together into a compact form (Fig. 49, c). Any ductile metal of good conductivity can be used for making capacitors. The most common electrode material is aluminum, but copper and tin are also used. The major requirement is that the metal can be easily rolled to very thin gages (about 0.00025 in.). A special high-grade wood pulp (Kraft) paper varying from 0.0003 to 0.001 in. in thickness is used. Metallized paper can also be used. This type is made by exposing lacquered

---

* The power factor is the ratio by which the apparent power must be multiplied to obtain the actual (working) power.

paper to a heated metal vapor (aluminum or zinc) in a vacuum.

Mica capacitors consist of two or more strips of metal foil separated by thin sheets of mica. Complete assemblies are pressed into a compact form and are incased in insulating material.

Ceramic capacitors can operate over a wide temperature range. Their capacitance can be very high, due to the large permittivity or dielectric constant of ceramic materials.

Compared to the types mentioned, the electrolytic capacitor has a large capacitance-to-volume ratio. Electrolytic capacitors depend on a chemical action to form a dielectric of a very thin film of oxide; this film is responsible for the large capacitance (Fig. 49, b). The metal (aluminum) is placed in an electrolyte that consists of a borax solution. In operation, a thin film of aluminum oxide forms on the aluminum and serves as the dielectric. Electrolytic capacitors are polarized — they have a positive and negative terminal (usually the container serves as the cathode) and must be properly connected in the circuit. A reverse current destroys the oxide film and, hence, the capacitance of the unit. The electrolytic types are used widely in power supplies and low-frequency amplifiers, where large values of capacitance are required. The so-called dry electrolytic capacitors have an absorbent material saturated with a solution. Electrolytic capacitors are unsuitable for low temperatures — to −55 C (−67 F) — and have relatively short shelf life. Capacitance at −55 C is approximately one fifth of its value at 25 C (77 F).

Tantalum electrolytic capacitors are made from pressed powdered metal (high surface area), which is mounted inside a silver cup containing acid (Fig. 49, d). This type has a high capacitance in a very small volume. An oxide with remarkable insulating properties forms on the surface of the tantalum. The metal-oxide combination has excellent corrosion resistance for electrolytic condensers. Tantalum oxide dielectric and a phosphoric or sulfuric acid electrolyte are common combinations. Porous tantalum disks are oxidized electrolytically, using 200 v dc in a 1% solution of ammonium carbonate, to form the element. The tantalum is the anode and the silver cup is the cathode.

A **voltage variable capacitor** is a semiconductor device (silicon junction) with a capacitance controllable by adjustment of bias voltage (175).* The combination of a dielectric (the depletion

---

* Bias voltage is a voltage whose principal function is to locate the operating point in an electron tube or transistor.

region, l) and two conducting regions, p and n, has capacitance properties (Fig. 50). The capacitance-voltage relationship for voltage variable capacitors is given in Fig. 51.

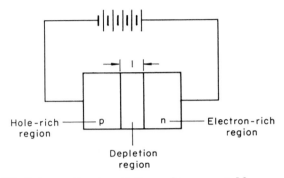

Fig. 50. *Schematic circuit for voltage variable capacitor*

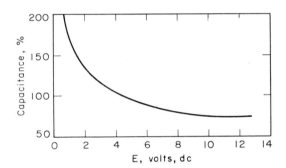

Fig. 51. *Capacitance-voltage relation-ship for a voltage variable capacitor*

Voltage variable capacitors are used for automatic frequency control, frequency modulation, amplitude modulation, voltage-controlled oscillators, amplifiers, and other circuits.

Thermocouples

A simple thermocouple (Fig. 31) consists of a measuring junction of two dissimilar metals, which develop an electromotive force that is measured when the junction is at a different temperature from the reference junction. The presence of the indicating instrument does not affect the generated electromotive force, as long as the instrument is at a uniform temperature. If the reference junction is maintained at some temperature, such as 0 C, the electromotive force developed by the thermocouple can be determined as a function of the temperature of the measuring junction. In many instances, the thermocouple is connected to the instrument by copper leads, as shown in Fig. 32.

In commercial installations where it is not convenient to maintain reference junctions, each thermocouple wire is connected to the instrument with lead wires or extension leads of essentially the same chemical composition and thermoelectric characteristics as the thermocouple wire. In most installations, the instrument is equipped with an automatic reference junction compensator and thus eliminates the necessity of correcting for the cold junction. The circuit is similar to that in Fig. 32, except that extension leads are substituted for the copper leads.

Thermocouple Materials. Platinum and the platinum-rhodium alloys are the most common thermocouple materials for high-temperature applications. Two types of platinum, platinum-rhodium thermocouples are used: (a) platinum versus 90 Pt – 10 Rh, and (b) platinum versus 87 Pt – 13 Rh. The platinum thermocouples are more stable than any other combination of metals. They are used for defining the international temperature scale from 660 C (1220 F) to the freezing point of gold (1063 C; 1945 F) — only the platinum versus 90 Pt – 10 Rh is used for this — and for very accurate temperature measurements from 400 to 1500 C (750 to 2730 F). These thermocouples are not suited for measurements below 0 C, because dE/dT is small (5 microvolts per °C at 0 C) and reaches zero at −138 C (−216 F). The Bureau of Standards calibrates platinum versus platinum-rhodium thermocouples at four fixed points on the International Practical Temperature Scales. The points used are the freezing temperatures of gold, 1063 C (1945.4 F), silver, 960.8 C (1761.4 F), antimony, 630.5 C (1134.9 F), and zinc, 419.56 C (787.1 F). The purified metals are melted in a graphite crucible, and electromotive-force readings are taken on cooling.

In general, Chromel-Alumel couples are more satisfactory than thermocouples of other base metals for measurements of temperatures from 650 to 1200 C (1200 to 2200 F). Chromel contains 90% Ni, 10% Cr and Alumel contains 95% Ni, plus aluminum, silicon and manganese.

The number of metals suitable for commercial use in thermocouples is limited, because the materials must be resistant to oxidation, melting, and contamination at high temperatures; they must develop an electromotive force that is sufficiently high to be measured without delicate apparatus; the thermal electromotive force must be reproducible.

The following combinations are in common use:

	Maximum temperature
Platinum versus 87 Pt – 13 Rh	1540 C (2800 F)
Platinum versus 90 Pt – 10 Rh	1540 C (2800 F)
Chromel versus Alumel	1200 C (2200 F)
Iron versus constantan	760 C (1400 F)
Copper versus constantan	370 C (700 F)

Table 40 lists typical relationships between temperature and electromotive force for precious and base-metal thermocouples, using the Centigrade scale; Table 41 gives the same type of information but uses the Fahrenheit scale.

Table 40. Typical Relationship of Temperature to Electromotive Force (in Millivolts) of Precious Metal and Base Metal Thermocouples
(Reference junction is 0 C.)

Temperature, C	Pt vs 13% Rh – Pt(a) British	U.S.	Pt vs 10% Rh – Pt(a) British	U.S.	Chromel P vs Alumel	Iron vs constantan	Copper vs constantan
0	0	0	0	0	0	0	0
100	0.646	0.646	0.643	0.643	4.10	5.40	4.28
200	1.461	1.463	1.434	1.435	8.13	10.99	9.29
300	2.386	2.394	2.316	2.315	12.21	16.56	14.86
400	3.387	3.397	3.251	3.250	16.39	22.07	20.87
500	4.444	4.454	4.220	4.219	20.64	27.58	....
600	5.557	5.561	5.230	5.222	24.90	33.27	....
700	6.724	6.713	6.270	6.261	29.14	39.30	....
800	7.942	7.927	7.349	7.330	33.31	45.72	....
900	9.202	9.176	8.459	8.434	37.36	52.29	....
1000	10.503	10.471	9.594	9 570	41.31	58.22	....
1100	11.836	11.811	10.756	10.736	45.14	....	....
1200	13.200	13.181	11.939	11.924	48.85	....	....
1300	14.584	14.562	13.133	13.120	52.41	....	....
1400	15.981	15.940	14.333	14.312	55.81	....	....
1500	17.394	17.317	15.542	15.497	....	....	....
1600	18.81	18.679	16.765	16.673	....	....	....
1700	20.16	....	....	....	....	....	....

(a) British values are from standard calibration tables issued by Johnson Matthey & Co., Ltd.; American values are calculated from tables issued by the Bureau of Standards.

For low temperatures, a high-output thermocouple can be made with bismuth. Bismuth containing 0.17% Ni can be formed into wire and, with a tin-antimony alloy, makes a thermocouple with a relatively high output of 0.03944 mv per °F in the temperature range from 40 to 176 C (118 to 350 F), with good linearity.

For temperatures over 1650 C (3000 F), platinum with 30% Rh versus platinum with 6% Rh is quite satisfactory as a thermocouple. Iridium versus iridium with rhodium (40, 50 or 60%

Table 41. Typical Relationship of Temperature to Electromotive Force (in Millivolts) of Precious Metal and Base Metal Thermocouples
(Reference junction is 32 F.)

Temperature, F	Platinum vs 87 Pt – 13 Rh	Platinum vs 90 Pt – 10 Rh	Chromel vs Alumel	Iron vs constantan	Copper vs constantan
32	0	0	0	0	0
100	0.220	0.221	1.52	1.96	1.52
200	0.596	0.594	3.82	4.92	3.97
300	1.030	1.016	6.09	7.95	6.64
400	1.503	1.473	8.31	11.02	9.52
500	2.012	1.956	10.56	14.09	12.57
600	2.546	2.457	12.85	17.16	15.77
700	3.102	2.975	15.18	20.23	19.09
800	3.675	3.505	17.52	23.31	22.53
900	4.263	4.044	19.88	26.41	26.06
1000	4.867	4.594	22.25	29.54	29.67
1100	5.436	5.155	24.62	32.74	. . . .
1200	6.122	5.725	26.98	36.04	. . . .
1300	6.773	6.307	29.33	39.46	. . . .
1400	7.438	6.898	31.65	42.96	. . . .
1500	8.118	7.500	33.94	46.48	. . . .
1600	8.810	8.122	36.20	50.00	. . . .
1700	9.518	8.734	38.43	53.52	. . . .
1800	10.237	9.365	40.62	57.04	. . . .
1900	10.970	10.006	42.77	. . . .	. . . .
2000	11.720	10.657	44.89	. . . .	. . . .
2100	12.478	11.315	46.97	. . . .	. . . .
2200	13.242	11.977	49.01	. . . .	. . . .
2300	14.010	12.642	57.00	. . . .	. . . .
2400	14.777	13.305	52.95	. . . .	. . . .
2500	15.543	13.968	54.85	. . . .	. . . .
2600	16.308	14.629	. . . .	. . . .	. . . .
2700	17.073	15.288	. . . .	. . . .	. . . .
2800	17.833	15.943	. . . .	. . . .	. . . .
2900	18.588	16.596	. . . .	. . . .	. . . .
3000	19.342	17.246	. . . .	. . . .	. . . .

Rh) is serviceable to 2040 C (3700 F), even in an oxidizing atmosphere. Tungsten versus tungsten-rhenium thermocouples, with proper protection, can be calibrated to 2315 C (4200 F) within 1% or better. A thermocouple of tungsten against tungsten with 26% Re has been used to 2985 C (5400 F). The use of tungsten with 5% Re versus tungsten with 20% Re makes a serviceable thermocouple that does not embrittle up to 1650 C (3000 F), as does the tungsten in the combination of tungsten versus tungsten-rhenium.

A thermoelectric pile, or a thermopile, consists of a group of thermocouples joined in series. The electromotive forces generated by each of the couples are additive, so that, if a sufficient number of couples is grouped, a considerable voltage and current can be developed.

Under development are thermoelectric-electroluminescent cells that will make it possible to cool, heat, and light home or office space with combination wall panels.

A thermionic converter that is used to convert heat into electricity is showing some commercial promise (176). The converter is similar to a diode in that the heated cathode emits electrons to the cold anode in a vacuum or a low-pressure gas. If the cathode and anode are connected by an external circuit, the difference in potential can be made to do useful work. For high efficiency, the space-charge effects must be reduced, and the difference between the work function of the cathode and of the anode must be large. These generators have operated at 10 to 15% efficiencies, and 25% efficiency is expected in a few years. The cathode is operated in the range of 1000 to 2000 C (1830 to 3630 F). In one reported experiment with a converter having a gap of 0.033 in., 11 watts per sq cm at an efficiency of 17.8% were produced with the cathode at 1780 C (3235 F).

Electron Tubes

Although electron tubes could include television, x-ray, klystron, magnetron and traveling wave tubes, consideration will be given only to large and small, receiving, transmitting and rectifying tubes. Electron tubes, in either the widest or restricted sense, are devices that operate in sealed, evacuated, usually glass, envelopes. Electron tubes, either the vacuum or gas types, can be considered as simple fast-acting valves that control cur-

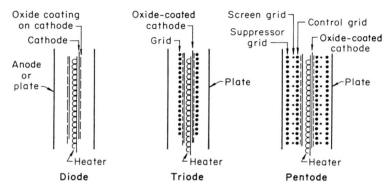

Fig. 52. *Schematic representation of tube construction of a diode, triode and pentode*

rent. The vacuum tube is a practical application of the phenomenon of electron emission. It is a throttling-type valve, whereas the gas tube is an on-off valve. The primary disadvantage of vacuum tubes is that they deliver low currents, because the cathode can emit only a limited number of electrons. Gas tubes overcome the disadvantage; they deliver large currents at high voltages because the gas is a source of electrons. Gases used in tubes are mercury vapor, nitrogen, neon, argon, or xenon. The great utility of either type of tube lies in its rapid response, because the electron has a small mass and its motion can be controlled readily. Both the vacuum and gas tubes require metals, glass, and ceramics of unique properties.

Electron tube manufacturers are plagued by a variability in performance of various cathode nickels or nickel alloys. The variations may be any of the following: electron-emission level, rate of formation and chemical composition of interface compounds between the cathode base metal and the emission coating, rate of sublimation of the alloy additions, influence of the base metal on sublimation of the emission coatings, and contact potential developed between the cathode and other electron tube electrodes. Vacuum induction melting and preparation of nickel strip by powder metallurgy methods are said to minimize the variability.

Types of Tubes. The simplest vacuum tube is the diode. As the name suggests, it contains two elements: a cathode and an anode (plate). A filament has to be included to heat the cathode from which electrons are emitted (Fig. 52). In diode operation, when the plate is made more positive than the cathode, negatively charged electrons emitted by the cathode are drawn to the more positive plate. If the plate is made negative with re-

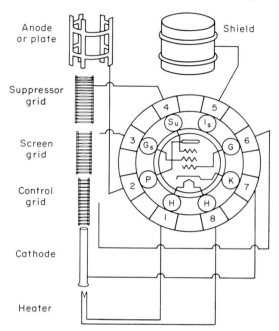

Fig. 53. Schematic (exploded) diagram of electron-tube (pentode) components and their relationship to tube base positioning (after Michaelson)

spect to the cathode, no current flows. This property allows the tube to be used for rectification and detection.

A triode is a diode with a third electrode, called the control grid. The control grid is a fine wire structure (for example, spiral) between the cathode and plate (anode). The spaces between turns on the grid allow electrons to flow from the cathode to the plate. The grid makes amplification possible.* A sche-

---

* Amplification is defined as the addition of outside energy to a signal without distorting it. Hence, an electronic amplifier consists of one or more tubes and associated circuits that increase a signal, either in voltage or current. An electron tube amplifies because a small input signal (grid voltage) controls the plate current. This plate current then produces an output signal of larger voltage across the plate load.

matic drawing of a triode is shown in Fig. 52. Gas-filled triodes, commonly known as thyratons, are used as rectifiers as well as to trigger devices, relays, and sawtooth generators. Thyratons used on low-frequency power, such as 60 cps, are usually of the mercury-vapor type. For higher frequencies, where ionization and deionization must be more rapid, helium, argon, and neon are used. A special type of triode is the mercury-pool tube, known as Ignitron. Used widely in resistance welding, the Ignitron can supply a 50,000-amp current for several cycles for spot welding.

The tetrode has another grid, called the screen grid, inserted between the grid and plate. The pentode has still another grid between the screen grid and the plate. The construction of the pentode is shown schematically in Fig. 52. Figure 53 diagrams the parts of a tube and their relation to each other. Multiple-function tubes, each containing a number of ordinary electron tubes, are available. One such tube combines a detector diode, a triode amplifier, a pentode beam-power amplifier, and a half-wave rectifier diode.

Cathode Construction (177, 178). Cathode surfaces of thermionic devices are made of special metals that, when electrically heated to high temperatures, release a copious flow of electrons. Cathodes are heated directly, by means of a current passed through a filament of base metal to which the emissive material has been applied, or indirectly, by means of a separate, insulated heating element, mounted within the cathode assembly. The objective in cathode design is to obtain the required thermionic current with a minimum of heating power consumption. Indirectly heated cathodes are used in most receiving tubes. In indirectly heated cathodes, tungsten insulated with alumina generally serves as a mechanical support for the cathodes.

For low-power tubes, the cathodes operate at 700 to 900 C (1290 to 1650 F). The base metal for these cathodes is almost pure nickel or nickel with small additions of other elements, such as tungsten. Cathodes are coated with alkaline earth oxides to facilitate electron emission. Active cathode alloys are recommended where high-speed activation is desired. Passive alloys offer low rates of barium evolution, minimum sublimation, and freedom from interface impedance. A cathode-base material is a compromise of various characteristics: rate of activation (controlled by reducing agents such as aluminum, magnesium, silicon, titanium, and carbon), rate of barium evolution, rate of sublimation of the alloy, interface impedance due to resistance and capacitance effects of compounds formed between alloying elements and the coating materials (these blocking layers are undesirable), heater-cathode leakage, and tube life. Cathode sleeves are available in 11 different materials and in four forms for receiving, power, industrial, and other types of electron tubes. There are three types of disk cathodes for cathode-ray tube guns.

Power-tube cathodes are generally made with tungsten and will operate at up to 2260 C (4100 F); those made with thoriated tungsten will operate to about 1800 C (3270 F). Cathode support members should have a low thermal conductivity to reduce the drain of heat from the cathode; Nilvar (36% Ni, remainder iron) meets this requirement.

Anode Construction. The anodes receive the electrons emitted from the cathode. To obtain a high degree of power dissipation from the anodes, their surfaces should have high thermal emissivity. Black surfaces radiate better than bright, metallic surfaces. Anodes for low-power receiving tubes are commonly made from high-purity nickel, carbonized nickel, aluminized steel, or carbonized nickel-plated steel. For high-power receiving and transmitting tubes, molybdenum, tantalum and graphite are used. Copper is used when the anode can be water cooled. Tantalum cannot be blackened, so its surface is roughened by grit blasting to improve emissivity.

Tube miniaturization has created high-temperature problems and increased dissipation ratings. These problems have been successfully solved by using copper-base anodes, made of layers of aluminum and steel over a copper core. The new copper-base anodes have made possible increased thermal conductivity, more effective heat radiation, a higher plate dissipation at a given temperature, and higher thermal efficiencies, which are reflected in a reduction in tube power inputs by as much as 40%. The new anode materials have been used successfully on rectifiers (the copper base faces the tube cathode) and amplifier tubes (179).

Grids (177). On low-power tubes, the No. 1 grid is generally made of nickel containing 4.5% Mn. The No. 2 and 3 grids can be molybdenum, nickel, and molybdenum-iron, nickel-molybdenum-iron, and nickel-chromium-iron alloys.

Power-tube grids, which must dissipate a fair amount of power, have low thermionic emission, and must maintain good mechanical strength at high temperatures. Molybdenum, tantalum, tungsten, and nickel are commonly used for grid wires. To keep grid emission from becoming high, the molybdenum or tungsten wire is clad with zirconium, platinum, gold or silver.

In receiving tubes, the oxide-coated cathode tends to deposit barium on the grid. In this instance, gold plating prevents undesirable primary emission. High temperatures lead to excessive primary electron emission in the presence of low-work-function films deposited from the cathode.

The grid-supporting side rods can be nickel, steel, nickel-plated iron, and copper alloys. In transmitting tubes, molybdenum side rods are used when the grid wires are made of molybdenum. The thermal conductivity of grid side rods and laterals should be as high as possible to reduce operating temperature.

Lead-In Wires. Tungsten wire is often used as a lead-in conductor for electronic power tubes, because it makes a perfect seal with hard glass. One reason for good sealing is that tungsten oxides dissolve readily in glass. Although the thermal expansions of tungsten and glass are not identical, proper heat treating of the glass makes gastight joints possible.

Dumet, a 42% Ni steel wire, coated with a 22 wt % OFHC copper layer, seals readily to soft glass and is widely used for incandescent and electronic tubes.

Platinum is also used as a lead-in wire for transistor leads, because it eliminates oxidation and cleaning problems and can be electroplated, soldered, and welded.

Glass-Metal Seals. The manufacture of sealed-beam automotive lamps, incandescent and fluorescent bulbs, transistors, vacuum and gas electronic tubes, x-ray and microwave tubes, and ceramic-coated resistors depends on the gastight seal produced between the metal and glass (or ceramic) sections of the item. The production of glass-metal seals depends in large part on the expansion and contraction characteristics of the glass and metal, and to a lesser degree on the design of the seal. Some metal systems, particularly the iron-nickel alloys, appear well suited for glass-metal seals. Alloys with 42, 45, and 52% Ni are widely used. Another popular alloy contains 42.5% Ni and 5.75% Cr. An iron-chromium alloy (28% Cr, remainder iron) has also found some application.

Kovar A alloy (29% Ni, 17% Co, remainder iron), with expansion characteristics that match a special glass (No. 7052), makes possible rugged metal-to-glass seals of electron and other special-purpose tubes. Oxygen-free high-conductivity copper is sometimes used for a tube envelope.

Photocells

Photocells, which include the photoconductive, photovoltaic, and photoelectric types, are used for two general purposes: measurement of light intensity, and operation of equipment by light-activated relays.

Measurement of light intensity involves phototubes in sound reproduction, picture transmission, television camera tubes, light-beam signaling, and infrared detection. For operation of equipment, there are light relays, traffic-control systems, safety devices, industrial controls, industrial inspection, photoelectric gages, photoelectric organs, and aids for the blind.

In the future, cells may be used for conversion of solar energy into electric power.

Photoconductive Cells (180). The selenium photoconductive cell was one of the first developed, and it is still in use today. These selenium cells were made by pouring molten selenium into a grid pattern and then annealing the grid and its support at about 200 C (392 F) for varying times up to several hours. This treatment converts the as-cast vitreous form of selenium into the gray crystalline variety that exhibits the photoconductive effect. Present-day cells are made by distilling selenium in vacuum or inert gas onto a grid of gold or platinum wires placed on heated glass. The hot glass favors the formation of the gray crystalline selenium. The cells may be mounted in vacuum or in helium-filled (for cooling) tubes.

Because selenium is opaque, the light does not penetrate to any depth; hence, it is essential to design the cell with as much irradiating surface as possible, without making the electrical resistance large. Within this requirement, a photoconductive cell consists of two electrodes separated by semiconducting material.

When a selenium cell is connected to a battery and meter, a small current will flow, even when the cell is not illuminated. Exposure to light, however, causes a large increase in the current. The ratio of the increase in current because of the light to the current without light is used as a criterion for the sensitivity of the device. A photoconductive circuit is shown in Fig. 28.

The selenium cell has held its position among photoconductors for almost 50 years, mainly because of its relatively high absolute sensitivity. The dark resistance of selenium cells is from 50.000 to 10 megohms and the corresponding operating voltages are from 9 to 500 v. A luminous flux of only 0.1 lumen may reduce the effective resistance of the cell by a factor of three. The spectral response of selenium cells is generally broad, with a peak at about 7000 A.

The thallous sulfide (thalofide) cell has replaced the selenium cell to some extent, because it is superior to the selenium cell in sensitivity and in dynamic response. The active surface is evaporated thallous sulfide (Tl_2S), which is an excess (n-type) semiconductor.

The lead sulfide cell was used in the Second World War for signaling purposes, because it could detect the far-infrared radiation. When cooled with dry ice (-80 C; -112 F), these tubes can detect bodies at ambient temperature from which about 10^{-8} w of radiant energy is incident on the cell surface. Lead selenide cells can be used with longer infrared radiation than the lead sulfide types, but they lack equivalent sensitivity.

Silicon cells, although intermediate in sensitivity between thallous sulfide and selenium, are exceedingly stable in performance. Cadmium sulfide cells are remarkable detectors of x-rays.

Photovoltaic Cells. The selenium cell, developed in 1876, is a barrier-layer photovoltaic cell and is a true solid-state device. In the semiconductor photocell, the incoming light is the energy source; no battery is required. In these photocells, light penetrates through a thin metal to the boundary between film and semiconductor (cuprous oxide or selenium). The light causes electrons to flow in the high-resistance direction — from the semiconductor to the conducting film. The electrons then return to the cuprous oxide, either through the external circuit or through the internal cell resistance.

The photoelectric yield and quantum yield of rectifier photocells are much greater than those for photoelectrically emitting surfaces used in vacuum and gas-filled phototubes. The over-all sensitivity in microamperes per lumen is only slightly better than that of a gas-filled phototube.

Photovoltaic cells are self-contained current and voltage generators that develop a potential difference between their terminals when exposed to light. Wet cells, no longer common, consist of two electrodes in an electrolyte. Dry cells consist of a semi-conducting layer between two metal electrodes.

The cuprous oxide and selenium barrier layer cells are very common photovoltaic devices. Schematic construction of these cells is shown in Fig. 54.

There are two types of barrier cells: back-wall cells and front-wall cells. Back-wall cells are those where the barrier layer —

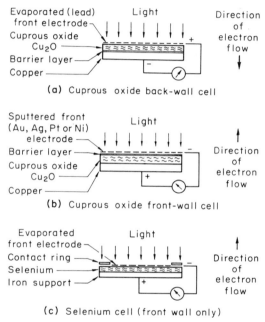

(a) Cuprous oxide back-wall cell

(b) Cuprous oxide front-wall cell

(c) Selenium cell (front wall only)

Fig. 54. *Typical photovoltaic cells*

junction of cuprous oxide and copper — is remote from the incidence of light. Front-wall cells are those where the action takes place at the boundary between the top electrode and the cuprous oxide. Front-wall cells have much greater sensitivity than the back-wall type. The front-wall type of cuprous oxide–copper cell has a spectral sensitivity of 3000 to 6000 A, while the back-wall type has a range of 6000 to 14,000 A.

Selenium cells are invariably front-wall cells. Selenium is a defect semiconductor. The photovoltaic effect in selenium is assumed to be analogous to that in the cuprous oxide–copper cell.

The spectral response of selenium cells is in the range of 3000 to 7000 A, peaking at about 6000 A, which is close to the maximum sensitivity of the human eye (5500 A). Selenium barrier-layer cells are used principally in light meters and for the operation of relays.

The silicon *p-n* junction photovoltaic cell converts solar (as well as radioactive) radiation into electrical energy with practical efficiency. These silicon cells are assuming an important role in the space satellite programs.

Photoelectric cells convert light energy into electrical energy, which is used either directly or with amplification.

One of the most important uses of the photoelectric cell, or "electric eye," is to operate a relay that opens or closes a circuit for some useful purpose, such as counting, sorting, and opening and closing doors. In this usage, the output of the cell is sufficient to actuate either a meter or a relay. Other examples of direct usage are light meters (photographic) and meters for colorimetric work.

The action of radiation (visible, ultraviolet, or x-ray) on a metal generally gives rise to a limited number of electrons per unit area of emitting surface, and the current from a photocell is small. The photocell is fundamentally a diode, and current flows only when the anode is positive with respect to the cathode. They are of two types: vacuum and gas-filled.

An important characteristic of a photocell is its spectral response. The graph of anode current versus wave length is called a spectral-response curve. This is different for the various photocells, for example, sodium and cesium–silver oxide.

Photoelectric cathodes can be classified (180) in the following manner:

1 *Pure metals:* Zinc, aluminum, and platinum. The work function, ϕ, is high; combination is useful in the ultraviolet region; efficiency is poor.
2 *Alkalies:* Potassium, rubidium, and cesium films. The work function, ϕ, is high; efficiency is low.
3 *Alkali-hydride* (hydrogen reacted with alkalies): Potassium base material; potassium hydride–potassium layers. The work function, ϕ, is high; useful in range of 3700 to 5200 A.
4 *Composite:* Silver base material; Cs_2O, Ag-Cs layers. Useful in range of 4000 to 5000 and 6000 to 9000 A. The cell is made by silver plating nickel; the silver is then oxidized and cesium is vaporized on the silver.

are measured by direct-current techniques. The current flowing in the reverse direction of the rectifier is called leakage current.

Metal rectifier cells are rated largely on a thermal basis. The ratings must be chosen so that the rectifier unit can dissipate the heat generated by the internal losses, without excessive temperature rise. Ratings are a function of load current, reverse voltage, type of cooling, spacing between cells, and ambient temperature — standardized at 35 C (95 F).

Characteristics of the metal rectifier change with time and operation. The major effect is an increase in the forward resistance. Aging, of course, will vary with types of rectifiers, as well as within the same type.

Two combinations of the metal oxide rectifier are in use: cuprous oxide and selenium oxide. These were the original semiconductor rectifiers. The selenium rectifier was discovered by Fritts in 1883, and the cuprous oxide rectifier was found by Grondahl in 1926.

The cuprous oxide rectifier found application in the new field of high-power low-frequency rectification. This type of rectifier consists of a thin film of copper oxide on a disk of copper. A spacer (usually lead) is placed between each rectifier element in the stack. The assembly of rings of oxidized copper (on which are cooling fins) and lead spacers into stacks of washers is comparatively easy. Because the thin coating of oxide cannot withstand high voltage (the maximum voltage of a single copper oxide disk is 11 v), several disks are stacked in series. Thus, a stack of ten disks can withstand 110 v.

The selenium oxide rectifier consists of a thin film of selenium oxide on a disk of any conducting metal, usually iron or aluminum. The resistance of the selenium rectifier in the forward, or conducting, direction is less than that of the copper oxide rectifier. For this reason, the selenium rectifier is more efficient and can pass a greater current than can a copper oxide rectifier of similar size.

The copper sulfide rectifier has found some application in low-voltage high-current duty.

Because of their construction, metal oxide rectifiers are particularly suited to supplying relatively large direct current. They are used to run small direct-current motors, operate relays, charge batteries, and for the basis of direct-current power.

The efficiency of a metal oxide rectifier is expressed in terms of the ratio of its resistance in the reverse (nonconducting) direction to its resistance in the forward (conducting) direction. A perfect rectifier would have a forward resistance of 0 ohms and a reverse resistance of infinity. The metal oxide rectifier has a forward resistance of several hundred ohms and a reverse resistance of several hundred thousand ohms. This magnitude of the reverse resistance shows that the rectifier conducts slightly in the nonconducting portion of the cycle. The diode tube has about the same forward resistance, but a higher reverse resistance of several hundred megohms. The metal oxide rectifier is less efficient than a diode, but it has the advantage of requiring no filament power. The disadvantage of the metal oxide rectifier is a relatively low peak inverse voltage. On the nonconducting half-cycle, the reverse voltage across the element must not exceed its rated peak inverse voltage or breakdown occurs.

The *p-n* junction is a crystallographic union of an *n* and a *p* region of a semiconductor. It is used for rectification. A net transfer of charge occurs when the regions are adjacent to each other.

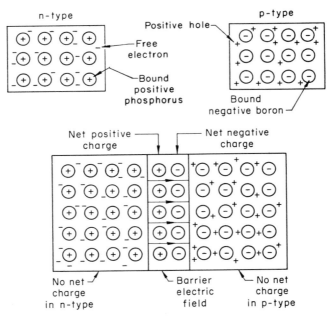

Fig. 60. Schematic representation of the operation of a p-n junction in silicon (after Chapin, Fuller and Pearson)

An electrostatic potential barrier is formed that produces the rectifying properties of an equilibrium *p-n* junction. Optimum electrical characteristics are obtained in single crystals, in which one part is made with an excess of acceptor impurities and the other part is made with an excess of donors. A schematic diagram of a *p-n* junction is shown in Fig. 60.

It is more difficult to move an electron from a *p*-type conductor to the *n*-type than the reverse. If an *n*-type region is made positive with respect to the *p*-type, the potential barrier is made much higher. In this situation, the electrons in the *p*-type region will

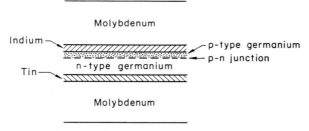

Fig. 61. Schematic construction of a p-n *junction germanium rectifier*

have to climb a potential hill to conduct current to the *n*-type region. However, if the *n*-type area is made negative with respect to the *p*-type, the potential barrier is decreased, and current flows easily. This principle is the basis for the rectifying action of the *p-n* junction. Silicon diodes can rectify up to 300 C (570 F).

In the construction of one type of germanium rectifier, a sandwich of five layers of material is prepared (Fig. 61). The protecting disks are of molybdenum, which has the same thermal coefficient of expansion as germanium and has good thermal conductivity. The rectifier is a slice of germanium that is doped so that it is an *n*-type conductor. The germanium is soldered to tin on one side and indium on the other. The indium, when it diffuses into the germanium, forms the *p-n* junction; the upper surface of the germanium changes from *n* to *p*-type. The molybdenum-tin junction is ohmic in nature.

The development of a reliable silicon rectifier diode has made practical the use of alternating-current generators on motor cars.

Because these generators (also called alternators) have no commutator, they operate at higher speeds than direct-current generators. Because of the increased speed, the generator can be made more compact, and output is increased at idling speed. Six diodes are used per automobile.

The p-n junctions of silicon carbide have been developed into high-temperature rectifiers, operating even at red heat. Currents as high as 10 amp can be passed.

When light is applied to a p-n junction, hole-electron pairs are created by the photoelectric process, and they allow current, which is proportional to the light energy absorbed, to flow. These photodiodes are used in headlight dimmers, automatic door openers, and exposure meters.

In the solar cell, which is a photovoltaic diode, there is a junction between the electron-rich n region and the hole-rich p region. This situation results in a strong electric field, which keeps the electrons on the n side and the holes on the p side. When light is absorbed at the p-n junction, electron-hole pairs are produced, and the electric field segregates the holes to the p side and the electrons to the n side. This segregation of charges is responsible for the voltage difference between the ends of the silicon crystal. In full sunlight, such a silicon cell has an open-circuit voltage of about 0.6 v (122).

Crystal Rectifiers. The "cat whisker" crystal galena detector, which was used in the early days of radio to rectify high-frequency, alternating current, was the first crystal rectifier. The discovery of the vacuum tube rapidly made the crystal rectifier obsolete, but, during the Second World War, it was revived. With the availability of semiconducting crystals such as germanium, stable, cartridge-type components became available. A typical crystal rectifier consists of a fine tungsten, phosphorus-bronze or platinum-iridium wire (cat whisker), whose point bears on the surface of the silicon or germanium (Fig. 62).

The principle of the crystal rectifier dates back to F. Braun in 1874. He discovered that the metal-point contact on a crystal, such as galena (PbS) or silicon, has a resistance dependent on voltage.

The germanium point-contact diode (182) is a very simple semiconductor rectifying device made from an n-type crystal. When the metal wire contact is positive with respect to germanium, a current passes much more readily than when the wire contact is negative. In this *n*-type rectifier, the impedance to voltage in one direction is extremely high so that, over a normal working range, no current flows. To an applied potential of opposite polarity, the crystal presents a relatively low impedance, but in a nonlinear fashion. A *p*-type crystal has polarity properties opposite to those of the *n*-type. The device is still used in microwave technology.

The metal-point combination can be considered as a tiny cold cathode diode; the crystal is considered the cathode and the

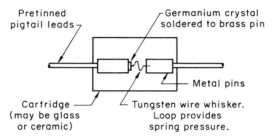

Fig. 62. A typical semiconductor diode

metal-point is the plate. Such an arrangement has low capacity, because of the small area of the point. Theoretically, the electrode spacing is about 250×10^{-6} in. (10^{-5} cm), so that the important property of electron transit time is negligibly small, due to the short distance. These characteristics of the metal-point combination help sustain the efficiency of crystal rectifiers up to frequencies of 30,000 mc.

Tunnel Diodes. Tunnel or Esaki diodes (108) are majority-carrier devices that depend for their operation on the quantum mechanical tunneling of electrons through a *p-n* junction. Tunnel diodes must be heavily doped, and they must have a carefully controlled and abrupt junction.

These diodes have high-frequency response (4 to 5 billion cps), low power consumption (less than transistors), and low noise level (transistors are noisier than tubes), and they are excellent switching devices, having switching times of 0.5 nanosec (0.5×10^{-9}). Amplifiers can be constructed by making use of the obscure phenomenon known as negative resistance (183) (see Fig. 63). In a tunnel diode, above a voltage V_p in the forward direction, the current decreases with increasing voltage, and above a voltage V_v, it increases again, but with a higher resistance than shown in the reverse direction. The effect is independent of temperature. A commercial tunnel diode is made of heavily doped gallium arsenide, germanium or silicon gallium antimonide. In the Esaki diode, chemical purity and crystal perfection do not seem to be as important as in the other semiconductors.

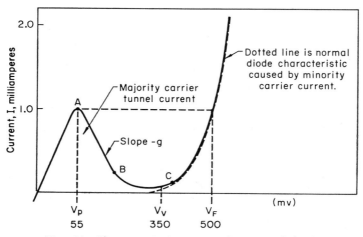

Fig. 63. Characteristic curve of a tunnel diode

The Zener diode is a semiconductor device, the chief characteristic of which is the sharpness and stability of its reverse breakdown. When a *p-n* junction is subjected to a sufficiently high, externally applied, reverse voltage, breakdown occurs, resulting in a very large increase in reverse current, while the voltage remains constant. In the germanium and silicon devices, the predominant mechanism is referred to as an avalanche effect. The characteristic curve of a Zener or an avalanche diode is shown in Fig. 64. The breakdown voltage in the semiconductor is adjusted by controlling the resistivity of the crystal through the use of impurities.

Because the *p-n* junction in a Zener diode is made extremely narrow, an electric field gradient of several hundred thousand volts per centimeter can be produced. At this field strength, the minority carriers may be accelerated to high velocities, so that upon collision with atoms they will strip off valence electrons, creating electron-hole pairs. These new carriers, in turn, are accelerated and create more electron-hole pairs by collision. In this way the avalanche effect is produced.

The sharp breakdown voltage, low alternating-current imped-ance, stability, and compactness make the Zener diode useful for voltage regulation, reference use in constant-current and

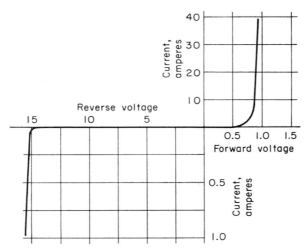

Fig. 64. Typical voltage-current relationship in a Zener diode

constant-voltage direct-current power supplies, surge protection in switching circuits, and coupling devices in coupled amplifiers, in which they perform like capacitors.

Other diodes (184) have and are being developed. The gold-bonded diode is replacing the point-contact diode. In this type, a whisker of gold is bonded to n-type germanium. The diode is use-ful in computer logic circuits, because it has high switching speed, from 0.6 to 20 nanosec ($\times 10^{-9}$).

Varactor diodes are microwave devices capitalizing on the phenomenon that diode junction capacitance decreases with a rise in reverse voltage. They are made of diffused-junction sili-con or gallium arsenide.

Four-layer trigger diodes are controlled rectifiers without a base connection. They are made of n-p-n-p layers of silicon.

The backward diode, also called a tunnel rectifier or a poor tunnel diode, is used in connection with tunnel diodes to obtain certain circuit characteristics.

The unijunction transistor is actually a double-base rectifying diode with two ohmic contacts. With this device, a negative resistance can be obtained: As the current increases, the voltage decreases.

Multiple diodes are made to conserve space. Several may be placed in one case. Clusters of several junctions on one sliver of silicon is a possibility.

There are two types of photodiodes. In the photoconductive type, conductivity increases with incident light. Doped germanium is commonly used. In the photovoltaic or junction-barrier type, the voltage is generated across a circuit element upon exposure to light.

Semiconductor Rectifiers (184). High-current silicon rectifiers are available in ratings of 0.5 to 240 amp to 1000 v. High and low-current rectifiers are alloy junction types made by diffusing gold-boron or aluminum disks into n-type silicon. High-voltage silicon rectifiers are produced in ratings of 1200 to 10,000 peak inverse voltage, with a current-carrying capacity of 1 to 50 amp.

Controlled rectifiers are three-terminal devices, which are actually transistors but their use puts them into the rectifier class. They are used mainly as high-speed switches.

Transistors (184, 187, 188)

The transistor, invented by W. H. Brattain and John Bardeen (186) in 1948, is a three-electrode amplifying device, using a semiconductor such as germanium or silicon. A preferred form, known as the junction transistor, was invented by W. Shockley.

The transistor can perform many of the duties of a vacuum tube, but it is far more efficient, because it requires no power to heat a cathode. Also, the transistor operates with much lower voltages and is smaller than a vacuum tube. Because of its low power dissipation and low voltage requirements, it can be miniaturized. The final result is that size, weight, and power consumption of apparatus employing transistors can usually be reduced to a small fraction of that required for vacuum-tube apparatus. Transistors are used in hearing aids, portable radios, television sets, computers, and other electronic gear. A missile-guidance system may contain as many as 6000 transistors.

The disadvantages of transistors are that they have low power capacity and high noise level. Their power-handling capacity is much less than that of either electron tubes or magnetic amplifiers. Early in the technology, transistors were best for low-power low-frequency applications, such as radio. However, transistors are being steadily improved for higher-power and higher-frequency use.

It is popularly believed that transistors will replace vacuum tubes in the near future. There are applications where transistors can replace tubes, and there are some areas where tubes and transistors will serve equally well, but certain uses (high-power applications) remain in which tubes are and will continue to remain superior (189).

Semiconductor devices based on germanium, and to a lesser extent on silicon, show wide variation in performance; they reach a limiting capability at junction temperatures of about 100 C for germanium and 200 C (390 F) for silicon. Silicon devices are preferred for most industrial and military applications. Temperature introduces serious degradation in performance of transistors. Because of inherently better insulation afforded by vacuum devices, it is expected that high-voltage tubes (diodes and multielement) will be favored over transistors. It is predicted that silicon will eventually replace germanium in 80 to 90% of the devices, because of greater stability, reliability, and higher-temperature performance.

The properties of semiconductors are harder to control in production than those of vacuum tubes. From available information, it appears that transistors are vulnerable to high-energy gamma radiation, whereas tubes are not. Fast and thermal neutrons affect transistors more than glass and ceramic vacuum tubes. Shelf life of a transistor is limited.

Transistors may be combined with sources of power and various circuit elements (resistors, inductors, capacitors) to form transistor circuits of many forms that are used for generation, amplification, and shaping and control of electrical signals. Many circuits are similar to vacuum-tube arrangements in performing corresponding functions, but there are many others that capitalize on the unique transistor characteristics — such circuits have no vacuum-tube counterparts.

The point-contact transistor (190) was the first commercial semiconductor device (1948) to amplify an input signal. Figure 65 shows the operation of the transistor. Two point contacts (tungsten tips) are placed about 0.001 in. apart on an *n* or *p*-

type germanium crystal. Opposite the pair of contacts is placed a large-area low-resistance contact. One contact, the emitter, which has a low impedance, is made positive. This emitter injects holes into the block. The other contact, the collector, which has a high impedance, is made negative. With this arrangement,

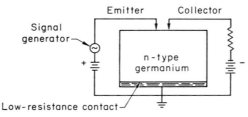

Fig. 65. Schematic diagram of a point-contact transistor

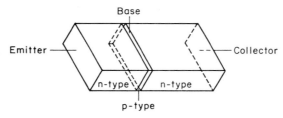

Fig. 66. Schematic representation of a junction transistor. Entire transistor is a single crystal.

there is a large voltage amplification, because the signal introduced at low impedance at the emitter flows into a high-impedance load. Some current amplification also occurs.

No current flows between the two point contacts, unless a small current is introduced at the opposite low-resistance contact. Then, a much larger current flows between the contacts (emitter and collector). In this way, amplification occurs. Noise limits the use of the point-contact transistor as an amplifier.

A junction transistor, developed in 1951, is one in which one type of semiconductor is sandwiched between another type, for example, the *n-p-n* transistor. Figure 66 shows the construction of the junction transistor. Low-resistance electrodes on the ends (the emitter and collector) make contact with the *n* portion of the crystal, while the third electrode (the base) makes contact at the *p* portion. The *p* region in actual junction transistors is only a few thousandths of an inch in thickness. A junction transistor based on a *p-n-p* sandwich operates in a reverse fashion.

The junction transistor bears a close analogy to the vacuum tube. The emitter corresponds to the cathode, the collector to the plate, and the base to the grid.

Transistor action can be illustrated in the following way: It is known that the simple *p-n* junction has rectifier characteristics.

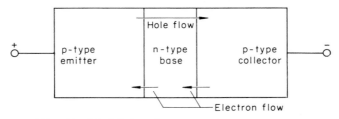

Fig. 67. Model for demonstrating movement of holes and electrons in a p-n-p *transistor*

If another *p*-type crystal is diffused to the *n*-type material and the *n* region is purposely made small, the *p-n-p* combination has a new set of characteristics. Its action, however, still depends on the existence of the two junctions. If the *n* region is small, few holes will have time to recombine before reaching the new *n-p* junction. This *p-n-p* arrangement is capable of producing amplification and is called a transistor. The *n* region is called the base and is grounded for convenience; the positively energized *p* region is referred to as the emitter, because it emits holes to the base; and the negatively biased * *p* region is known as the collector, because it collects holes reaching it from the base.

Electrons flow from the base to the emitter, but this flow does not provide transistor action, because there is no link to the collector. This electron flow is useless, and, to minimize it, the conductivity of the base is made lower than that of the emitter. An electron flow also occurs from the collector to the base, but this flow is small, because the collector is biased. The action of the holes and electrons is shown schematically in Fig. 67.

Transistor action, then, depends on the fact that the current from the emitter is composed mainly of holes. The modification of the base-collector barrier by the holes injected by the emitter

* Application of a voltage to obtain an operating condition.

makes possible the modulation of the collector current by the emitter current. Current amplification and power amplification are then possible.

Junction transistors are stable, have a relatively low noise level, and should have virtually an indefinite life. The earlier limitations of frequency response have been removed by making thin semiconductors with sharp junctions.

The first diffused base-junction transistor was a high-frequency germanium device (1958). The mesa transistor has been operated at 50 to 100 mc per sec; this is five to ten times faster than the older germanium transistor.

The n-p-n fused-junction transistors have been produced from high-purity silicon (one part impurity in six billion parts silicon) and are capable of handling up to 1 kw in the 2 to 5-amp units and up to 3 kw in the 10 to 20-amp units. The silicon transistors are used in high-speed switching operations.

The performance of a transistor (its current-carrying capacity, power dissipation, output capacitance and switching characteristics) is dependent on both the size and geometry of its p-n junctions.

Preparation of Transistors. Ultra-high-purity semiconductor materials are required for transistor use. Pfann's development (191) in 1954 of zone refining or purification was a great contribution to this new technology. Four common techniques are used for single-crystal growing after the purified (intrinsic) semiconductor is provided: the Czochralski, Bridgman, floating-zone, and gradient-freeze methods.

After a high-purity single crystal is available, the transistor is made in one of several ways (184):

1 *Diffusion.* Impurities can be placed or evaporated on opposite sides of germanium or silicon slices, and the impurities are then diffused into the crystal in one, two, or even three operations. The diffusion method can also be performed by heating the semiconductor slices in an atmosphere containing the proper impurities. By this procedure, the base layer can be controlled to within a millionth of an inch. Both p and n-type impurities can be introduced simultaneously into silicon, because the acceptor atoms diffuse faster than the donor atoms.

2 *Grown Junction.* By adding impurities to a melt as the single crystal is being withdrawn from a melt (Czochralski method), impurities can be placed across the diameter of the crystal. Then, by cutting the crystal longitudinally, the impurity layers can be spaced.

3 *Alloy Junction.* A metal containing donors or acceptors is fused directly to the semiconductor crystal; indium can be fused to germanium and aluminum to silicon. The fusing is done at high temperatures, and, after the operation, the crystal is cooled and two *p-n* junctions result.

The above procedures are used in the formation of the following classifications of transistors: mesa, planar, epitaxial, and electrochemical.

The mesa structure, akin to the land form that is bounded by steep walls, is produced as a *p-n-p* transistor by solid-state diffusion and etching operations. The emitter is kept very small in comparison to the base. At the annealing temperature, etching occurs, leaving mounds or mesas on the crystal surface. A mesa structure reduces capacitance, because the junction area is small. Mesa transistors are high-frequency devices used for switching.

The planar structure is a flat construction in which the *p-n* junctions are diffused down into very accurate etch patterns on the wafer by means of a series of passivations, precision etchings, and diffusion processes. The starting material is an *n*-type silicon slice or wafer, on which silica is first formed by passivation. By masking, a portion of the oxide is etched away and boron is diffused. During this operation, silica forms again. Another window in a different area is etched away and phosphorus is diffused. The diffused areas are etched, and leads are attached by first metallizing electrode areas with aluminum, followed by cold welding or thermocompression bonding the leads. The planar device has low capacitance as a result of small junctions.

Epitaxial structures are those in which a very thin film is grown on a substrate of the same crystal to obtain crystal registry. The formation of layers by epitaxial growth produces very thin, sharply defined boundaries between different impurity levels. Furthermore, epitaxially grown layers can be deposited faster than they can be diffused in the usual impurity layers. In silicon epitaxy, a heavily doped crystal is heated to 1300 C (2370 F) for 10 min. The temperature is allowed to drop somewhat, and silicon tetrachloride is introduced. Through dissociation, a silicon film (about 0.0001 in.) is deposited to obtain an emitter surface. Then phosphorus tetrachloride is introduced into the silicon tetrachloride, to form an *n* collector on the crystal. Epitaxial transistors form ideal *n-p-n* switches, because the structure has low impedance when the switch is on and infinite impedance when it is off. Planar epitaxial transistors have a great future, because of improved transistor performance, increased reliability, and lower cost.

Electrochemical transistors have been made by plating metal electrodes on opposite sides of thin wafers of semiconductor material. These are referred to as surface-barrier transistors. They were the earliest of the high-frequency transistors.

Microelectronics (184, 185) can be considered under three categories: miniaturized conventional components, thin-film and solid-state devices. In the component class, circuit elements are reduced in size and are mounted on a printed circuit or a ceramic wafer. The thin-film approach uses methods of depositing circuit elements as films on glass or ceramic substrates. The solid-state devices, also called molecular electronics, micrologic elements, or solid circuits, are based on use of semiconductors to form various circuit elements within the solid.

Microelectronics is a new and fascinating technology; devices are produced for miniaturization of circuits. Production costs increase exponentially with the degree of miniaturization and the required precision. Microminiaturization is very common in computer modules and networks.

In one miniaturized circuit of conventional components, a multilayer microcircuit plate is produced so that four independent memory and delay circuits, consisting of 64 resistors, 8 capacitors, 16 transistors, and 32 diodes, can be placed in a space 2 by 3.7 in.

In the thin-film technique, deposited films can form resistive, conductive, and capacitive elements of a circuit on one substrate.

Solid-state circuits have as their goals the arrangement of functions within solid blocks of materials that will perform the conventional circuit functions. For instance, it is possible to form 40 diodes in a single block of silicon. In other instances, it is possible to form diodes, transistors, resistors, and voltage variable capacitors within a single block of semiconductor material. The only circuit element that remains to be developed is a solid-state inductor.

Thin-film amplifiers or majority-carrier amplifiers (184) are an outgrowth of the tunnel diode technology and are basic amplifiers. Electrically, they are three-terminal devices, corresponding roughly to *n-p-n* transistors, but physically they are tunneling devices with two barrier junctions. They rely on one charge carrier, the electron.

The device is made as a film sandwich of metal, metal oxide, and metal, deposited on a germanium substrate. The two metal layers and the germanium serve as injector, control, and collector, respectively, and correspond to emitter, base, and collector of a transistor.

Hall-Effect Devices

Although the Hall effect has been known since 1879, it has remained a laboratory curiosity, because of the small voltages obtainable, until the nature and possibilities of modern semiconductors were known. The Hall effect has been used as a simple, portable method for probing magnetic fields, because the output of the generator is exactly proportional to the magnetic field. The generator is usable to 10^{12} to 10^{14} cycles. Grubbs (192) lists several (20) Hall-effect devices. The devices are classified into

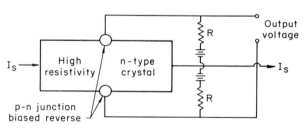

Fig. 68. Junction Hall generator made from a single-crystal semiconductor. The magnetic field is perpendicular to the plane of the sketch.

two groups: (a) devices that use a constant magnetic field, and (b) those in which a signal or an oscillator produces at least part of the magnetic field.

Materials for Hall-effect devices are indium arsenide, indium antimonide, indium phosphide, germanium, silicon, and indium arsenic phosphide.

Hall generators suffer from one important limitation: Their output impedance is low — 0.01 to 20 ohms. Because of this low impedance, many measuring circuits will not match the peak power output of the device. This difficulty can be circumvented by a modification of the Hall generator. Instead of using polycrystalline material, a junction Hall generator can be made from a single crystal. This junction device has high resistivity and a high output impedance. The construction of the junction Hall generator is shown in Fig. 68. The current, I_s, through the load resistor, R, changes by an appreciable factor due to the leakage characteristics of both junctions. Because of the high load resistance and high voltage applied to these devices, the output impedance may be of the order of 500,000 ohms.

With most metals, the voltage produced by a Hall generator is about 1 micro-v. Semiconductors, however, have outputs of 1 or more volts; this is sufficient power to operate a sensitive relay or switch. The junction Hall generators are nonlinear. They generate low power and exhibit low-frequency cutoff.

The Hall generator provides a voltage output that is proportional to the product of two quantities: the current being fed to it and the magnetic field perpendicular to it. This relationship permits novel applications in electronic circuitry. A Hall generator can be designed to have an output exactly proportional to the product of the magnetic field and the current. Such a generator can be used as an analog computer element. The element will multiply two electrical quantities, one being expressed as a current and the other as a magnetic field. Similarly, an electrical quantity can be squared, merely by expressing it as a field and as a current.

The characteristics of a Hall generator make it suitable for detector elements in magnetometers, clip-on dc-ac ammeters, electrical compasses, dc-ac converters, low-level amplifiers, transducers (converting mechanical motion into electrical signals), magnetic-field variation meters, and wattmeters (193).

Electrical Contacts

The field of electrical contacts is as old as the science of electricity, yet few laws underlying the theory of electrical contacts have been formulated. Excellent reviews on the subject are available (194, 195).

Efficient contacts are essential to the successful operation of innumerable types of electrical equipment. Two general classifications of contacts can be made: switching (make-and-break) contacts and sliding contacts. The requirements of electrical contacts are that they shall successfully close the circuit, carry the current without overheating, and interrupt the current without deterioration. The successful operation of contacts depends on the following:

1 *Chemical Properties*

Contact material must resist tarnishing and oxidation to preserve low contact resistance.

2 *Physical Properties*

High hardness contributes to low electrical wear (arc loss).

High melting point, like hardness, also contributes to low electrical wear.

High thermal conductivity is necessary to dissipate heat to prevent temperature rises.

High electrical conductivity is required to obtain current-carrying capacity.

3 *Electrical Conditions*

High voltage at make and break favors electrical wear.

Increasing current, to be carried and interrupted, favors electrical wear.

Electrical wear on direct current is greater than on alternating current for a given voltage.

Inductance of circuit: Interrupting an inductive circuit will cause more wear than interrupting a noninductive circuit on the same voltage.

Arc suppression reduces electrical wear; condensers, resistors used singly or together, and, on large equipment, magnetic blowout and deionizing devices are helpful.

4 *Mechanical Conditions*

Size and form of contacts are related to the heating effect.

Increasing contact pressure increases, within limits, the contact resistance, and greater currents can be carried.

As frequency of operation increases, electrical wear increases.

The higher the speed of make and break, the shorter will be the duration of the arc.

A rolling or wiping contact action is preferred to butting action, as the former tends to break oxide films.

The maximum current that can be carried by contacts is determined by the permissible temperature rise. The temperature rise will depend on the contact resistance and on the dissipation of heat. Contact resistance is lowest for metals that do not form surface films, when these are used with the maximum available contact pressure. The maximum current that can be interrupted is governed, therefore, by the resistance of the contact material to electrical wear. Electrical wear will depend on the conditions just outlined.

In a given material, for voltages between 24 and 250, a

Table 42. Limiting Arcing Currents for Contact Materials at 250 Volts

Material	Limiting arcing current, amp	Material	Limiting arcing current, amp
Silver............	0.45	10% Au-silver alloy............	0.25
Platinum........	0.90	10% Pd-silver alloy............	0.30
Palladium........	0.60	10% Ir-platinum alloy.........	1.0
Gold............	0.40	40% Ag-palladium alloy........	0.5
Rhodium........	0.35	40% Cu-palladium alloy........	0.6
Tungsten........	1.4	Platinum-silver-gold...........	0.35

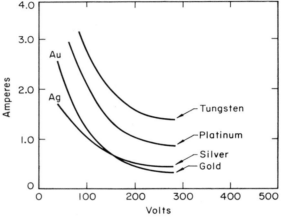

Fig. 69. Volt-ampere characteristics required to maintain a direct-current arc. When the critical values of current at a given voltage are exceeded, arcing occurs.

limiting current exists that can be interrupted with only a small contact gap without the maintenance of an arc. Below these certain voltages and currents, electrical wear is slight and is principally due to bombardment of the positive contact by free electrons emitted from the negative contact. In direct-current circuits, a small amount of material transfers from the positive to the negative contact, and, in extended and frequent use, there may be a growth on the negative contact and a crater on the positive.

Below a specific voltage, which is characteristic of the material and of the order of 12 to 15 v, a current of any magnitude may theoretically be interrupted without arcing; below a certain limiting amperage, any voltage up to the minimum breakdown voltage of the air gap will not maintain an arc. Table 42 shows the approximate limiting currents for contact materials operating at about 250 v.

The limiting current-voltage curves are hyperbolas (Fig. 69), and tend asymptotically toward a minimum voltage and a minimum current, below which an arc will not form. When the critical values of current are exceeded, arcing results. The amount of metal removed depends greatly on the energy of the arc, since the effect is one of bombardment by ions.

Types of Contacts. Contacts, whether sliding or butting, can be classified into four groups:

1 Light-duty contacts
2 Medium-duty contacts
3 Contactor contacts
4 Circuit-breaker contacts

Light-duty contacts include instrument, radiofrequency and sensitive relay contacts on which no arcing occurs, because they operate at low currents and voltages. Sliding contacts come under this classification.

Contact metals used are palladium, silver, platinum, rhodium, gold and such alloys as 10 Ir-Pt, 7 Pt – 26 Ag – 67 Au, 30 Ag-Au, 40 Cu-Pd, 40 Ag-Pd, and 14 Ru-Pt.

For sliding contacts, it is necessary to maintain a low, or uniform, contact resistance and freedom from wear of the fixed or moving member. Rhodium against rhodium is excellent for radiofrequency work; rhodium-plated copper is also used.

Medium-duty contacts operate in currents from 0.4 to 5 amp at voltages up to 660, and at 20 amp at voltages up to 250, and at even higher amperages at battery voltages. These contacts should have low contact resistance, as well as resistance to arcing. Films, tarnish, grease, and dust do not affect these contacts as they do light-duty contacts, as the arc readily punctures such obstructions.

Silver fulfills the greater part of contact requirements in the medium-duty group, especially at low voltages and currents. If conditions are severe, silver-base alloys, such as silver-copper, silver-gold, and silver-platinum, are used. Powder metallurgy compacts, such as silver-tungsten, are very useful, as they resist material transfer and welding of contact due to their composite nature.

Contactor contacts include contactor starters and various con-

Table 43. Physical Characteristics of Common Contact Metals and a Few Composite Materials

Material	Contact yield point, psi	Rockwell hardness	Specific resistance, ohm-in. $\times 10^{-6}$	Heat conductivity, watts per in. per °C	Wiedemann-Franz law, $\rho\kappa = LT$ ($T = 300$ K), $\times 10^{-8}$
Contact Metals					
Silver (hard)	68,000	15T–34	0.64	10.64	2.27
Silver (soft)	46,000	15T– 0	...	...	...
Copper (hard)	175,000	15T–75	0.68	9.86	2.24
Copper (soft)	64,000	15T–41	...	...	...
Molybdenum	430,000	30T–80	2.2	3.71	2.72
Tungsten	665,000	30T–87	2.2	4.07	2.98
Nickel (soft)	175,000	15T–75	3.1	1.49	1.54
Graphite	6,700	15T–60(a)	320	0.399	36.2
Platinum (hard)	230,000	15T–81	3.87	1.77	2.28
Platinum (annealed)	105,000	15T–58	...	...	...
Palladium (hard)	250,000	15T–83	3.94	1.71	2.25
Palladium (annealed)	90,000	15T–51	...	...	...
Iridium	860,000	15T–95	1.94	1.50	0.97
Gold (hard)	52,000	15T–12	0.95	7.50	2.38
Gold (annealed)	49,000	15T– 8	...	...	...
Sintered Contact Materials (Composition by weight)					
70 W – 30 Ag	480,000	30T–82	1.6	5.0 (b)	2.67 (c)
62 W – 38 Ag	430,000	30T–80	1.2	6.5	2.60
50 W – 50 Ag	220,000	30T–60	1.0	7.6	2.52
60 Mo – 40 Ag	240,000	30T–64	1.3	5.9	2.54
30 Mo – 70 Ag	170,000	30T–48	0.86	8.9	2.41
95 Ag – 5 graphite (hard)	120,000	15T–63	1.0	5.7	2.28
95 Ag – 5 graphite (soft)	89,000	15T–50	1.0	5.7	2.28
93 Ag – 7 graphite (soft)	81,000	15T–45	1.3	4.1	1.78
60 Ag – 40 Ni (hard)	160,000	30T–46	1.1	5.3	1.96
40 Ag – 60 Ni (hard)	270,000	30T–68	1.4	3.9	1.80
40 Ag – 60 Ni (soft)	107,000	30T–15	1.6	3.4	1.80

(a) Hardness reading on graphite taken with $\frac{1}{2}$-in.-diam ball. (b) The heat conductivities of the composite contact materials have been calculated from the values of the Weidemann-Franz law constant and the measured values of the specific resistance. (c) The Wiedemann-Franz constant for the composite contact materials has been taken as the average on a volume basis of the values for the separate materials in the composition.

trol gear. They interrupt relatively heavy current safely and quickly, and when closed they carry the rated load with a limited temperature rise. Principal problems with this type of contact are overheating, excessive wear, and welding.

Copper is often used for this application, because of its high electrical and thermal conductivity, but its biggest limitation is oxide formation. Silver is superior to copper. Generally, silver-copper (7.5% Cu) alloy, cadmium-copper-silver alloy, or compacts of silver and nickel or silver and tungsten are used.

Circuit-breaker contacts should be able to carry rated currents indefinitely without deterioration, must be able to operate safely and dependably under abnormal or fault conditions, must handle initial peak current on reclosing, and must return to normal operation after line difficulties have been cleared.

Low contact resistance and high thermal conductivity are principal requirements of these contacts. Silver and its alloys are frequently used. Once copper was used extensively, but now it is superseded by silver. Generally, silver facings are applied to copper blocks. Silver-nickel and silver-molybdenum compacts are sometimes used. Table 43 lists some physical characteristics of common contact materials and a few of the composites.

Electromechanical Transducers

Electromechanical transducers are of two types: those that use the Joule effect (change in dimensions with magnetization) and those that use the Villari effect (change in magnetization because of stress). Although the Joule effect, $\Delta l/l$, is small, 30×10^{-6}, large amplitudes may be built up by resonance in a suitably designed core. Materials for magnetostrictive transducers must have a high rate of change of linear magnetostriction, low electrical losses, good mechanical properties, a high Curie point, and, in some instances, good corrosion resistance.

Nickel, iron-nickel, nickel-cobalt, and iron-cobalt alloys have high magnetostriction and are used for transducers. A nickel alloy with 4.5% Co is said to be most suitable for the magnetostrictive element of receivers, such as hydrophones, whereas a nickel alloy with 1.4% Co and 2.3% Cr is preferred for high-frequency power (196), because of its high electrical resistivity (30 microhm-cm compared with 8.1 microhm-cm for nickel). The soft ferrites are finding increasing use in transducers. High-efficiency transducers are made with laminated metal cores to obtain low eddy current losses. Stacked laminations of about 0.015 in. can be used for frequencies to 30,000 cycles. For higher frequencies, 0.002 and 0.005-in. tapes are used. With Permendur (49 Fe – 49 Co – 2 V) at frequencies of 20 to 60 kc, a high intensity of 400 w per sq in. of surface can be readily obtained.

Magnetostrictive transducers are used for sonar and related devices for detecting submarines and ships. A transducer sends out sound waves that are reflected by objects in the water; the reflected waves are detected by a hydrophone. The Fathometer, used for determining depth of water and locating schools of fish, is a similar device. Here, too, a transducer sends out a signal and a hydrophone receives the signal. By noting the time interval between the sending and receiving of the signal, the target distance can be established.

One method of generating ultrasonic waves (elastic waves of frequencies far beyond the range of audibility) is with high-frequency transducers. The effects of ultrasonics are becoming better known. For instance, ultrasonics can be used to homogenize and sterilize milk, and chemical reactions can be accelerated.

Magnetostrictive transducers are used for cleaning applications in electroplating aluminum bus bars with silver, cleaning printed circuits for television and radio receivers, and decontaminating pieces of nuclear apparatus. The transducer produces sound intensity high enough to produce a secondary effect, called cavitation. The creation and collapse of millions of vapor bubbles in the medium produce the cleaning effect.

Strain Gages (197)

The widespread growth and application of experimental stress analysis since 1940 is almost entirely due to the introduction of the bonded-wire resistance strain gage. Although other methods of measuring strain have been used for decades, the wire resistance gage is now by far the most important single tool used for stress analysis.

The gage consists of a grid or pattern of special, very-small-diameter wire cemented between two pieces of paper. It is about the size of a postage stamp. The wire has the property of linear variation of electrical resistance with strain. The strain gage is cemented to the structure to be studied, and is then connected to a measuring instrument, such as a wheatstone bridge, strip chart recorder, or oscilloscope. The gage will faithfully follow and indicate (or record) the strains occurring in the surface of the structure being studied.

The gage factor, G, is defined as follows:

$$G = \frac{\Delta R/R}{\Delta L/L} \tag{49}$$

The gage factor is a measure of the amount of resistance change for a given strain, and is thus an index of strain sensitivity of the gage. The higher the factor, the more sensitive the gage. The fact that a gage factor can be either positive or negative is unimportant.

The ideal gage wire would have high resistance, a large change in resistance with strain, a high elastic limit, insensitivity to temperature with respect to the physical and electrical properties, and a constant ratio between resistance and unit strain. Some possible materials for strain gages are given in Table 44.

The change in resistance is not due solely to dimensional strain accompanying longitudinal stretching of the wire. Addi-

Table 44. Wire Characteristics as Related to Strain Gage Materials

Material	Gage factor, G	Temperature coefficient of resistance per °C, $\times 10^{-6}$	Resistance, ohms per ft in 1-mil diam	Stress equivalent to 10 C on steel, psi	Remarks
Nichrome(a)	+2.0	+300	638	+2,000	Temperature coefficient too high
Manganin(b)	+0.47	0	260	−400	Low gage factor
Advance(c)	+2.1	....	...	−66	Good for gages
Copel(c)	+2.4	±2	290	−200	Good for gages
Constantan(c)	+2.1	....	...	−60	Good for gages
Chromel C(d)	+2.5	....	640	+980	....
Iso-elastic(e)	+3.5	+175	680	+5,000	For dynamic strain measurement
Nickel(f)	−12.1	+6000	70	−13,500	Unstable thermal properties
Platinum	+4.8	+3000	80	....	Too expensive
Soft iron	+4.2	+5000	68	....	Easily corroded
Carbon	+20.0	−500	45,000	....	For comparison only

(a) 80 Ni – 20 Cr. (b) 84 Cu – 12 Mn – 4 Ni. (e) 55 Cu – 45 Ni. (d) 64 Ni – 25 Fe – 11 Cr. (e) 52 Fe – 36 Ni – 8 Cr – 0.5 Mo. (f) 99.9 + % Ni.

tional effects result from tension in nonmagnetic materials and the effect of tension on resistance, as well as on magnetostriction, in ferromagnetic wires.

Relays (198)

A relay is a low-power switching device that either enables large power to be controlled in another circuit or allows a series of subsequent switching operations to be performed in a time or process sequence.

Originally, a relay was a switching device actuated by an electromagnetic movement. This type of elementary relay is shown in Fig. 70. Currently, the meaning of relay has been modified to include innumerable electronic devices. One classification of relays includes electromagnetic (moving iron, moving coil, or alternating-current induction), thermal (bimetal), electronic (trigger action of vacuum or gas-filled tubes), and miscellaneous devices. Relays can also be divided into those that operate

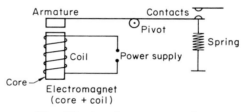

Fig. 70. An elementary relay

Table 45. Compositions and Melting Points of Fusible Alloys

Composition, %					Melting point,	
Bi	Pb	Sn	Cd	Hg	C	F
20	20	..	..	60	20	68
50	27	13	10	..	72	162
52	40	..	8	..	92	198
53	32	15	..	..	96	205
54	26	20	..	..	103	218
29	43	28	..	..	132	270
..	32	50	18	..	145	293
50	50	..	..	..	160	320
15	41	44	..	..	164	327
33	..	67	..	..	166	331
20	..	80	..	..	200	392

instantaneously (in less than 0.1 sec) and those that operate with a time lag.

In an electromagnetic device, the part of the relay that is attracted by the electromagnetic coil is called the armature; the iron in the electromagnet is referred to as the core. The armature and the core are made of soft magnetic materials, such as ingot iron, low-carbon steel, or 1 to 3% Si iron. Where corrosive conditions exist, annealed ferritic stainless steels (type 410 with 12% Cr and type 430 with 17% Cr) are used. For highly sensitive relays, iron-nickel alloys have found some application.

Spark Plug Electrodes

In the automotive engine, nickel with 4.5% Mn has found considerable service for spark plug electrodes, because of its resistance to sulfide corrosion. Nickel with up to 0.20% Ba (to improve thermionic emission) has been used for electrodes. For electrodes in aircraft spark plugs, nickel-clad (64% Ni) copper wire performs well, whereas for spark plug electrodes in heavy-duty aircraft engines, where maximum resistance to highly leaded fuels is required, drastically cold worked (for hardness) 84 Pt – 10 Pd – 6 Ru has been used.

Fuses and Circuit Breakers

For the protection of circuits in electronic and electrical equipment, it is necessary to provide open-circuit devices. The simplest and oldest method is the use of fuses of easily fusible metals; this goes back to Thomas Edison.

Fuse metals for electric fuses of the open-link, enclosed and expulsion types are usually made of some low-fusible alloy. Aluminum is also used to some extent. A predetermined load will melt the alloy in the fuse, and thereby break or open the circuit and in this manner protect it.

Sufficient current melts the fuse and this opens the circuit, provided the resultant arc is self-extinguishing. Metals that volatilize in the arc are preferred to those that leave a residue or globule of hot metal. The rating of a fuse depends critically on its shape, dimensions, mounting, and enclosure. Some typical compositions of fuse alloys are given in Table 45.

Circuit breakers, like fuses, protect circuits from damage. A circuit breaker trips and opens the circuit. If the load is of a temporary nature, the circuit breaker can be closed again by resetting it. Earlier breakers were actuated by the thermal expansion of a bimetal strip. Modern breakers combine thermal and magnetic action or use a magnetic coil with a hydraulically delayed plunger or core. The breaker is designed to hold under temporary overloads, but will open the circuit if an overload continues; it will break in less than a hundredth of a second in case of a short circuit.

Chapter 5

Magnetism

THE ONLY known source of magnetism until the nineteenth century was the lodestone — the iron ore called magnetite, so named for the rich deposits at Magnesia, Asia Minor. In 1819, Oersted discovered electromagnetism — that a wire carrying an electric current has a magnetic field around it. Barely three weeks after Oersted's observation, Ampere showed that current-carrying wires repel or attract each other like magnets. A few years later William Sturgeon made the first electromagnet; he placed a piece of iron inside a coil of wire, thereby intensifying the magnetic field. Since then scientists have been striving to produce magnets that are more and more powerful.

Magnetic Fields. Permanent magnets are not strong when compared with electromagnets. The magnetic field of an ordinary bar magnet may be 2000 or 3000 gausses.* The better permanent magnets (for example, Alnico V) may develop 10,000 to 14,000 gausses in a small air gap. An electromagnet using a core of metal to intensify the magnetic field by the electric current in the coil can reach 60,000 gausses; this is about the limit, because of the magnetic capacity of metals. To attain greater field strengths, ferromagnetic cores are abandoned and the field is produced in air or vacuum.

With high electrical power, extremely high fields can be generated, but there are difficulties. High currents place severe strains on the coil, because a magnetic field produces both me-

* The term "gauss" is sometimes used as the unit of magnetic field intensity. Because flux density equals permeability times field intensity ($B = \mu H$), these quantities have the same units, if permeability is considered dimensionless. In 1930, the International Electrotechnical Commission adopted the following names: For magnetizing force or intensity, the oersted; for magnetic flux density, the gauss. Strengths of magnets are commonly given in gausses.

chanical and heating effects. Kapitza (199), at the University of Cambridge, produced fields of 300,000 gausses with pulsed currents. A unit is now commercially available that will produce field strengths in excess of 500,000 gausses for 0.5 millisec in a space 0.5 in. in diameter and 1.5 in. long. Bitter (200) succeeded in producing fields of about 100,000 gausses with a continuous current, using a million-watt generator. The field produced is proportional to the square root of the input power, limiting greatly the design of large electromagnets.

The Model C Stellarator at Princeton University required two main coils to create the magnetic field, to confine and stabilize the plasma (ionized gas consisting of electrons, ions, and neutral atoms). The coils, producing 55,000 gausses for 1 sec, re-

Table 46. Magnetic Fields

Magnitude, gausses	Origin of field
0.01	Almost any iron object has a residual field.
0.01 to 1	Earth's field; small (bar) toy magnets
1 to 100	Toy magnets
100 to 10,000	Simple electromagnets; pole gaps in magnets of measuring instruments; loudspeaker magnets; bar and horseshoe magnets
10,000 to 50,000	Commercial electromagnets for lifting iron objects
50,000 and greater	Specially designed electromagnets; higher fields are obtained by pulsed currents. Superconducting magnets.

quire a current buildup from a generator of 157,000-kw power. The current density varies from 20,000 to 40,000 amp per sq in. Experts in cryogenics predict that a superconducting magnet weighing 20 lb, exclusive of refrigeration equipment, and started with a pulse from a 6-v battery will produce a field comparable to that of a 100-ton electromagnet operated by a 100-kw power supply.

The discovery of nuclear magnetic resonance in 1945 introduced a new era in the development of magnets and electromagnets, and the measurement of magnetic fields. It became necessary to measure fields with an accuracy of one part in 40,000. Further, the resonance experiments demand magnets with a high degree of field homogeneity (one part in ten million over a volume of 0.1 cu cm) and stability (one part in ten million over a period of 30 sec or more).

Table 46 lists the strengths of various fields and their origins.

Magnetization. A substance is said to be magnetized when it possesses the property of attracting iron in the form of bits, rods, wire, and filings. There are three ways in which a material can be magnetized to attract iron:

1 Certain materials can be magnetized by rubbing them with a permanent magnet. A piece of steel, a needle for example, can be transformed into a magnet by rubbing it with a magnet. This is a crude manner of magnetization, because it affords little, if any, control over the resultant magnetization.
2 Magnetization may also be produced by induction. A soft * piece of iron, such as a nail, will not attract iron filings. If, however, a permanent magnet is held to one end of the nail, the nail immediately attracts filings and other ferrous materials. When the magnet is removed, the iron specimen (nail) will lose wholly or in part the magnetism that had been induced in the iron. The soft iron was induced into a state of magnetization by the presence of the magnetic field of the permanent magnet. This method of magnetization is also crude, and is not amenable to easy and accurate control of magnetization.
3 In the third method of magnetization, a coil, preferably one with many loops, is brought near the soft iron; when a current flows through the coil, magnetization is induced in the soft iron. With the coil and the current, a simple, accurate, easily reproducible method of controlling magnetization is available; further, much higher magnetic fields are obtainable with this arrangement than with the others.

In these situations, the iron behaves as a magnetic conductor; lines of force pass through it more easily than through air. In all instances, the outside magnetic environment causes the microscopic domains of the iron to align themselves to the external field, and in this way add their lines of force to those of the adjacent magnets and coils.

Any conductor, carrying a current, I, has a magnetic field around it; this is Oersted's fundamental discovery (201). This field, for an infinitely long conductor, is given by the equation:

$$H = \frac{0.2I}{r} \tag{50}$$

* "Soft" is used in the mechanical sense, in contradistinction to hard or permanent magnet materials, which historically were quenched and tempered steels. Soft permanent magnets are now available.

where H is the magnetic field in oersteds, I is the current in amperes, and r is the perpendicular distance, in centimeters, from the conductor.

If the current-carrying conductor is formed into a loop, the magnetic field is concentrated within the area of the loop. If the

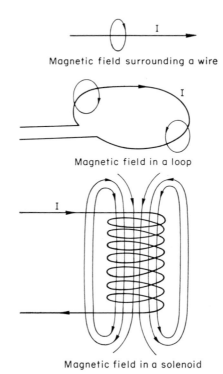

Magnetic field surrounding a wire

Magnetic field in a loop

Magnetic field in a solenoid

Fig. 71. Schematic diagram of the magnetic field generated in various current-conducting arrangements

conductor is wound into a helix, the construction is referred to as a solenoid, and the magnetic field becomes more concentrated (Fig. 71). A solenoid with a soft iron core is known as an electromagnet.

The magnetic field in a coil or a solenoid can be controlled either by increasing or decreasing the current, or by varying the number of turns of the conductor. The magnetizing force or field, H, therefore is given by the current and the geometric configuration of the conductor. For a single coil or loop, the field in the center of the area is given by equation (51) as:

$$H = \frac{0.2\pi I}{r} \tag{51}$$

where r is the radius of the loop. For a coil of n turns, the field is:

$$H = \frac{0.2\pi nI}{r} \tag{52}$$

For slim solenoids, where the length is large with respect to the radius of the solenoid, the field is accurately given by:

$$H = 0.4\pi n'I \tag{53}$$

where n' is the number of turns per unit length (cm).

The oersted is the unit of magnetic field strength in the centimeter-gram-second electromagnetic unit system (cgs emu), and these equations define it. In the English system, the magnetiz-

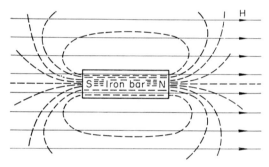

Fig. 72. *When a long rod of iron is placed in a uniform magnetic field,* H, *the bar becomes magnetized with* N *and* S *poles. The lines of force due to the poles (dashed lines) combine with the external field (solid lines). The actual field is distorted so that most of the field in the vicinity of the iron goes through the iron.*

ing force is given by the ampere-turns per inch and has no special name.

Under ordinary circumstances, a piece of iron or steel displays no magnetism. In the presence of a magnetic field (for instance, by placing the iron in a solenoid), the situation is quite different. The magnetization of a piece of iron by induction means that the magnetic field inside a coil may be greatly enhanced by a core of iron. Iron magnetized by induction will have polarity and from these poles will emerge or enter lines of flux, just as they do from a permanent magnet.

Consideration of what happens in a solenoid into which a bar of iron is introduced can be very informative (Fig. 72). The excess number of lines over those that would be present if the iron were not in the field H may be expressed in terms of the pole strengths that have been induced. At the poles, where both sets of lines coincide, the pole strengths of the induced magnets are given as m. The following relation between lines of flux, ϕ, then holds:

$$\phi_{\text{iron}} - \phi_{\text{air}} = 4\pi m \tag{54}$$

The factor 4π results from the definition of a unit pole that gives rise to a unit field everywhere on the surface of a sphere of unit radius enclosing the pole; this sphere has an area of 4π.

In terms of flux density (lines per unit area),

$$\frac{\phi_{\text{iron}}}{A} - \frac{\phi_{\text{air}}}{A} = \frac{4\pi m}{A}$$

where A is the cross-sectional area of the iron bar. Here, ϕ_{iron}/A is defined as the induction or flux density, and ϕ_{air}/A, as the magnetizing force.

Table 47. Susceptibilities of Some of the Elements

Element	Mass susceptibility(a), χ, $\times 10^{-6}$	Element	Mass susceptibility(a), χ, $\times 10^{-6}$
Hydrogen	-1.97	Copper	-0.086
Helium	-0.47	Zinc	-0.157
Lithium	$+0.50$	Zirconium	-0.45
Beryllium	-1.00	Columbium	$+1.5$
Boron	-0.69	Molybdenum	$+0.04$
Carbon	-0.49	Palladium	$+5.4$
Nitrogen	-0.80	Silver	-0.20
Oxygen	$+106.2$	Cadmium	-0.18
Sodium	$+0.51$	Tin	-0.25
Magnesium	$+0.55$	Antimony	-0.87
Aluminum	$+0.65$	Lanthanum	$+1.04$
Silicon	-0.13	Cesium	$+15.0$
Phosphorus	-0.90	Praseodymium	$+25.0$
Calcium	$+1.10$	Neodymium	$+36.0$
Titanium	$+1.25$	Tantalum	$+0.93$
Vanadium	$+1.4$	Tungsten	$+0.28$
Chromium	$+3.08$	Platinum	$+1.10$
Manganese	$+11.8$	Bismuth	-1.35

(a) Mass susceptibility $\chi = \kappa/\rho$.

The pole strength, m/A, is known as the intensity of magnetization, I,* so that the equation can be written:

$$B - H = 4\pi I$$
$$\text{or } B = H + 4\pi I \qquad (55)$$

The last equation states that the flux density, B, through a bar of iron placed in a uniform magnetic field is composed of two parts: the imposed magnetic field, H, and the magnetization, I, produced in the iron.

In the cgs emu system, the magnetic induction or flux density, B, is given as gausses or kilogausses (lines of flux per square centimeter or maxwells per square centimeter). In the English system, the induction is given as lines or maxwells per square inch.

Types of Magnetic Materials

Faraday (202) demonstrated that all matter reacts to a magnetic field and the interaction is of three types, identified as:

1 *Diamagnetic materials.* These orient themselves perpendicular to a strong magnetic field.
2 *Paramagnetic materials.* These orient themselves parallel to a strong magnetic field.
3 *Ferromagnetic materials.* These include iron, nickel, cobalt, and their alloys, and are strongly attracted to a magnet or electromagnet.

Quantitative work on diamagnetic and paramagnetic materials was to come later, particularly in the classic work of Curie (203). Diamagnetism was shown to be temperature independent and paramagnetism was shown to follow the law:

$$\chi = \frac{C}{T} \qquad (56)$$

where χ is the mass susceptibility, ** C is a constant, and T is the absolute temperature.

---

* The intensity of magnetization, I, can also be defined as the magnetic moment per unit volume. If $I = m/A$, it follows that $I = mL/AL = M/V$, where L is the length of the magnet, M is the magnetic moment, and V is the volume.

** Mass susceptibility, χ, is defined as

$$\chi = \kappa/\rho \qquad (57)$$

where ρ is density and κ is the volume susceptibility. The atomic or molar susceptibility, χ_A or χ_M, is the product of χ and the atomic or molar weight.

Table 48. Types of Magnetic Phenomena

Kind of magnetism	Cause	Temperature dependence	Volume susceptibility, κ, at 20 C (68 F)	Examples
Diamagnetism	Closed electronic shells with spins in antiparallel pairs	None	$\sim -10^{-5}$	Rare gases, H_2, N_2, Hg
Normal paramagnetism	Moments of free electrons; orbital or spin moments or both	$\chi = C/T$	$\sim +10^{-3}$	Hydrogen atom, alkali atoms, rare earths, elements with partly filled shells
Degenerate paramagnetism	Conducting electrons	None	$\sim +10^{-5}$	Na, K, Mg, Al, carbides, nitrides
Ferromagnetism	Exchange forces between atomic moments	$\chi = C/(T - \theta')$(a)	$\theta' > 0$	Fe, Ni, Co, Gd at less than +16 C
Antiferromagnetism	Exchange forces between atomic moments	$\chi = C/(T - \theta')$	$\theta' < 0$	Pt, Pd
Anomalous diamagnetism	Valence electrons in certain lattices	None	$\sim -10^{-4}$	Bi, Sb, gamma brass
Ferrimagnetism	Moment resulting from two antiferromagnetic lattices	$\chi = C/(T - \theta')$	$\theta' > 0$	$MO \cdot Fe_2O_3$(spinel), $MO \cdot 6Fe_2O_3$ (hex) See note (b).

(a) θ' is the paramagnetic Curie point. (b) M is a divalent element of the group magnesium, zinc, copper, nickel, cobalt, and manganese for spinel structures and calcium, strontium, lead, and barium for hexagonal structures.

Table 49. Magnetic Properties of Some Soft Ferrites

$NiO \cdot Fe_2O_3$, mole %	$ZnO \cdot Fe_2O_3$, mole %	$MnO \cdot Fe_2O_3$, mole %	$ZnO \cdot Fe_2O_3$, mole %	Magnetic saturation, B_s	Curie temperature, θ, C	Initial permeability, μ_0	Coercive force, H_c	Electrical resistivity, microhm-cm
..	..	48	52	3300	100	1400	0.2	20
..	..	79	21	5200	210	700	0.5	80
36	64	..	..	3600	125	650	0.4	10^5
64	36	..	..	4100	350	90	2.1	10^5
100	..	..	..	2300	500	17	11.0	10^5

Apart from the exceptional cases of the ferromagnetic materials, the induction, B, is linearly proportional to the field, H. The proportionality factor, called the permeability, μ, relates the quantities B and H as follows:

$$B = \mu H \tag{58}$$

The permeability is a constant of matter and is characteristic for a given medium. The permeability of a vacuum is 1. If the permeability is slightly less than unity, the substance is diamagnetic; if the permeability is slightly greater than unity, the substance is paramagnetic. Only if permeability is large and positive is the material considered ferromagnetic. The word "susceptibility" has been chosen to express the difference in permeability of matter relative to a vacuum. The volume susceptibility, κ, is related to the permeability through the following relation:

$$\mu = 1 + 4\pi\kappa \tag{59}$$

The susceptibility can be negative (diamagnetic materials) or positive (paramagnetic materials), as indicated in Table 47.

Diamagnetism is exhibited by elements possessing an even number of electrons and no incomplete inner shells; the rare gases belong to this group. In the simplest, and incidentally the most specialized case, an electron moving in a circular orbit generates a magnetic field exactly as does a current flowing in a conductor. The strength of the current generated is measured by its magnetic moment. Also, the sense (clockwise or counterclockwise) in which the electron revolves determines the direction of the moment. With the aid of the quantum theory, an equation can be derived for the diamagnetism of various elements. For a summary of the characteristics of diamagnetism, see Table 48.

Some elements, notably bismuth, that have loosely bound valency electrons are able to have anomalously high diamagnetism; the volume susceptibility of bismuth is -0.000013.

Paramagnetism is exhibited by elements with an odd number of electrons, namely the transition elements from the scandium group to the iron group and the lanthanides, the rare earths that follow lanthanum. The susceptibility results from the interaction of the magnetic field and the disordering effect of thermal motion.

Langevin (204) was able to show that the atomic susceptibility can be calculated with the following equation:

$$\chi_A = \frac{N\mu_A^2}{3kT} = \frac{C}{T} \tag{60}$$

where μ_A is the magnetic moment, N is Avogadro's number, k is Boltzmann's constant, and T is the absolute temperature. This temperature dependence is shown in Fig. 73. The theory remains valid in light of current quantum theory.

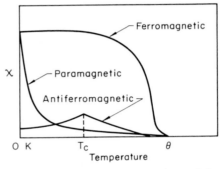

Fig. 73. Variation of susceptibility with temperature for ferromagnetic, paramagnetic, and antiferromagnetic materials. The critical temperature, T_c, for antiferromagnetic substances is generally referred to as the Néel temperature. Theta is the Curie temperature.

Paramagnetism has two distinct causes: It can arise from the orbital moment or the spin moment of the electrons, or it can arise from a vectorial addition of both moments.

In a metal, the electrons may be present as conducting electrons, between which there is no marked interaction. The conduction electrons cause a weak paramagnetism, which Pauli (205) refers to as degenerate paramagnetism. This type of paramagnetism is temperature dependent and is of the order of $\kappa = +10^{-5}$. Superimposed on this degenerate paramagnetism is the diamagnetism of the metal ions, which remains after subtracting the effect of the conduction electrons; in such instances, the diamagnetism is not always apparent. However, in larger atoms, diamagnetism predominates. Degenerate paramagnetism occurs in sodium, potassium, magnesium, and aluminum. Diamagnetism predominates with cesium, copper, silver, and gold. Carbides and nitrides that are metallic conductors, such as titanium carbide, titanium nitride, and zirconium nitride, show degenerate paramagnetism.

The extension of the ideas of Langevin (204) and Curie (203) to quantum mechanics has been made with some success by Van Vleck (206). He was able to calculate the diamagnetic susceptibility of simple atoms, as well as the strong paramagnetism of the rare earths and the paramagnetic gases (for example, oxygen). For a summary of the characteristics of paramagnetism, see Table 48.

Antiferromagnetism. An anomaly in the temperature dependence of susceptibility of some strongly paramagnetic materials

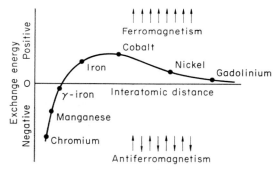

Fig. 74. *Magnitude and sign of the exchange energy determine whether the element is ferromagnetic or antiferromagnetic. When exchange energy is greater than zero, the electron spins are aligned parallel and ferromagnetism results. When the exchange energy is less than zero, the electron spins are aligned antiparallel and antiferromagnetism results.*

was observed by Bizette, Squire, and Tsai (207, 208). These substances, known as antiferromagnetic materials, display the following anomalous properties: a maximum in the χ-versus-T curve; a maximum in the specific heat, C_p-versus-T curve; an anomaly in thermal expansion; and mass susceptibility dependent on magnetic field. At the critical temperature, T_c, known as the Néel temperature, the susceptibility reaches a maximum value and then decreases as the temperature decreases (see Fig. 73 and Table 48).

The general characteristics of antiferromagnetic materials can be explained by the fact that the exchange energy is negative in sign. A consequence is that the electron spins are aligned antiparallel, in contradistinction to the situation that exists for ferromagnetism (Fig. 74).

Ferrimagnetism. Originally the ferrites were variants of magnetite, the oldest magnetic material known. In a magnetite molecule, given as Fe_3O_4 but more correctly as $FeO \cdot Fe_2O_3$, one iron atom is divalent (Fe^{++}), two iron atoms are trivalent (Fe^{+++}), and the four oxygen atoms are doubly ionized (O_4^{--}). Crystallographically, the structure is that of a spinel (face-centered cubic crystal); the binding force is ionic in nature. The ferrites have a relatively low saturation (less than 5000 gausses), a low Curie temperature, and very high electrical resistivity, compared to ferromagnetic elements or alloys.

The ferrites comprise the general class of the type $MO \cdot Fe_2O_3$, where M is any divalent metal (Mg, Zn, Cu, Ni, Co, and Mn). These ferrites are known as the soft ferrites, because of their high initial and maximum permeabilities. Because of the ease of substitution of foreign ions for the Fe^{++} ion (usually) and the Fe^{+++} ion (sometimes), it is possible to tailor-make the magnetic properties to some degree. With Ni^{++} substituted for Fe^{++}, the resultant has the highest Curie temperature of the ferrites. Substituting Mn^{++} for Fe^{++} increases the electrical resistivity. Substituting Al^{+++} for Fe^{+++} reduces the net magnetization (209). Some typical ferrites are given in Table 49, page 214 (210).

Later work with these oxide materials showed that the hexagonal ferrites of the formula $MO \cdot 6Fe_2O_3$ were good permanent magnets or hard magnetic materials (211). In the formula, M is a divalent metal of the group including barium, strontium, calcium, and lead.

Ferrimagnets are much weaker than ferromagnets, and the strongest ferrite has only about one third the saturation of iron. Because of the low saturation, ferrites are not used in power applications, but are widely employed in electronic circuitry.

Néel (212) has developed a theory to explain the magnetism of the ceramic ferrites. In his theory, the origin of the magnetism is different from that of ferromagnetism. The magnetism of the ferrites is the result of ferrimagnetism. This ferrimagnetism arises from nonidentical substructures that have different magnetic structures containing more than one kind of magnetic ion or more than one kind of crystallographic site or both (213). In one lattice, the atomic moments order parallel to the other moments of their sublattice and antiparallel to the moments of the other sublattice. This kind of material has magnetic properties, because the net moment of one lattice is greater than that of the other.

The first example of a first-order phase transition from ferrimagnetic to antiferromagnetic with decreasing temperature has been found in $Mn_{2-x}Cr_xSb$ for $0.02 \leq X \leq 0.2$ (214). The magnetization of the material increases with decreasing temperature, but at a critical temperature decreases to zero. The critical temperature increases with chromium content: Above the critical temperature, the intermetallic compound is magnetic, and below, it is nonmagnetic. The transition temperature can be varied from absolute zero to over 100 C. This exchange inversion is dependent on the changes in the interatomic distances: When the distance is a certain magnitude, the material is ferrimagnetic, and, when it is less, the material is aligned in a nonmagnetic pattern.

Another ferrimagnetic system is that of the garnet $3M_2O_3 \cdot 5Fe_2O_3$, where M_2O_3 is one of the rare earth oxides. The oxide crystal can accommodate the heavier rare earths, starting with samarium. Garnets are less magnetic than ferrites, but they have some useful characteristics. They are more complicated structurally than ferrite: A unit cell contains 24 rare earth ions, 40 iron ions, and 96 oxygen ions. The series $Y_{3-y}Gd_yFe_{5-x}Al_xO_{12}$ yields flux densities of 100 to 500 gausses and, in proper circuits, switching times of the order of 0.1 microsec. The garnets are transparent materials.

Ferromagnetism. In some lattices, a strong interaction of the electron spins occurs. If the spins orient themselves parallel to one another, ferromagnetism occurs (Fig. 74). If the spins orient themselves antiparallel, a strong paramagnetism, know as antiferromagnetism, results. The temperature dependence of these two phenomena is different from that of ordinary paramagnetism. Because of the strong interaction between the electron spins in a lattice leading to either ferromagnetism or antiferromagnetism, only the crystalline state gives rise to these phenomena; diamagnetism and paramagnetism exist in gas, liquid, and solid states of matter.

A special circumstance obtains in the case of the ferromagnetic materials, iron, nickel, cobalt, their alloys, and certain rare earth elements, namely, gadolinium and its alloys. A unique force, which has its origin in the so-called exchange energy, comes into play. This exchange energy is electrostatic in nature. Heisenberg (23) suggested that the Weiss molecular field might be accounted for by this exchange interaction between the spinning electrons.

In iron, nickel, and cobalt, the electrons outside the closed argon core (see Table 3) are the s and d electrons. The s, or valence, electrons form the electron gas in the metal structure, and are responsible for electrical conductivity and the metallic bond. The d electrons are localized in the 3d shell, and they carry the net magnetic moments responsible for ferromagnetism. Some degree of interaction between the s and d electrons is strongly suspected. In the rare earths, the carriers of the net magnetic moments are the f electrons. However, the f-f interactions cannot account fully for the ferromagnetism of gadolinium, and it is assumed that the s and f electrons interact.

According to Heisenberg, whose explanation of ferromagnetism of 30 years ago is still widely accepted, the exchange energy between two atoms is a function of the ratio of atomic separation to the diameter of the unfilled shell. The exchange energy is zero at large atomic separations, increases rapidly and causes parallel coupling as the separation diminishes, passes through a maximum, and then decreases. At a still closer spacing, the exchange energy becomes negative. In this situation, there is antiparallel coupling of the unfilled shells, giving rise to antiferromagnetism (Fig. 74). Except for the rare earth elements, the ratio of the atomic spacing to the unfilled shell diameter is largest for iron, nickel, and cobalt. The ratio is not sufficiently large for manganese, which is antiferromagnetic. However, by proper alloying, to increase atomic separation, the manganese becomes magnetic, as in the Heusler alloys (215), the most common of which are Cu_2MnAl, Cu_2MnSn, and Ag_5MnAl.

Above the ordering or Curie temperature, ferromagnetic materials become paramagnetic. Well above the Curie temperature, the susceptibility follows the Curie-Weiss law:

$$\chi = \frac{C}{T - \theta'} \tag{61}$$

where C is the Curie constant, and θ' is the paramagnetic Curie temperature, which is a few degrees higher than the more common Curie temperature θ, and T is the absolute temperature (see Table 48).

Slater (216) and his school have given us an energy-band picture of ferromagnetism. Zener (217) has recently proposed another theory of ferromagnetism based on interactions of conduction s electrons and d shell electrons.

Characteristics of Ferromagnetic Materials

Ferromagnetic materials, in contrast to paramagnetic or diamagnetic substances, are characterized by the following behavior:

1 A magnetization curve that approaches magnetic saturation is readily obtainable.
2 A hysteresis phenomenon accompanies the magnetization process when the field is reversed.
3 A temperature exists (the Curie temperature) above which ferromagnetic effects disappear and the material becomes paramagnetic.

From the study of independent elementary magnetic moments in paramagnetic materials, it is known that only about one magnetic moment in one billion is oriented by a very weak field. For example, in a ferromagnetic iron-silicon crystal, it is possible to achieve saturation in the same weak field. The atomic chaos in a paramagnetic material is due to the important role of thermal agitation in a system where there are no interactions between magnetic moments.

Domains. To reconcile fact with theory, Weiss (28) showed that the difficulty introduced by thermal agitation could be circumvented by considering the existence of an internal molecular field. The consequence of this molecular field was that a ferromagnetic material consisted of a large number of small areas, called domains, magnetized to saturation and dispersed in a random fashion, so that the net macroscopic magnetization was essentially zero.

There is now a wealth of experimental information to substantiate the existence of domains. Bitter (218) discovered that domain boundaries could be delineated on a polished surface with colloidal magnetic powders. Because his samples were mechanically polished, his patterns were distorted and generally

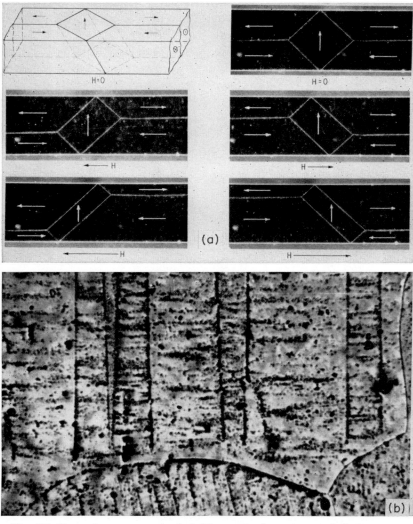

Fig. 75. Domain structures. (a) *Magnetic domains and their move-ment in a single crystal iron whisker (about 200×). In upper right is the domain configuration for zero field. Upper left is a derived three-dimensional domain structure. Arrows below figures indicate the direction of the field and its relative magnitude. Arrows drawn in domains show direction of magnetization. (Courtesy of R. W. DeBlois and C. D. Graham, Jr., General Electric Co.) (b) Domain structure in a 3.25% Si polycrystalline steel (about 19×). (Cour-tesy of R. W. Fowkes, Crucible Steel Co. of America)*

unintelligible. Williams and co-workers (219, 220), by using electropolishing and thereby avoiding a cold worked surface layer, were able to obtain domain patterns that were more easily analyzed. Electron optics can be used to demonstrate the presence of domains (221). Also, it is possible to observe domains directly in barium ferrite crystals by means of the Faraday effect (rotation of transmitted polarized light by a magnetic field) (222). Figure 75 shows the domain structures on an iron whisker single crystal and a grain in a polycrystalline silicon steel.

The domain picture in single crystals is shown schematically in Fig. 76. Sketch (a) shows the unmagnetized condition, while (b) illustrates the domain movement in an applied magnetic field.

The domain structure represents the minimum energy state of the material. Obviously, the structure changes with the application of a field. Explanation of domains in terms of magnetic field energy was given by Landau and Lifshitz in 1935 (223).

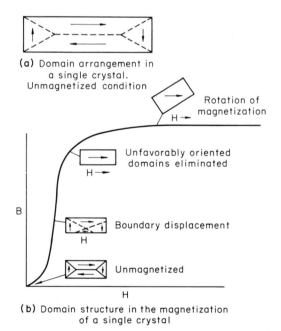

(a) Domain arrangement in a single crystal. Unmagnetized condition

Rotation of magnetization

Unfavorably oriented domains eliminated

Boundary displacement

Unmagnetized

(b) Domain structure in the magnetization of a single crystal

Fig. 76. Domain structure in an unmagnetized condition and changes produced by application of a magnetic field

Domains in a single crystal are essentially dependent on the size and shape of the crystal. Superficial domain structures may be small (about 10^{-6} cu cm), while the inner domains may be quite large (about 10^{-2} cu cm); these values are illustrative of size only.

In polycrystalline materials, where grains are oriented mostly at random, each crystal will behave as if it were an isolated

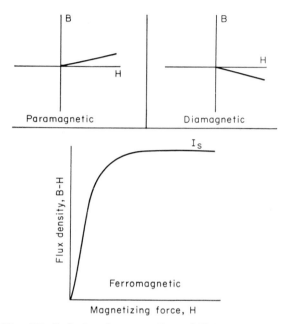

Fig. 77. Relation between B *and* H *in paramagnetic, diamagnetic, and ferromagnetic materials*

single crystal, and the domain may be smaller than the grain. In polycrystalline materials with preferred orientation, where the crystallographic axes align themselves parallel to a direction of deformation (for example, rolling direction in sheet), the domain may extend over several grains.

Magnetization Curve. For diamagnetic and paramagnetic materials, there is a linear relationship between the magnetizing force, H, and the flux density, B (Fig. 77). In ferromagnetic materials, there is no linear relationship. In ferromagnetics, a very small change in H gives a large change in B. The relationship is best shown in the magnetization or *B-H* curve,* also shown in Fig. 77. As *H* increases, the flux density increases rapidly up to the knee of the curve. It is evident from this *B-H* curve, as drawn, that the permeability (the ratio B/H) up to the saturation magnetization, I_s, is constant at no point. The manner in which the permeability varies as a function of *B* is shown in

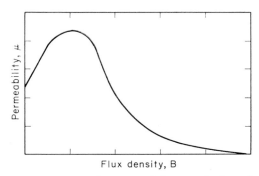

Fig. 78. *Variation of permeability with flux density*

Fig. 78. The largest value on this curve is known as the maximum permeability, μ_{max}. Another important quantity is the initial permeability, μ_0, measured at very low fields at the toe of the magnetization curve.

When a further increase in *H* causes no useful increase in *B*, the material is said to have been saturated. (See Table 50 for values of the saturation magnetic moment of the elements.)

Marked changes in the shape of the magnetization curve are produced by the introduction of an air gap (or a nonferromagnetic material) into the magnetic circuit. The presence of the air gap forces the magnetization curve to the right on a *B-H* plot, because of the creation of free poles producing demagnetizing fields.

The magnetization curve for either a single crystal or a polycrystalline material can be explained in terms of domain motions, in the manner indicated in Fig. 76. Three distinct domain phenomena occur during magnetization of the ferromagnetic material. In the initial stages of magnetization — at the toe of

* The *B-H* quantity actually represents *B* minus *H* and not *B* and *H*. Except for very high fields, *B* is large with respect to *H*. In the *B-H* curve, *H* must be subtracted in order that a saturation induction (which is constant) is obtained.

the *B-H* curve — the domain walls move in such a manner that domains favorably oriented with the applied field grow at the expense of unfavorably oriented domains; this is reversible boundary displacement: Upon removal of the field, the domains resume essentially their original positions. As the field is increased

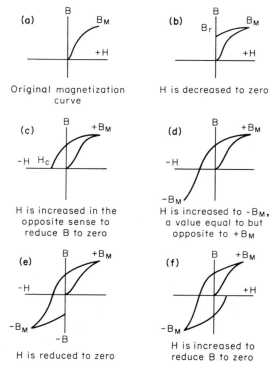

Fig. 79. *Development of the hysteresis cycle*

further, more and more of the domains that are less favorably aligned with the field suddenly swing over to the larger, already aligned domains and form larger domains parallel to the lattice edge, with the smallest angle to the field. This process is referred to as irreversible boundary displacement. The anisotropy energy of a crystal causes the magnetization of a domain to be aligned parallel to crystallographic axes or directions. When stronger fields are applied and the material approaches saturation, the direction of magnetization is rotated from the favorable, easy direction of the applied field. This rotation is reversible: When the field is reduced, the direction of magnetization returns to the position where the domains are essentially aligned along the easy crystallographic direction. The shapes of magnetization curves are variable, because some domains are more or less favorably oriented with respect to the applied field direction than others.

Hysteresis Loop. The magnetization curve shows how the flux density, B, changes with increasing magnetizing force, H. However, if H is reduced to zero, the B-H curve does not retrace itself; the induction in the steel lags behind the magnetic field,

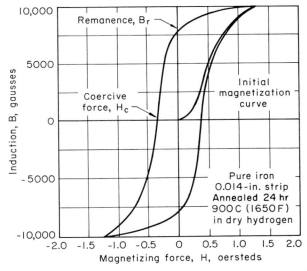

Fig. 80. Hysteresis loop for pure iron. Note relationship of the initial magnetization curve to the hysteresis loop.

and therefore the phenomena responsible for the B-H curve are not reversible. This situation leads to the hysteresis cycle.

When the magnetizing force is reduced to zero, the flux density is only partially reduced. A residual flux remains; this is called remanence, B_r (Fig. 79, b). As the magnetizing force is applied in the opposite or negative direction (by reversing the direction of current flow in the windings), a point is reached where the flux density is zero. The magnetizing force required to reduce the flux density to zero is known as the coercive force, H_c (Fig. 79, c). Increasing the magnetizing force further in the same direction causes the flux density to increase. Increasing H to the value it had at its greatest point increases B to the same flux density but in the opposite direction (Fig. 79, d). Removing the magnetizing force leads to another residual induction, also B_r (Fig. 79, e). Increasing the magnetizing force to the point where the flux density is zero is shown in Fig. 79(f). This point is equivalent to the coercive force, but of opposite sign; it is also called H_c. Increasing H does not cause the B to follow the initial or virgin B-H curve. Actually, by increasing H, the maximum flux density, $+B_M$ is attained, as in Fig. 79(b). The typical hysteresis loop is given in Fig. 80. In alternating-current applications, the magnetic material goes through this cycle for every reversal in current — 60 times per second on a 60-cps power line.

The hysteresis loop is a measure of the energy lost as heat in magnetizing a core. It is apparent that as H increases, the flux density increases, and as a consequence the loop becomes larger — that is, the energy loss increases. In soft (nonretentive) magnetic materials, the loop should be as small as possible. Hysteresis loops for three soft magnetic materials (Supermalloy, Molybdenum Permalloy, and Armco iron) are given in Fig. 81. For hard or permanent magnet materials, the loop should be large.

Magnetic losses are represented by the area of the hysteresis loop, and these energy losses (as heat) are attributable to domain-wall motions. If these domain walls are impeded by inclusions and lattice strain due to cold work or precipitation, the hysteresis loss is increased. A portion of the domain wall may be held back by imperfections, while most of the wall continues to advance with the application of a field. Eventually, at higher values of field, the arrested portion snaps back into alignment with the moving wall. The coercive force is a measure of the field necessary to force the domain wall past imperfections. The more imperfections, the greater is the coercive force.

Square hysteresis loops have been known since the middle 1930's, when they were discovered in connection with magnetic annealing experiments. Figure 85 compares conventional and square-loop hysteresis diagrams. Criteria for measuring and comparing square loops are discussed by Legg (224).

The magnetic after-effect, which manifests itself as an elliptical loop on a B-H four-quadrant plot, may be superimposed upon the common hysteresis loop (225). This magnetic after-effect occurs as a result of the diffusion of interstitials.

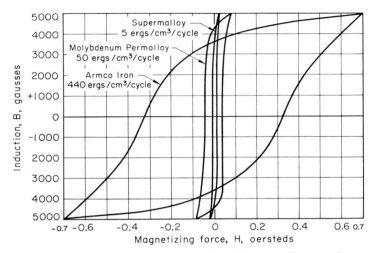

Fig. 81. Hysteresis loops for Supermalloy and Molybdenum Permalloy compared with Armco iron

Curie Temperature. The temperature at which a ferromagnetic material becomes paramagnetic is called its Curie temperature. Above this temperature, the regions of magnetic moments that are parallel to each other (domains) become disordered. This point was named in honor of Pierre Curie. That iron or magnetite lost its magnetism when heated was well known to William Gilbert in 1600.

Superparamagnetism. Particles that are single domain but whose direction of magnetization fluctuates with temperature were first discussed by Néel (226). These particles have no remanence and no coercive force, but they do have the temperature-dependent magnetization curve of a paramagnetic material with a very large moment. Bean (227) refers to this phenomenon as superparamagnetism.

Structure-Insensitive Properties

Structure-insensitive properties (actually physical constants of either soft or permanent magnet materials) are as follows:

Saturation magnetization, I_s
Curie temperature, θ
Saturation magnetostriction, $\Delta l/l$
Crystalline anisotropy, K_1, K_2

Once a composition is established, it has a unique set of the structure-insensitive characteristics. Table 50 gives the values of these properties for iron, nickel, and cobalt, and other ferromagnetic elements. There is also a set of structure-sensitive properties, which will be discussed presently.

Saturation Magnetization. The magnetic moment of a ferromagnetic material placed in a magnetic field of increasing strength will increase toward a limit, called the saturation, for that particular material. Specifically, as the field, H, is increased, the intensity of magnetization, I, and the intrinsic induction B-H of a ferromagnetic material approach a limiting value known as saturation. The induction, B, however, increases indefinitely. The quantity B-H at saturation is equal to $4\pi I_s$.

The saturation decreases with increasing temperature and reaches zero at the Curie point. Table 50 shows the saturation values for the ferromagnetic elements. With the addition of any element to iron, except cobalt, the saturation magnetization is decreased.

Curie Temperature. Table 50 also gives the Curie temperatures for the ferromagnetic elements. The loss in magnetism of iron

Table 50. Summary of Some Structure-Insensitive Properties of Ferromagnetic Elements

Property	Iron	Cobalt	Nickel	Gadolinium	Dysprosium
Saturation magnetic moment per gram, σ_s	218.0	161	54.39	253.3(a)	215(b)
Saturation magnetic moment per cu cm, M_s or I_s	1,714	1,422	484.1	....	...
Intrinsic induction, $4\pi M_s$ or $4\pi I_s$	21,580	17,900	6084	....	...
Curie temperature, θ, °C(c)	780	1,131	358	16	−181
Saturation magnetostriction, λ_{100}, $\times 10^{-6}$	20	−46	−51	....	...
Saturation magnetostriction, λ_{111}, $\times 10^{-6}$	−20	−24	−28	....	...
Crystalline anisotropy, K_1, ergs per cu cm, $\times 10^6$	0.460	−0.051	4.3 5.3	....	...
Crystalline anisotropy, K_2, ergs per cu cm, $\times 10^6$	.....	.....	1.2 1.0	....	...

(a) At 0 K. (b) For $H = 10,000$ oersteds at 88 K. (c) For terbium, $−40$ C.

with temperature is shown in Fig. 82; other ferromagnetic elements show similar curves. Cobalt has the highest Curie temperature, 1131 C (2068 F). The Curie temperature of iron is 780 C (1436 F).

Saturation Magnetostriction. Magnetostriction, while generally referring to the Joule effect (the increase or decrease in

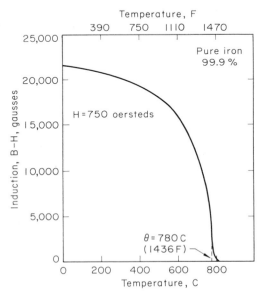

Fig. 82. Dependence of magnetization of iron on temperature

length of a ferromagnetic rod placed in a longitudinal magnetic field), actually refers to three other less well-known phenomena:

The Guillemin Effect: The tendency of an elastically bent rod to straighten when placed in a longitudinal magnetic field

The Wiedemann Effect: The twisting of a rod carrying an electric current when it is subjected to a magnetic field

The Villari Effect: The change in magnetic induction when a magnetized iron rod is put under longitudinal stress

For the Joule magnetostriction, the symbols λ or $\Delta l/l$ are ordinarily used. The changes are either plus or minus: The material increases in length in a magnetic field (as iron does) or decreases in length (as nickel does).

Magnetostriction also reaches saturation. Saturation magnetostriction, λ_s, is a property most easily determined on single crystals; the property is anisotropic, giving different values in different crystallographic directions. Saturation magnetostriction, exhibited in polycrystalline materials, is an average of values determined for magnetostriction in the three principal directions in single crystals.

Figure 83 shows the polycrystalline magnetostriction of polycrystalline iron, cobalt, and nickel. The values for polycrystal-

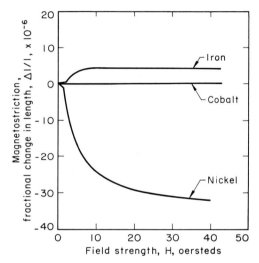

Fig. 83. Magnetostriction of polycrystalline iron, cobalt and nickel

line materials are quite variable, depending on composition, grain size, nature of surface (presence of oxide), orientation, and so on. Values for saturation magnetostriction for single crystals of these elements are constants and are listed in Table 50.

The origin of magnetostriction is not completely understood, but it is ascribed to spin-orbit coupling. Calculations give results of the right order of magnitude.

Crystalline Anisotropy. In single crystals, there are directions of easy and difficult magnetization. This characteristic of single crystals is known as crystalline anisotropy or magnetocrystalline anisotropy. In polycrystalline materials, the highly anisotropic single crystals are generally so oriented that the magnetic properties in different directions are quite similar; the material is then said to be isotropic. In certain polycrystalline materials, such as critically rolled and heat treated sheet, a pronounced preferred orientation can be developed, and the magnetic properties can be highly anisotropic, often approaching single-crystal properties.

Honda and Kaya (228) and Kaya (229, 230) have shown that ferromagnetic crystals, when magnetized along different crystallographic directions, give rise to different magnetization

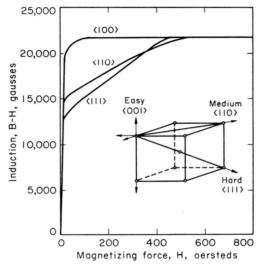

Fig. 84. Crystal structure of iron, and the types of magnetization curves obtained in principal crystallographic directions

curves. In body-centered cubic iron, the cube edges — the <100> family of directions * — are the directions of easy magnetization, while the body diagonals corresponding to the family of <111> directions are difficult to magnetize; the <110> family of directions are intermediate between the easy and difficult directions (Fig. 84). In face-centered cubic nickel, the easy directions of magnetization are the <111>, the difficult are the <100>, and the intermediate are the <110>. In hexagonal cobalt, the [0001] is the easy direction while the [10$\bar{1}$0] is the difficult one.

The anisotropic or magnetocrystalline energy of a crystal acts in such a manner that magnetization tends to be directed along

* The family of cubic directions represents the [100], [010], and [001].

certain crystallographic axes. As shown in Fig. 84, a lower energy is required to saturate the iron crystal in an easy direction (for example, [100]) but considerable energy is required to saturate the crystal in a difficult direction (for example, [111]). The excess energy required in the difficult direction over the easy direction is the anisotropic energy. The anisotropic energy is evaluated in terms of the anisotropic constants for specific crystal directions (Table 50). The origin of this anisotropy, like magnetostriction, is not completely understood, but it is also believed to result from the effect of spin-orbit interaction.

Structure-Sensitive Properties

In addition to certain unique structure-insensitive properties, ferromagnetic materials also possess a set of structure-sensitive characteristics; these properties, readily influenced by elastic and plastic strains, impurities, grain size, and order-disorder, are as follows:

Permeability. Mainly initial and maximum, but also at arbitrary values of B or H

Hysteresis loss, and the related quantities, coercive force, H_c, and remanence, B_r

For soft magnetic materials, it is essential to eliminate strain and to minimize impurities in order to achieve high permeability and low hysteresis loss. For permanent magnet materials, permeability is unimportant, but it is desirable to have high coercive force and high remanence, that is, a large hysteresis loop.

Because core loss is composed of hysteresis and eddy-current losses, the core loss is influenced not only by any factors that influence hysteresis loss but also by those that characteristically determine the eddy-current loss. Eddy currents are affected directly by strip thickness and indirectly by the electrical resistivity of the steel. Both the hysteresis and eddy-current components are affected by frequency and flux density. The thin laminations in transformers and rotating machinery also must be insulated from each other or the eddy currents will rise, defeating the objective of thin gages.

Permeability. The dimensionless ratio, μ,* is a very important

---

* It is dimensionless only in the centimeter-gram-second electromagnetic-unit (cgs emu) system. See Appendix, page 362.

index of the quality of the material. As a rule, the lower the coercive force, the higher the permeability. Commonly, the initial, μ_0, and maximum permeability, μ_{max}, are considered criteria for comparing quality; they are very sensitive to strains and impurities. These values are of little design importance.

Coercive force, H_c, is the value of the demagnetizing field, H, corresponding to $B = 0$ on the major hysteresis loop (Fig. 80). The coercive force is usually defined with reference to the saturation hysteresis cycle, although it is sometimes given for arbitrary inductions, for example, for $B = 10,000$ gausses.

The coercive force is one of the most sensitive properties of a ferromagnetic material. It characterizes well the difference

Table 51. Coercive Forces in Ferromagnetic Materials

Material	Composition	Coercive force, H_c, from saturation, oersteds
Supermalloy	79% Ni, 5% Mo	0.002
Oriented silicon steel	3.25% Si	0.1
Hot rolled silicon steel	4.5% Si	0.5
Mild steel (normalized) (a)	0.2% C	4.0
Carbon magnet steel	0.9% C, 1% Mn	50
Alnico V	24% Co, 14% Ni, 8% Al, 3% Cu	600
Alnico VIII	35% Co, 14.5% Ni, 7% Al, 5% Ti, 4.5% Cu	1450
Barium ferrite (oriented)	$BaO \cdot 6Fe_2O_3$	1900
Bismanol	MnBi	3650
Platinum-cobalt	PtCo (77% Pt)	4300

(a) Heating to above the transformation range followed by cooling to room temperature in still air.

between soft magnetic and permanent magnet materials. Coercive forces of the various magnetic materials extend over a range of one million oersteds (Table 51).

Remanence, B_r, has a great usefulness for both hard and soft magnetic materials. The value is related to the saturation induction. Where good crystalline orientation or domain orientation has been achieved, it is possible to obtain rectangular hysteresis loops in both soft and permanent magnet materials. In such cases, remanence is very close to the saturation induction. Figure 85 illustrates the difference between a conventional loop and a rectangular one for a 50 Fe – 50 Ni alloy.

Eddy Currents. When a core material is subjected to an alternating field, energy is lost in several different ways (231). One type of energy loss, already discussed, is the hysteresis loss. Another important loss is that due to eddy currents, sometimes called Foucault currents. Eddy currents are induced within the

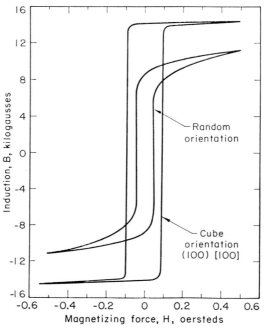

Fig. 85. *Direct-current hysteresis loops for a 50 Fe –*
50 Ni alloy, for random and preferred orientation

core material by the changing flux. The current induced flows in such a direction that its magnetic field opposes the change in magnetic flux that produces it. The secondary magnetic field associated with eddy currents opposes domain-wall motion, which is producing the flux change: The secondary field always opposes the primary field, partially canceling it.

The magnitude of the eddy currents depends on the frequency and the flux density imposed by the application, and by the physical characteristics of the material, the specific resistance, and thickness of the core material. The eddy currents are very undesirable, both because of the large amount of heat that they produce and because of the flux that they set up.

In calculation of eddy-current losses, uniform permeability is assumed. On this basis, the eddy-current losses are always smaller than the measured losses. Actually, the permeability is not uniform. The difference between the measured core loss and the sum of the hysteresis (measured) and eddy-current loss (calculated) is known as the anomalous loss. This anomalous loss is particularly large in oriented materials. However, in engineering discussions of core loss, it is not usually considered.

Classical eddy-current loss is calculated from the following relationship:

$$W_e = K \frac{\pi t^2 B^2 f^2}{\rho} \tag{62}$$

where t is thickness, B is maximum induction, f is frequency, ρ is electrical resistivity, and K is a constant.

Two factors can be used to reduce eddy currents: reducing thickness and increasing electrical resistivity. The ceramic ferrites ($MnO \cdot Fe_2O_3 + ZnO \cdot Fe_2O_3$) have resistivities about a million times greater than iron, and hence are useful for electronic cores operating in a frequency range of 1000 to one million cycles per second. Thin metallic tapes (1 mil or under) can also be used for these high frequencies.

Core Loss. The total sum of the losses in a core material exposed to an alternating flux is called the core loss. Core loss is considered to consist of two parts: the hysteresis and the eddy-current losses:

$$W = W_h + W_e, \text{ or}$$
$$W = (A_h) \cdot f + K \frac{\pi t^2 B^2 f^2}{\rho} \tag{63}$$

where A_h is the area of the hysteresis loop.

Core-loss measurements at $B = 10,000$ or $15,000$ gausses (but not both) and at 60 cps are used as a basis of grading iron and nonoriented silicon steel sheets; core loss at $B = 15,000$ gausses only is used for classifying grain-oriented silicon steels. These measurements are usually made in accordance with the ASTM specification A-34.

The variation of core loss with induction at 60 cps for nonoriented material of increasing silicon content is shown in Fig. 86. The variation of core loss with induction for three frequen-

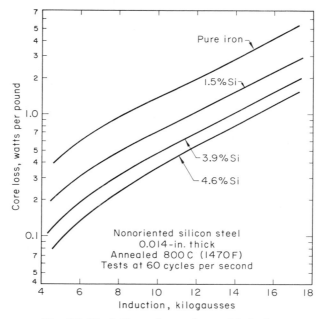

Fig. 86. Variation of core loss with induction for steels of different silicon content

cies is shown for grain-oriented 3.25% Si steel in Fig. 87.

Insulating Coatings. Because short circuiting of laminations increases core loss, by defeating the gains in eddy-current reduction realized from thin gages, care must be exercised in insulating laminations from each other. Where laminations are not annealed after punching, as with fully processed steel, sheets are coated with an organic varnish; this coating also helps to prolong die life. Where laminations are strain-relief annealed, as with semiprocessed steel, inorganic coatings (for example, phosphate) are applied after the heat treatment. For silicon steels that are annealed at temperatures over 1100 C (2012 F) in hydrogen, magnesia serves not only as a mechanical separator but also reacts to some degree with the metal surface to give a high-resistance coating.

Flatness is required in armature, stator, and transformer construction, because of the space factor requirement in construction and control of dimensions of the laminated structure. Any mechanical flattening (roller leveling, skin pass) after anneal-

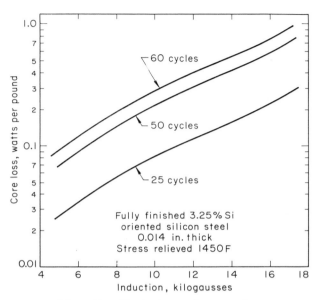

*Fig. 87. Variation of core loss
with induction at three frequencies*

ing destroys magnetic quality. Flatness is essential in material used for transformers, because flat material tends to give a lower noise level.

Factors that Influence Properties of Soft Magnetic Materials

The factors that influence the properties of soft magnetic materials are as follows:

Alloying elements	Order-disorder
Impurities	Preferred orientation
Solid solution	Magnetic annealing
Precipitates	Temperature
Grain size	Radiation
Strains	Pressure

Effect of Alloying Elements. In some ways, pure iron is a good ferromagnetic material. However, in ultrapure form, it is expensive and has a low electrical resistance, making it unsuitable for alternating-current circuits, where it is necessary to reduce eddy currents. Its low resistance can be offset by rolling it to very thin gages, but the magnetic properties deteriorate at thin gages and rolling to gages under 0.01 in. is expensive. One of the main objectives of adding alloying elements (such as silicon or aluminum) to iron is to increase the electrical resistivity.

Silicon and aluminum form substitutional solid solutions and do not distort the lattice to affect adversely the magnetic properties. Silicon and aluminum have another important effect: They eliminate the allotropic transformations in iron. As a consequence, alloys can be annealed at a high temperature without undergoing a phase change. In this way, desirable large grains, formed by grain growth or secondary recrystallization, can be preserved.

More than about 4.5% Si or 8% Al makes the iron alloy too brittle for most commercial use. About 3.25% Si is the limit to avoid excessive breakage in cold rolling.

One undesirable effect of alloying elements is that they lower the saturation induction of iron. Cobalt is the only element that increases the saturation value. As a matter of fact, the highest saturation known ($4\pi I_s = 24{,}200$) is obtained with 35% Co.

Because silicon and aluminum are excellent deoxidizers, oxide inclusions are formed when they are added to undeoxidized iron. Inclusions are harmful to magnetic properties. Oxides formed with aluminum appear to be more harmful than those formed with silicon.

Valuable magnetic alloys are obtained by combining iron with nickel or cobalt, or both, and by adding to these combinations other elements, such as copper, vanadium, molybdenum, or chromium.

Addition of nickel to iron forms an important series of alloys of high initial and maximum permeability. About 78% Ni gives an alloy of zero crystalline anisotropy and zero magnetostriction. When these properties are zero or relatively small in magnitude, alloys of high permeability and low hysteresis loss result (232).

Effect of Impurities. Because ferromagnetic properties depend on the perfection of the crystal lattice, it is not surprising that impurities in solid solution and as coherent and incoherent precipitates should influence magnetic properties. Interstitial impurities, such as carbon, nitrogen, and boron, are more harmful than the substitutional impurities, such as sulfur and oxygen; hydrogen is also an interstitial element, but no effects on magnetic quality have been traced to it, probably because it is difficult to retain hydrogen in thin-gage material.

Carbon and nitrogen are the most harmful interstitial elements in soft magnetic materials. Usually, in commercial materials, nitrogen is about 0.005% after open hearth melting, so that it poses no serious problems; also some nitrogen can be eliminated by annealing at elevated temperatures in hydrogen. Carbon is a very harmful element that it is difficult to keep out of iron. Maximum for meltdown carbon in oriented silicon steels is about 0.03%. To obtain good quality steel, the carbon must be re-

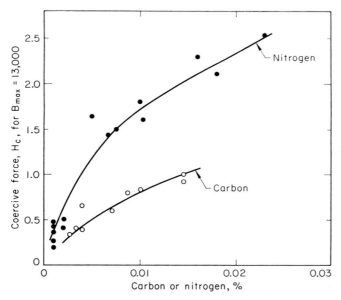

Fig. 88. *Effect of carbon and nitrogen
on the coercive force of 3% Si iron*

duced by proper processing to below 0.005%. Figure 88 shows the greater harmful effect of nitrogen over carbon in a 3% Si steel (208). Reference also should be made to the classic work of Yensen and Ziegler (234), who showed quantitatively the harmful effect of carbon and oxygen in iron-silicon alloys.

The solubility of the interstitials in iron is low at room temperature, and it is reduced further by silicon. Any supersaturation results in slow precipitation of particles in the grains, causing harmful effects. This precipitation and the simultaneous effect on chemical and physical properties is referred to as aging.

In iron and iron-silicon alloys, the carbon should be kept below 0.005% in order to obtain low hysteresis loss and high maximum permeability with no aging, which would have an undesirable effect on magnetic properties.

The solubility of carbon in alpha iron at 700 C (1290 F) is 0.02%, but, in an alloy containing 3% Si, the solubility is reduced to 0.005% at the same temperature (235).

Effect of Grain Size. Optimum magnetic properties are obtained with single crystals. The lattice disregistry between crystals in a polycrystalline material is a source of energy loss and is

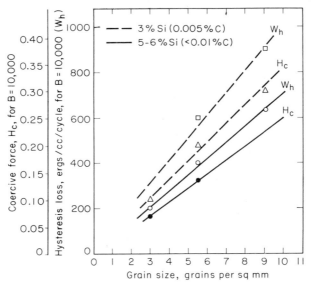

Fig. 89. Effect of grain size on the hysteresis loss and coercive force of iron-silicon alloys

undesirable. Hence, larger grains favor lower energy losses and greater permeability. Figure 89 shows the effect of grain size on the coercive force and hysteresis loss for $B_m = 10,000$ gausses. Grain size effect varies with carbon and silicon (234).

Elastic and plastic strains have a profound influence on magnetic properties. For materials with a positive magnetostriction (for example, iron), a tensile strain improves the permeability (increases the slope of the *B-H* curve) up to a certain stress level, and then harms it (Fig. 90). In materials with a nega-

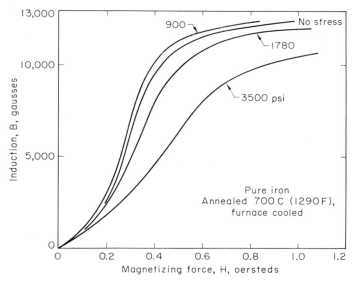

Fig. 90. Effect of elastic strain on the magnetization of iron

tive magnetostriction, the permeability is decreased by a tensile stress. The effect of elastic strain in bending on core loss is shown in Table 52 (236).

Plastic strains are harmful to all soft magnetic materials, decreasing the permeability, increasing the hysteresis, and increasing the core loss (237). In some instances, however, the crystal properties (anisotropy energy and magnetostriction constants) are also influenced. The nature of the crystal determines

**Table 52. Effect of Elastic Bending on Magnetic Properties
of Oriented 3.25% Si Iron(a)**

Radius, in.	Maximum permeability	Coercive force, oersteds	Residual induction(b), kilogausses	Total loss(c), w per lb
Flat	104,000	0.066	13.9	0.55
130	85,000	0.077	13.0	0.63
68	62,000	0.096	11.1	0.71
44	47,000	0.108	9.6	0.76
15	24,000	0.123	5.8	. . .
8	18,000	0.127	5.1	. . .

(a) D-C magnetic data for 8 and 15-in. radii refer to single strips; all other data to 20-strip Epstein samples. (b) From 15 kilogausses. (c) At 15 kilogausses and 60 cps.

which of its properties are affected by plastic deformation (238).

Order-Disorder. Ordering in metals occurs when species of atoms diffuse more or less completely to preferential lattice sites, leaving atoms of other kinds in the remaining positions. The segregation of atoms to certain positions results in an ordered solid solution or superlattice; little or no deformation of the lattice accompanies this ordering. Arrangements of atoms at elevated temperatures are random, and, at a relatively low but well-defined temperature, atomic segregation occurs. Compositions

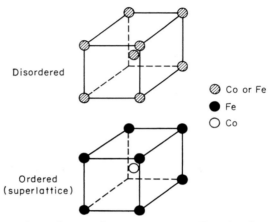

Fig. 91. Superlattice formation in 50 Fe − 50 Co alloy

forming superlattices are AB or AB_3, or compositions close to these formulas. Figure 91 shows a disordered and ordered lattice in a 50 Fe − 50 Co alloy.

The effect of order on ferromagnetic properties is discussed by Muto and Takagi (239).

The Heusler alloys (Cu_2MnAl, Cu_2MnSn, Cu_2MnIn, and Cu_2MnGa) are ferromagnetic when in the ordered condition. Ni_3Mn is also ferromagnetic in the ordered state. Both systems are paramagnetic when disordered. A slight increase in saturation magnetization occurs in FeCo and $FeNi_3$ (Permalloy) when ordering occurs. In the ordered condition, $FeNi_3$ has marked crystalline anisotropy; in the disordered state the anisotropy is zero (240). High initial and maximum permeability occur in this system in the disordered state. Ordering increases the magnetostriction in $FeNi_3$ (Permalloy), FeCo, and FeAl alloys (241).

Preferred Orientation. Anisotropy of magnetic properties also exists in polycrystalline materials as a consequence of the magnetic anisotropy of the grains. A high degree of anisotropy or orientation can be developed by a proper combination of critical cold working and annealing operations. Oriented silicon steel and iron-nickel alloys are common alloys of commerce. The sharp

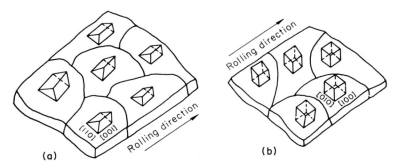

Fig. 92. (a) Schematic representation of the cube-on-edge orientation that can be described crystallographically as the (110)[001]. This is the common orientation found in oriented 3.25% Si steel. (b) Schematic representation of the cube orientation that is described crystallographically as the (100)[100]. This orientation is commonly obtained in 50 Fe – 50 Ni alloys, and under special conditions in 3.25% Si steel.

texture is developed through the secondary recrystallization process.* Through this process, the grain size becomes much larger than the thickness of the sheet. The growth of grains is determined by the relative energy of the surfaces of the grains in different orientations with respect to the plane of the sheet. Temperature, nature of the restraining impurities (if any), and the purity and dryness of the atmosphere become important in determining these energies.

In iron-silicon (3.25% Si) alloys, the common preferred orientation is the so-called cube-on-edge texture, which is described

---

* A cold worked metal will recrystallize on heating. This phenomenon is called primary recrystallization. The recrystallized structure on further heating, or heating at higher temperatures, then changes by enlargement of the grains either through ordinary grain growth (growth of more or less equiaxed grains at the expense of neighboring grains) or exaggerated grain growth (growth of exceedingly large grains of a unique orientation at the expense of less favorably oriented grains), also called secondary recrystallization.

crystallographically as the (110)[001]. This description indicates that the (110) planes of the crystals are in the rolling plane and that the [001] direction is in the rolling direction.

In iron-nickel (50% Ni) alloys, it is possible to develop the cube texture or the (100)[100]. In other words, the (100) plane becomes parallel to the rolling plane and the [100] direction is in the rolling (as well as in the transverse) direction. This cube orientation has recently been developed in 3.25% Si steel (242, 243). The two orientations are depicted graphically in Fig. 92. One of the advantages of oriented silicon steel is evident from Fig. 93; lower core losses are obtainable with orientation.

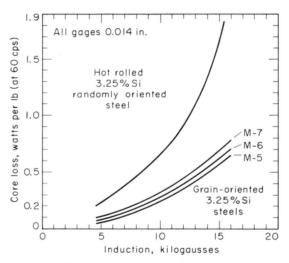

Fig. 93. Comparison of core loss of randomly oriented and grain-oriented 3.25% Si steel

The cube texture in iron-nickel alloys gives a rectangular hysteresis loop. The difference in hysteresis loops between an oriented and unoriented loop is shown in Fig. 85.

Magnetic Annealing. When heat treated and cooled in a magnetic field, some magnetic materials are found on testing to have a direction of easy magnetization parallel to the direction of the magnetic field. In soft magnetic materials, such annealing (when effective) fixes the domains to the crystal lattice, so that when the field is removed, the domains remain in the direction of magnetization determined by the anneal. In permanent magnet materials, such as Alnico V, the magnetic field improves the magnetic quality by causing the preferential nucleation of the precipitating particles.

In soft magnetic materials with a zero or low magnetostriction and a zero or low anisotropy, the usual mechanisms for orienting domains are absent or weak. In such a situation, it is possible to orient the domains by cooling the material through the Curie temperature in the presence of a field, or by holding it in the field below the Curie temperature. The domains thereby tend to become fixed in the direction of the heat treating field. An alloy with 65% Ni cooled from 600 to 400 C (1100 to 752 F) in a magnetic field of 10 oersteds will have its maximum permeability increased by a factor of 50 (244).

Iron-silicon alloys containing 4 to 6.5% Si show increases in permeability when given a magnetic annealing cycle: The maximum permeability of a 6.5% Si iron single crystal magnetized in the [100] direction increased from 50,000 to 3,800,000 (245); that of a 5% Si polycrystalline iron increased from 17,000 to 70,-000 (246).

There is no satisfactory explanation for all effects produced by magnetic annealing. In some instances, the field causes a change in the shape anisotropy of many-atom regions, and in others it influences the orientation of nucleating particles. In iron-nickel alloys, the soft ferrites, and thin films, the crystal orientation is not affected by the magnetic field, nor is the long-range or short-range order. It is feasible, believes Bozorth (244), to consider an induced anisotropy of crystallographically oriented imperfections (dislocations and vacancies) caused by the magnetic field.

Influence of Temperature on Ferromagnetic Phenomena. Temperatures up to 540 C (1000 F) will not usually harm soft magnetic materials, if they are in a neutral atmosphere. Thermal cycling may harm Supermendur. In most soft ferromagnetic materials, the permeabilities at high induction decrease with increasing temperature, but the permeabilities at low induction will increase.

The magnetic induction and hysteresis loss of iron decrease with increasing temperature until the critical temperature is reached (247); there is a remarkable increase in permeability just before the Curie temperature is reached. Both the anisotropy and magnetostriction decrease as temperature increases and reach zero before the Curie temperature is reached.

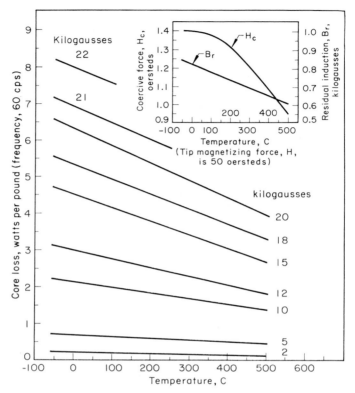

*Fig. 94. Variation of magnetic properties of 35%
Co iron with temperature (after Clark and Fritz)*

The direct and alternating-current (60 cps) properties of
many materials in the range of 24 to 800 C (75 to 1470 F) were
investigated by Pasnak and Lundstan (248). In general, high
temperature decreased the maximum induction and the residual
induction. The coercive force decreased, except for Supermendur and 11.7% Alfenol. The maximum and initial permeabilities
increased with temperature as the Curie temperature was approached, and then decreased. Grain-oriented silicon steels were
more affected by thermal cycling than the nonoriented grades.
The iron-silicon and iron-cobalt alloys oxidized very rapidly. The
properties of Supermendur, Perminvar, and iron-aluminum alloys were critically dependent on cooling rates.

The core loss of AISI M-36 (1.0 to 1.8% Si), M-22 (2.5 to 3.5%

Si), and M-19 (2.5 to 3.5% Si) steels at 10 kilogausses and 60 cps decreases as the temperature is raised from -80 to $+95$ C (-110 to 200 F) (249). The decrease in loss with increasing temperature can probably be explained by the increase in resistivity and consequent decrease in eddy-current loss. Grain-oriented silicon steel deteriorates if heated above 500 C (930 F), whereas nonoriented silicon steel does not.

The core loss of six iron-nickel materials has been investigated as a function of temperature at -60 to 250 C (-76 to 482 F) by Clark and Fritz (250). In 50% Ni alloys, with inductions up to 15 kilogausses, the core loss decreases linearly as temperature increases; at 15 kilogausses, the core loss increases as temperature increases.

Irons containing 27 and 35% Co experience relatively small changes in magnetic properties in the -60 to $+500$ C (-76 to 930 F) range. Supermendur (50% Co, 2% V) in the range of 400 to 500 C (750 to 930 F) experiences a lowering of permeability, and the measurement of room-temperature properties after exposure to 500 C reveals a decrease in permeability (for values under $H = 10$ oersteds) of as much as 200% (251). Figure 94 shows the variation of core loss, coercive force, and remanence as a function of temperature; these properties decrease with increasing temperature.

Irradiation Effects in Soft Magnetic Materials. In metals, electromagnetic radiation (x-ray and gamma-ray) is without effect on magnetic quality, but neutrons may have sufficient energy to produce harmful atomic displacements. Core materials with a coercive force greater than 0.5 oersted are generally unaffected by neutrons. Silicon steels, 2V Permendur, 16% Al iron, and soft (ceramic) ferrites are insensitive to a neutron flux of 2.4×10^{18} neutrons per sq cm. However, high-permeability materials, such as 4-79 Permalloy and 50% Ni alloys, when subjected to neutron irradiation, suffer significant damage; remanence is decreased, coercive force is increased, and permeability is reduced.

Hydrostatic Pressure Effects. For pressures up to 20,000 psi, little change is found in direct-current properties of metallic materials, or square loop or low-permeability ferrites, although the high-permeability ferrites do show reduced permeability (252). The nickel-zinc ferrite decreased 60% in permeability at 20,000 psi.

Lamination Factor (Space Factor). The measure of the compactness of a core or stock is known as the lamination factor. A high lamination or space factor is always desired. The lamination factor is the ratio of the volume of the steel (calculated from its weight and density) to the total volume of the compressed pack (measured from its dimensions at some arbitrary

Table 53. Influence of Thickness on the Lamination Factor

Thickness, in.	Lamination factor, % Oriented (type C core)(a)	Nonoriented (punchings)
0.013	95	90
0.005	90	80
0.002	85	70

(a) Rectangular cores are wound and the cores are then cut on the long dimension to give two C-sections. These are ground, etched, and banded together after the coils have been positioned.

pressure). Lamination factor varies with strip thickness, and oriented material has a higher factor, as a wound core, than nonoriented, as a stacked core (Table 53).

Punchability is a property that is difficult to define, because so many factors affect it. The mechanical properties of the magnetic material, its hardness, the surface coating (if any), and the die clearances and sharpness influence punchability. The harder alloys are preferred for punching. If proper die clearance is maintained and sharp dies are used, good punchability is said to result when the strip undergoes 50% plastic flow and 50% break, through the thickness of the lamination. Surface coatings can minimize die wear. Oxides and abrasive coatings, of course, are objectionable.

Gage. Uniformity of gage on flat-rolled materials is becoming increasingly important. Edge-to-edge variation must be small; crowns must be minimized. Not quite so important is variation from end to end of a coil, although users object to wide variations. Variable gages in laminations lead to nonuniform stack heights or mismatching in the case of E and I punchings.

Thin Films (253)

Thin films are less than 1000 A thick, although films up to 10 times thicker have been studied. Films thinner than 3000 A are single-domain structures. In ultrathin films, ferromagnetism goes to zero at 20 A for nickel and between 8 and 12 A for Permalloy (80% Ni).

Intense interest in these films exists because their magnetization can be made to reverse extremely rapidly. This feature makes thin films attractive for digital computers. In addition, thin films of magnetic materials provide unique opportunity to study some of the basic problems of magnetism. Present research is directed toward improvement of memories by several orders

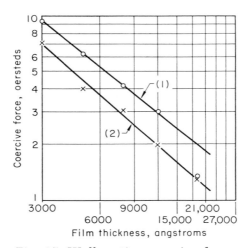

Fig. 95. Wall motion coercive force, H_c, versus film thickness for two Permalloy films of different roughness. Curve No. 1 was for a roughness corresponding to that of 600-grit polishing paper, and curve No. 2 for a roughness corresponding to Linde B compound on a wet felt wheel.

of magnitude through the use of films rather than ferrite cores. The speed of such memories is determined by the speed at which the magnetization can be reversed between two stable states by clockwise or counterclockwise magnetization.

Thin films (for example, Permalloy) use a means of magnetization reversal requiring a greater field, H, than is necessary for domain-boundary displacement. The reversal mechanism, known as spin rotation, involves changing the orbital momentum of individual electrons. These reversals can take place in one hundredth or thousandth of the time required for domain movement. Speed of magnetization reversal in films is 3 to 10 millimicrosec. This compares with 1 microsec in ferrite cores.

The films can be prepared by vapor deposition, electroplating, or chemical deposition onto various substances, of which glass is a common one. Thin electrodeposited and evaporated films generally have low permeability and high coercive force. The coercive force of films is proportional to film thickness raised to a power n, where n varies from -1.4 to a value close to zero (Fig. 95) (254). Films can be produced with quasirectangular hysteresis loops by depositing the material in the presence of a magnetic field. Permalloy films from 85% Ni, remainder iron to 55% Ni, remainder iron are preferred, because the low or zero magnetostriction of this material results in strain-free films. Films about 2000 A thick are of most interest.

The most common measurement made on films is the determination of the hysteresis loop. Current practice is to view the loop on the screen of a cathode-ray oscilloscope at a frequency of 60 cps. Values of coercive force, H_c, saturation flux density, B_s, and remanent flux density, B_r, are observed. For a magnetic film to be used as a computer element, the squareness ratio, B_r/B_s, should approach one. Usually, films have much squarer loops than bulk material.

Ultimate objectives for computers of the future are higher operating speeds, greater capacity, smaller size, improved reliability, and lower cost per item of information.

Permanent Magnets

The method of evaluating permanent magnets is based on the hysteresis loop of the material; more correctly, it is based on the demagnetization portion of the loop in the second quadrant (Fig. 96, a). The important values obtained from the curve are B_r, the residual induction, and H_c, the coercive force; both should be as large as possible for good magnets. The H_c is highly sensitive to strain, particularly of the coherency type. Permanent magnets are almost always operated with an air gap.

Any permanent magnet that is supplying flux to an air gap is working somewhere on the demagnetization curve. It is natural to inquire as to whether there is some particular operating point on the curve that is more advantageous in a design than some

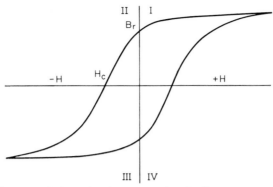

(a) Hysteresis loop. Quadrants are given by Roman numerals.

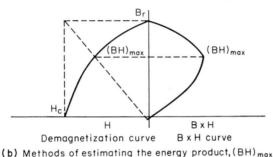

Demagnetization curve   B x H curve

(b) Methods of estimating the energy product, $(BH)_{max}$

Fig. 96. Graphic methods used in estimating the quality of permanent magnets

other point. There is; the reason is evident from the following:

$$V_m = \frac{FfB_g^2 V_g}{B_m H_m} \tag{64}$$

where V_m and V_g are the volumes of the magnet and gap, B_m and B_g are the flux densities in the magnet and gap, H_m is the magnetizing force, and F and f are leakage coefficients to correct for leakage flux.

The equation indicates that the volume of magnetic material used to supply the flux density, B_g, to the gap is inversely proportional to the product of B and H of the magnet at an operating point. This volume of magnet will be a minimum when the product of B and H is a maximum. For this reason, the so-called energy-product curve is important in design work.

Another way of looking at the energy product is to consider the following equation:

$$\frac{B_m H_m}{8\pi} = E \text{ ergs per cu cm} \tag{65}$$

The external energy is zero at both B_r and H_c, but reaches a peak value at a point known as the maximum energy product. This point represents the maximum energy that can be maintained by a unit volume of magnetic material; the aim is always to maximize the quantity $B_m H_m/8\pi$.

The maximum energy product $(BH)_{\max}$ is an important criterion for comparing the magnetic quality of permanent magnets.

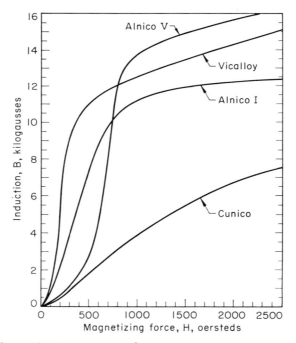

Fig. 97. Magnetization curves of some permanent magnet materials

The $(BH)_{\max}$ is, of course, related to the product of B_r and H_c. Hence, in alloy development, it is necessary to follow, in addition to $(BH)_{\max}$, the influence of alloy content and heat treatment on both B_r and H_c.

Referring to the demagnetization curve in the second quadrant only in Fig. 96(b), one can see how the energy product is derived from the coordinates. The B and H values of the demagnetization curve are plotted against the corresponding values of $B;$ this plot gives the maximum energy product.

In discussions of permanent magnet properties, it is unusual to refer to a magnetic normal magnetization curve, its permeability, or its hysteresis loss, although these quantities are attributes of any ferromagnetic material, hard or soft. Note in Fig. 97 the large values of magnetizing force that are necessary to develop high flux densities.

Factors Influencing the Properties of Permanent Magnet Materials

The following factors, singly or in combination, affect the quality of a permanent magnet material:

Precipitation (coherency hardening); second phases
Plastic deformation (where ductility exists)
Combination of precipitation and deformation
Ordering
Particle size (as in products made by powder metallurgy techniques)
Grain structure and crystal orientation
Annealing in a magnetic field
Degradation influences
    Extraneous fields
    Elevated temperature
    Contact with magnetic material
    Temperature cycling
    Vibration or impact
Temperature
Radiation

Strains (Coherency Hardening). The most important strain mechanism in permanent magnets is precipitation or coherency hardening (255). In this form of hardening, the atoms segregate from a solid solution into one or two phases, but the lattices are not separated from the matrix; they have not yet lost their registry. When incoherency sets in, the phases lose registry with the matrix and become separate entities. Geisler (256) discusses coherent and incoherent precipitation.

This type of precipitation occurs in the martensitic steels (the earliest permanent magnets), the popular Alnico family, Silmanal (Heusler alloy), Cunife, Cunico, and Vicalloy.

Coercive force is little affected by dispersion hardening (dispersion of an incoherent phase in a matrix structure). However, coherency strains in a ferromagnetic material are the source of high coercivity. If the precipitate instead of the matrix is ferromagnetic, coherency strains in the precipitate are responsible for the coercive force. If both the matrix and precipitate are ferro-

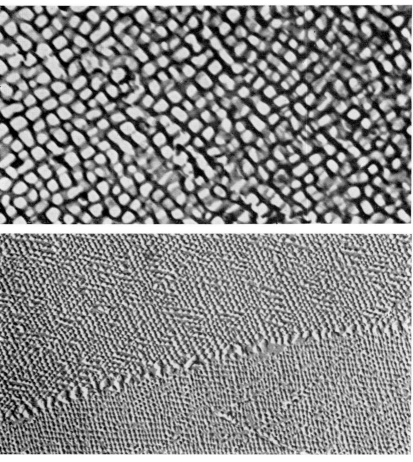

Fig. 98. Electron micrographs of Alnico V (upper) and Ticonal 1500 (lower). Sections perpendicular to direction of magnetic field during heat treatment. Alnico V specimen prepared by thin-foil technique; 85,000×. Ticonal 1500, shadowed surface replica; 25,000×. (Courtesy, J. Capenos, Crucible Steel Co. of America)

magnetic, the coherency strains of both affect the coercive force.

By way of illustration, consider the popular Alnico permanent magnet alloys. These compositions are, as is well known, susceptible to heat treatment. At high temperatures, they consist of a single body-centered cubic phase that decomposes by precipitation at low temperatures into two body-centered cubic phases of differing lattice parameters; one phase is rich in iron and the other is rich in nickel and aluminum. Figure 98 shows the nature of the precipitates in a properly heat treated Alnico V alloy.

The magnetic heat treatment consists of three basic operations: a solution treatment, conditioning, and an aging treatment. A single phase is produced by solution treatment at an elevated temperature. The Alnicos are extremely sensitive to the cooling rate, and optimum magnetic properties are obtained only after carefully controlled cooling. After the solution treatment, the material is conditioned by controlled cooling from the solution temperature (with or without a magnetic field). Then, the magnets are aged to obtain controlled reprecipitation to realize high coercive forces. Elements such as copper and cobalt make the decomposition reaction more sluggish and decrease the critical cooling rate required to obtain good magnetic quality.

Bradley (257, 258) has explained the high coercivity of the alloys on the basis of atoms segregating into the two phases without the two lattices separating; that is, the new phases retain the lattice constant of the parent phase. This condition of coherency gives high strain and hence high coercivity. It is currently assumed that each precipitate accommodates a single domain.

Occurrence of a nonmagnetic phase, such as the gamma phase in Alnico, is undesirable, because it affects adversely the magnetic properties.

Strains (Plastic). The coercive force is little influenced by plastic strain in comparison to the gains to be realized by coherency hardening. Iron-nickel-copper alloys (Cunife) (259) and iron-cobalt-vanadium alloys (Vicalloy) (260) can be formed by rolling or drawing into fine wire before heat treating. These alloys, even though hard magnetically, are relatively soft mechanically. In some instances, good properties have been developed by plastic deformation without resorting to aging treatments. For instance, in an alloy containing 45% Fe, 15% Ni, and 40% Cu, a coercive force of 240 oersteds and a remanence of 4400 gausses can be obtained in cold drawn wire.

Ordering. The phenomenon of ordering has been discussed in connection with soft magnetic alloys. Ordering appears to play an important role in Vicalloy, 77 Pt – 23 Co, and 78 Pt – 22 Fe. When iron-platinum or cobalt-platinum alloys become ordered during cooling, they transform from the face-centered cubic to the face-centered tetragonal ($c/a = 0.968$) structure. A cobalt-platinum alloy develops one of the highest coercive forces known, about 4300 oersteds.

Combined Coherency, Ordering, and Plastic Straining. The ductile iron-nickel-copper, iron-cobalt-vanadium, and cobalt-nickel-copper alloys obtain their high coercive force from aging (giving rise to coherency hardening) and cold work (rolling, swaging, and wiredrawing).

With an alloy of 20% Fe, 20% Ni, and 60% Cu (Cunife), a coercive force of 400 oersteds and a remanence of 4800 gausses can be obtained by quenching the alloy from 1000 C (1830 F), aging at 650 C (1200 F), and cold rolling. By additional aging at 650 C after rolling, a coercive force of 440 oersteds and a remanence of 5000 gausses can be realized (259). Cunico is similar to Cunife, except that it contains cobalt instead of iron.

Whether the hardening in the iron-nickel-copper or cobalt-nickel-copper alloys is the result of strain alone or strain and aging, the good magnetic properties are obtained by coherency hardening.

Vicalloy is ordinarily hot worked, cold worked, and aged at 600 C (1110 F). After this processing, typical properties are a coercive force of 525 oersteds, and a remanence of 10,000 gausses. As mentioned, Vicalloy hardens largely by ordering.

Particle Size (Single-Domain Particle Magnets). Fine particles have high coercive forces, because there is no domain boundary formation, and the usual mechanism of magnetization by wall displacement cannot occur. Magnetization can occur only by domain rotation; rotation is a process that takes place only in strong magnetic fields.

Although work as early as 1934 (261) showed that high coercivity was associated with fine particles, little work on fine powders was carried out until Guilland (262) reported that the coercive force of manganese-bismuth alloys increased to 600 oersteds as the particle size became extremely fine (3×10^{-4} cm in diameter). Kittel (263) showed by energy considerations that materials with single domains should have high coercive forces.

Later, both Néel (264) and Stoner and Wohlfarth (265) showed theoretically that fine particles have high coercive force, with either high crystal anisotropy or shape anisotropy (preferably rod or cigar-shaped particles). Table 54 gives properties of some fine-particle magnets.

The Alnicos are considered to be made up of fine particles (264, 265) having the dimensions of about 10^{-6} cm (Fig. 98).

Table 54. Fine-Particle Permanent Magnets

Material	Coercive force, H_c, oersteds	Remanence, B_r, gausses	Energy product, $(BH)_{max} \times 10^6$, gauss-oersteds
Fine iron (spherical)	330	7000	1.0
Bismanol (MnBi)	3650	4800	5.3
Barium ferrite (isotropic)	1500	2000	0.8
Barium ferrite (anisotropic)	1930	4000	3.7
ESD iron (50%) (a)	715	8800	3.3
ESD iron (30%) (a)	1105	5700	2.9
ESD iron-cobalt (about 50%) (a)	1025	9050	5.04

(a) Packing percentage; remainder is bonding material. ESD stands for "elongated single domain."

These particles are too small to permit the existence of domain boundaries, and therefore the processes of magnetization take place by the more difficult process of rotation (263).

Crystal Orientation. Some grades of Alnico have equiaxed grains and can be isotropic or anisotropic depending on whether they are heat treated in a magnetic field. Further improvement in energy products can be obtained by growing large columnar grains of proper orientation by chilling the molten metal in sand or shell molds (266). Structures with large columnar grains, when magnetized along the long axis of the aligned crystals, give improved magnetic properties. These are the so-called DG (directional grain) magnets. Many DG magnets are only partially columnar, and, if a completely columnar crystal is realized (100% DG), the properties are further improved.

For instance, Alnico V has a coercive force of 650 oersteds, a remanence of 12,700 gausses, and an energy product of 5.5 million gauss-oersteds, while Alnico V (DG) has a coercive force of 685 oersteds, a remanence of 13,300 gausses, and an energy product of about 6.5 million gauss-oersteds. Magnets of 100% DG will have an energy product of about 7.5 million gauss-oersteds.

Single crystals of Alnico V will have energy products of the order of 10 million gauss-oersteds.

Annealing in a Magnetic Field. Oliver and Shedden (267) showed that cooling an Alnico-type magnet from a high temperature in a strong magnetic field prior to final aging improved both the coercive force and remanence, and more than doubled the energy product.

During heat treatment, most Alnico grades are influenced by a magnetic field. After the material has been given a solution treatment, it is cooled at a controlled rate in a magnetic field and is then aged. With this treatment, the energy product is increased in the direction of magnetization but is decreased in a direction transverse to it.

The role of the magnetic field is not completely understood, although observations on the mechanism of precipitation have been made. Under normal conditions of precipitation, the plate-like phases form equally favorably on all crystallographic planes that constitute the family. Application of a magnetic field to Alnico V causes the preferential nucleation of particles (268) on one or two of the three possible planes {100}. Not all Alnico compositions respond to magnetic heat treatment, for example, Alnico XII (8% Ti).

Degradation Influences. The field in the air gap of a permanent magnet should be as constant as is possible. Extraneous magnetic fields, elevated temperatures, contact with iron or other magnetic material, aging due to structural changes, and mechanical vibration will influence the magnetization of a permanent magnet:

> *Extraneous magnetic fields* (alternating or direct current), if of sufficient magnitude, will reduce the induction in a magnet. Magnets of large dimensional ratios (length to diameter) show some superiority in stability over magnets of a small ratio. After a field is applied to a magnet and is then removed, the flux of a magnet is stabilized at a lower value against any disturbing fields not exceeding the initially applied field. A "keeper" (iron or low-carbon steel) in the air gap of a magnet when it is not in use protects the magnet against effects from extraneous fields.
>
> *Temperature.* If a magnet is heated with no applied field, the induction will generally decrease as the temperature rises; it will increase as the temperature falls to room temperature, but not all of the induction will return. This recovery is largely dependent on the type of material. Chromium magnet steels (3.5% Cr) lose

10% of their remanent induction by heating to 200 C (390 F) in ½ hr; Alnico V magnets, under equivalent conditions, remain essentially unchanged up to 500 C (930 F).

Physical Contact. Induction in a magnet can be changed when it comes in momentary contact with soft iron or other magnetic material. Changes in direction and amount of induction in the magnet can result. Sheathing with nonmagnetic material can protect magnets from these influences.

Temperature Cycling and Aging. Temperature cycling in some of the older steels (chromium or tungsten) gave rise to both irreversible and reversible changes in magnetization. The irreversible changes are caused by structural changes in the steels. Such changes are serious in chromium steels, and, for this reason, these steels have to be aged 24 hr at 100 C (212 F) in order to prevent subsequent changes in magnetization at room temperature. Where hardening is due to carbon, the alloys will age. In the newer materials (Alnicos), aging at room temperature is unimportant.

Vibration or repeated impact can cause loss of remanent magnetization. This effect is important in martensitic magnets hardened by carbon; it is small, or absent, in Alnicos, depending on grade.

Temperature. Some applications of permanent magnets require temperatures above and below ambient. The various high-temperature effects on the remanent induction can be classified as reversible, irreversible, and material (269). For small temperature rises, the remanent induction, B_r, decreases but returns reversibly to the original value. For wider temperature ranges, an irreversible loss of remanence is likely to occur on return to room temperature, in addition to the reversible change; this loss is recoverable by remagnetization. At higher temperatures, material damage can set in, and the entire hysteresis loop is influenced. Here, obviously, the material must be completely re-heat treated.

Irreversible losses are greater with smaller length-to-diameter ratios (L/D) of the magnets. Reversible losses can also depend on L/D ratios.

Both reversible and irreversible changes occur in the hard (barium) ferrites at low temperatures. When temperature is reduced, the remanence increases, whereas the coercive force decreases. When the magnet is returned to room temperature, the coercive force is regained, but the remanence may or may not be regained.

Radiation. All important permanent magnet materials can withstand 10^{17} neutrons per sq cm at 90 C (195 F). The radiation damage threshold (10% change in magnetic properties) lies above 10^{17}. The Alnicos, chromium (3½% Cr) steel, and Cunico irradiated with 10^{20} neutrons per sq cm at 55 C (130 F) show only slight (less than 10%) changes in open-circuit induction, whereas barium ferrite (oriented and nonoriented), cobalt (36% Co) steel, and Silmanal indicate severe damage (37 to 63%); the change in Cunife is intermediate (+13%) (270). In an environment of 5×10^{20} neutrons per sq cm and 325 C (615 F), the Alnicos change less than 5%, Cunico about 10%, and all others decrease from 23 to 97% in open-circuit induction.

Miscellaneous Magnetic Matters

In this section, such items as demagnetization of magnetized materials, the pull of a magnet, shielding, and the relation of magnetization to other physical properties will be discussed.

Demagnetizing Magnetized Materials. The correct procedure in demagnetizing a magnetized material (including, for example, a watch) involves primarily a slow and steady decrease in an applied field. One method involves insertion of the material into a coil, application of an alternating-current voltage and reduction of the voltage to zero by means of an autotransformer or variable inductance. In another method, the full alternating-current voltage is applied to a coil with the magnet to be demagnetized at its center, and the magnet is withdrawn along a line perpendicular to the plane of the coil (distance should be about four times the coil diameter). Heating a magnetized material above its Curie temperature will also demagnetize it.

Pull of a Magnet. The air gap force, F, in dynes of any electromagnet or permanent magnet with flat, parallel, attracting surfaces on an external body is given by the following equation:

$$F = \frac{B^2 A}{8\pi} \text{ dynes} \qquad (66)$$

where B is the flux density in gausses and A is the area in square centimeters perpendicular to the flux.

By application of the above equation to magnet design, a permanent magnet could be made that could lift 3500 and 5000 times its own weight (270). The ratio of the lifting power to the weight of a magnet forms a better measure of the quality of a permanent magnet than the lifting power alone.

Shielding. Magnetic lines of force are strongly refracted when they pass into a second medium of high permeability: Lines of force will travel through the highly permeable material with greater ease than in air or some other medium. As shown in Fig. 99, the lines of flux will be prevented from entering the inside

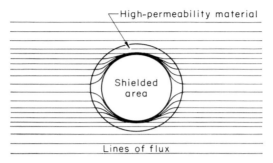

Fig. 99. How a high-permeability cylinder will shield the inside area from a magnetic field. In the actual situation, the external field, above and below the cylinder, is also distorted toward the shielding material.

of the cylinder; the inside is then said to be shielded from the flux. An assembly of several concentric shells of high permeability is more effective than a single layer.

Shielding is used to protect instruments from stray or external magnetic fields.

Relation of Magnetization to Other Physical Properties. Some important relationships exist between magnetism and the following physical properties: thermal expansion, electrical resistance, specific heat, Young's modulus and other elastic constants, and the magnetocaloric effect.

The thermal expansion anomalies in certain ferromagnetic and antiferromagnetic metals have recently been considered by Zener (272) and Chandrasekhar (273). Zener was particularly successful in explaining the low thermal expansion of Invar and the high expansion of certain copper-manganese alloys. Chandrasekhar qualitatively applied Zener's localized shell model to explain the thermal expansion of such ferromagnetic elements as gadolinium, terbium, and dysprosium.

The electrical resistivity of ferromagnetic, as well as diamagnetic and paramagnetic, materials is influenced by a magnetic field. Over a hundred years ago, William Thomson (Lord Kelvin) observed that the electrical resistivity of iron changes when it is magnetized (274). The magnitude of the change in resistivity caused by magnetization to saturation rarely exceeds 5% at room temperature. The resistivity of nickel is increased by about 2% in a large field. See Chapter 2 for a further discussion of the magnetoresistance effect.

A considerable anomaly in the specific heat exists just below the Curie temperature. The specific heat rises rapidly, and then drops even more rapidly at the Curie temperature.

In ferromagnetic materials, Young's modulus will vary with magnetization. The modulus, E, of a magnetized material may increase as much as 35%.

A magnetocaloric effect (the rise of temperature in a ferromagnetic material with the sudden application of a strong field) was discovered by Weiss and Piccard (275). A rise of 1 °C occurs in nickel with the application of a field of 10,000 to 20,000 oersteds.

There is also a unique coexistence of piezoelectricity * and ferromagnetism. Remeike (276) has prepared $GaFeO_3$ that is ferromagnetic below 260 K and piezoelectric from room temperature down to 50 K.

A coexistence of ferroelectricity ** and ferromagnetism was discovered by Fang and Roth (277). They found that in the system $(Ba_{6-2x}R_{2x}) \cdot (Cb_{9-x}Fe_{1+x})O_{30}$, where R is a trivalent rare earth (samarium, europium, gadolinium, or neodymium), both phenomena were possible.

---

* The piezoelectric effect is a phenomenon observed in certain crystals, and relates mechanical and electrical parameters. Compression generates an electrostatic voltage across the crystal; conversely, an electric field may cause a crystal to expand or contract in certain crystallographic directions.

** The ferroelectric effect is the phenomenon whereby certain crystals exhibit a spontaneous permanent dipole moment. The effect is often compared with ferromagnetism — the existence of a permanent magnetic moment.

Chapter 6

Soft Magnetic Materials and Their Applications

MUSHROOMING electrical, radio and television industries, radar and related fields, automatic controls, and electronic instrumentation encourage the improvement and development of special and improved materials, particularly magnetic alloys. Without soft, or high-permeability, materials, the production, transmission, and use of electricity would be virtually impossible. Wire communication, radio, and television would be nonexistent without high-permeability materials and permanent magnets.

Magnetic materials can be divided into two general categories: (a) magnetically soft materials, used for communications engineering and for power applications (motors, generators, transformers), and (b) magnetically hard materials, employed for instruments, radio loudspeakers, electric motors, attractive and holding devices, and general gadgetry.

For communication engineering, two types of magnetic properties are useful. On the one hand, a constant and high initial permeability is required; on the other hand, a high initial and maximum permeability, together with a low coercive force, is needed.

The requirement of constant permeability with low hysteresis loss is met in the initial part or toe of the magnetization curve. Any nonlinearity between magnetizing force, H, and induction, B, leads to undesirable nonlinear distortions of the signals. In the early stages of the communications industry, shearing by air gaps was used to flatten the steep magnetization curve to obtain constant permeability. Wire and compressed iron powder cores were also used. With the development of the Perminvars, a constancy of permeability up to $H = 5$ oersteds could be obtained. Later, the Isoperms were introduced.

For loading or inductance coils, a constant permeability with a high initial permeability is required. This requirement is met with either subdivided ferromagnetic materials, such as compressed iron powder cores, or rolled magnetic materials of the required composition and corresponding heat treatment (Isoperm). For transformers, choke coils, relays, soft iron devices (electromagnets), and shields, high initial and maximum permeabilities together with low coercive force are required. Rolled magnetic materials of the Permalloy type (78% Ni) and, in many instances, the 50 Fe – 50 Ni alloys are used.

For power engineering, high permeability, high flux density at low magnetizing forces, and low core loss, which implies a low hysteresis loss, are essential. These are properties of the iron-silicon alloys. Alloys with up to about 3% Si are used for motors and generators, and alloys containing up to 5% Si are used for transformers. For transformers, alloys with a high degree of preferred orientation, which results in high permeabilities and low core loss in the direction of rolling, are used extensively in high-efficiency cores.

Square-loop soft magnetic materials occupy an important niche in our technology. Applications include cores for saturable reactors, magnetic amplifier coils, magnetic pulse modulators, choke coils in mechanical rectifier circuits, and memory or switching coils in electronic computers. Square loops have been obtained in most of the soft magnetic alloys, namely, 3% Si steel, 45% Ni and 50% Ni iron alloys, Molybdenum Permalloy, 65 Permalloy, and 49% Co, 2% V alloy, by proper time-temperature anneals or by the application of a magnetic field during cooling, or both (224).

Historically, the hard magnetic materials were truly hard; these were the quenched and tempered martensitic steels. At present some of the high-quality permanent magnets (for example, the fine-powder single-domain magnets bonded with lead) are physically rather soft. Unfortunately, the most useful and powerful permanent magnets (the Alnicos) are so glass-brittle that they can be shaped only by careful grinding. The important magnetic criteria of permanent magnets are high coercive force, high remanence, and high maximum energy product.

The magnetic properties of both hard and soft materials are due to their chemical composition and heat treatment. The soft magnetic materials are carefully melted, processed, and annealed at elevated temperatures for strain relief, purification, and grain growth. The hard magnetic materials are also carefully melted, processed, and heat treated to develop high internal strains or to obtain single-particle magnetic performance in the total volume of the magnet. Every composition, whether it is a soft or hard magnetic material, has its own unique heat treatment for bringing about maximum quality.

As a class, soft magnetic materials have, in varying degrees, many characteristics in common. Often, certain compromises must be made and tolerated for either technical or economic reasons. The important characteristics are as follows:

1 The magnetic permeability should be high. If the maximum permeability (a quality value rather than a design index) is high, so is the initial permeability. As already mentioned, sometimes a constant permeability at low field or induction is essential.

2 The saturation induction should be high, particularly in power equipment, which requires a high flux density, preferably at a low magnetizing force. High flux densities make it possible to

Table 55. Typical Uses of High-Permeability and Low-Core-Loss Magnetic Materials

Uses	Property requirements
Power Applications	
Distribution and power transformers⎫ High-quality motors and generators⎭	Low core losses; high permeability at low and medium inductions; high saturation
Instrument Transformers	
Audiofrequency transformers	Low core losses; high permeability at low and medium inductions
Pulse transformers	High permeability
Inductance Coils	
Audiofrequency	Low hysteresis and high permeability
Carrier-frequency	Very low hysteresis and eddy-current loss
Radiofrequency	High permeability at low magnetizing force
Miscellaneous	
Relays ⎫ Magnetic shielding⎭	High permeability; low remanence and low coercive force. For alternating-current applications, core loss should be low.
Magnetic amplifiers	Rectangular hysteresis loops; low hysteresis

Table 56. Properties of High-Permeability Materials

Material	Composition, %	Heat treatment(a), C	Permeability, Initial, μ_0	Permeability, Maximum, μ_{max}	Coercive force (b), oersteds	Saturation induction, B_s, gausses	Electrical resistivity, microhm-cm	Curie temperature, C	Density, g/cu cm	Typical applications
Iron............	99.8 Fe	950	150	5,000	1.0	21,500	10	770	7.88	Small motors
Purified iron......	99.95 Fe	1480 + 880	10,000	200,000	0.05	21,500	10	770	7.88	......
Silicon iron......	1.5 Si	800	640	9,350	0.52(c)	20,900	29	760	7.77	Small motors and generators
Silicon iron.......	3.3 Si	800	1,250	9,200	0.49(c)	20,000	50	740	7.65	High-efficiency motors and generators
Grain-oriented silicon iron....	3.20 Si	1200	2,250(d)	70,000	0.11	20,000	48	740	7.66	High-efficiency transformers
Silicon iron.......	4.6 Si	800	1,250	9,750	0.39(c)	19,500	63	720	7.57	High-efficiency transformers
Sendust.........	9 Si – 5 Al – 85 Fe	Cast	30,000	120,000	0.05	10,000	80	500	7.1	HF transformers
45 Permalloy....	45 Ni – 54 Fe	1050	2,500	25,000	0.30	16,000	50	440	8.17	Specialty transformers
Hipernik........	50 Ni – 50 Fe	1200	4,000	80,000	0.05	16,000	35	500	8.25	Specialty transformers, shields
78 Permalloy.....	78 Ni – 21 Fe	1050 + 600	8,000	100,000	0.05	10,000	16	580	8.60	Loading coils, shields, tape-wound cores, transformers
4-79 Permalloy..	79 Ni – 4 Mo – 16 Fe	1100	20,000	150,000	0.05	8,700	57	420	8.72	Loading coils, transformers, tape-wound cores
Mumetal.........	75 Ni – 2 Cr – 5 Cu – 18 Fe	1100	20,000	150,000	0.03	7,200	60	430	8.58	Loading coils, transformers, tape-wound cores
Supermalloy.....	79 Ni – 5 Mo – 15 Fe	1300	100,000	1,000,000	0.004	8,000	60	400	8.87	Transformers, tape-wound cores
Hiperco.........	35 Co, 0.4 Cr	850	650	10,000	1.0	24,200	20	970	8.0	Electromagnets
Permendur......	50 Co – 50 Fe	800	800	5,000	2.0	24,000	7	980	8.3	Electromagnets
V Permendur....	49 Co – 2 V – 49 Fe	800	800	4,500	2.0	24,000	26	980	8.2	Receiver diaphragms
Supermendur....	49 Co – 2 V – 49 Fe	850	2,500	66,000	0.20	24,000	26	980	8.2	Magnetic amplifiers

(a) In dry hydrogen. (b) From saturation induction. (c) For $B = 10,000$ gausses. (d) Permeability at $B = 20$ instead of at $B = 0$.

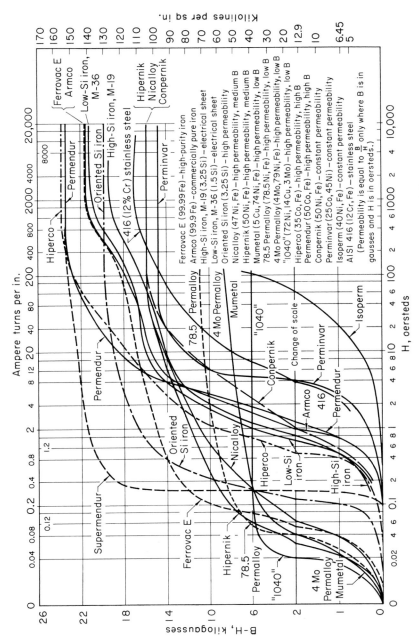

Fig. 100. Magnetization curves for soft magnetic alloys

build equipment of lower weight or smaller volume, or both, for a given rating.

3 The core or energy loss should be as low as possible, because this loss shows up as unusable energy (heat). Core loss is composed of eddy-current and hysteresis loss.* Hysteresis is kept low by having the material free of plastic strains, free of impurities, particularly those of interstitial nature (carbon and nitrogen), and by the development of a coarse grain size. The eddy-current component is reduced by increasing the resistivity of the material or decreasing the lamination thickness. For some applications, squareness of the loop is also essential.

4 The interlamination resistance should be high enough so that eddy currents are not increased. The resistance coating should be as thin as possible in order to get a high stacking factor, that is, to get as much steel into a unit volume as possible.

5 Economics, of course, are important. Often use of the best material is not justified because of the expense. In general, the costs, along with performance, determine the material used.

Table 55 gives some typical applications and the magnetic characteristics of soft magnetic materials, and Table 56 gives their compositions and some of their characteristic properties. Figure 100 shows their normal magnetization curves.

Motors and Generators

There is no fundamental difference between a generator and motor; a machine is capable of operating either as a generator or motor. The electromotive force of a generator is produced by movement of a system of conductors, the armature windings, relative to the lines of force of a magnetic field set up by the field system. Figure 101 shows schematically the construction of a four-pole generator or motor.

The generator or motor uses three types of materials:

1 The magnetic materials, iron or iron-silicon alloys, that have to carry the magnetic flux in the poles (stator) and armature (rotor)

2 The copper electrical conductors of the armature winding and of the field or exciting winding

3 The insulating materials used to insulate the armature and field windings from the rest of the machine, as well as the individual turns of copper in these windings

For the yoke, cast iron has been replaced by cast steel or welded low-carbon steel plate. The pole cores are made of lami-

---

* In low-loss materials, for example, grain-oriented silicon steels, a component called anomalous loss has not yet been satisfactorily explained.

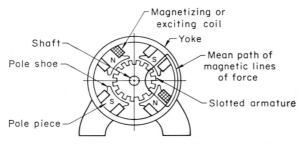

Fig. 101. Diagram of the field system of a
direct-current, four-pole generator or motor

nated iron or silicon iron. These pole cores, besides carrying flux, have the copper windings (exciting coils) wound around them. The armature is also made of laminated iron or iron-silicon alloy.

For armatures, cores up to about 30 in. in diameter can be punched in one piece. For larger diameters, it is necessary to build up the core in sectors. Current trends are for production of 36-in.-wide electrical sheet, but industry plans call for 48-in.-wide material within the next five years. Increasing labor costs are responsible for the trend to wider punchings, in order to eliminate or to reduce handling of sector punchings. Figure 102 shows the stacking of silicon steel laminations in a generator for the Fort Peck Dam, Fort Peck, Montana.

Fig. 102. Stacking of stator laminations (sectors) on a Fort Peck
38,889-kva generator. (Courtesy, Allis-Chalmers Manufacturing Co.)

The armature winding consists of straight copper conductors arranged in the slots parallel to the shaft and grouped around the periphery of the armature cores. In small rotating machines, the winding consists of insulated small-diameter wire, and, in larger machines, formed bus bar is used (Fig. 42). In small induction motor construction, the rotor conductors—aluminum or copper—are die cast into the assembled laminations.

Transformers

There are no moving parts in a transformer, nor is there any electrical connection between the two circuits; the energy is transferred by magnetic induction, usually with a change of volt-

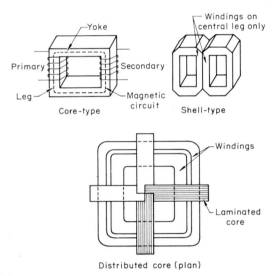

Fig. 103. *Types of transformer construction*

age. Regardless of voltage, the energy-supply circuit is called the primary, and the energy-receiving circuit is called the secondary. Transformers are sometimes classified as follows: (a) according to use (power, distribution, instrument), (b) according to the arrangement of the magnetic circuit (shell-type, core-type), (c) according to electrical connections (single-phase, three-phase), (d) according to cooling (air-cooled, oil-filled), (e) according to purpose (constant-voltage-ratio, constant-current).

The important "use" category deserves some discussion. Power transformers are those with capacities of over about 200 kva and voltages of over 17,500. Distribution-type transformers distribute energy of less than about 200 kva and secondary voltages of about 500 v or lower from the high-voltage mains.

Power transformers are more complicated than the distribution types, and three types of construction are common: core, shell, and distributed core (Fig. 103). The core-type has a structure with a single magnetic circuit. The shell-type can be regarded as two core-type transformers placed side by side, giving a central leg of twice the cross section of the outer leg. The primary and secondary windings are placed on this center leg only; thus, the shell-type construction has two magnetic circuits. The distributed core-type construction calls for a number of core-type cores arranged in such a way that, in a plan, they have radial symmetry similar to spokes of a wheel. The center leg again carries the primary and secondary windings. There are as many parallel magnet circuits as there are cores. Figure 104 shows the assembly of a power transformer of the core type.

Fig. 104. Yoke laminations complete the magnetic circuit of a power (core-type) transformer. (Courtesy, Allis-Chalmers Manufacturing Co.)

Distribution transformer cores are generally made from grain-oriented steel that is wound continuously, with the direction of rolling coinciding with the direction of magnetization. Power transformers, made from grain-oriented steel, are generally stacked.

For distribution transformer applications, the core is wound with 0.012-in. steel; for power transformers, the core is made of 0.014-in. laminations. For electronic transformers that operate at high frequencies, the electrical steel is rolled to 0.001 in. and sometimes less. For all types, it is important that laminations be insulated from each other to avoid short circuits and a consequent rise in eddy-current loss. For electronic transformers, the core is often made from wound cores, such as are illustrated in Fig. 105. The construction of transformers from punchings in the form of gapless laminations and from E and I punchings is still practiced.

Instrument transformers, which may be either current or po-

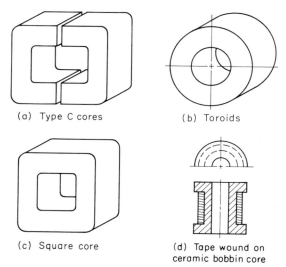

(a) Type C cores   (b) Toroids

(c) Square core   (d) Tape wound on
                                 ceramic bobbin core

Fig. 105. Types of wound-core construction for electronic cores.
(a) Type-C cores are available in 1, 2, 4, and 12-mil thicknesses in
silicon steel. Widths vary from 0.025 to 3 in. (b) Toroids are avail-
able in 1, 2, 4, and 12-mil thicknesses in silicon steel and 0.5 to 14-
mil thicknesses in iron-nickel alloys. Widths are from 0.125 to 3 in.
(c) Widths and thicknesses are the same as for toroids. (d) Usually
iron-nickel alloys; strip width, 0.062 to 0.250 in.; thicknesses, from
0.000125 to 0.001 in.

tential types, are important links in power metering and relay-ing. These transformers insulate and convert the high potentials and currents used for power transmission to lower values, which can be handled more easily with standard instruments, meters and relays, normal instrument ratings usually being 5 amp and 120 v. For potential transformers, major applications cover ranges of 600 to 2400 v, and, for current transformers, ratings are from 1.2 to 25 kv.

The windings on a transformer (the primary and secondary) are usually of copper, and must be insulated from each other.

Electromagnets

Electromagnets are solenoids made of insulated wire surround-ing soft iron cores. When electricity flows through the coil, the iron core is magnetized; when the current ceases to flow, the core loses virtually all its magnetism. Common devices using electromagnets are electric bells, telephone receivers, telegraph instruments, and lifting magnets.

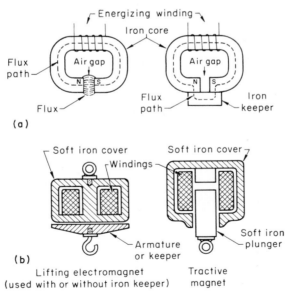

Fig. 106. (a) *Principle of magnetic trac-tion.* (b) *Two types of electromagnets.*

The action of an electromagnet can be easily understood by reference to Fig. 106. In Fig. 106(a), the energizing of the iron core causes a flux in the air gap. The introduction of a piece of iron alongside the air gap causes the lines of flux to travel through the iron rather than through the air gap. The flux flows through the iron more easily than through the air. This tendency of flux lines to flow more readily through high-permeability iron rather than low-permeability air is the reason for the iron being attracted to the electromagnet.

The sketches in Fig. 106(b) show the construction of a lifting and a tractive magnet. Elementary relays were mentioned in Chapter 5.

Iron and Steel as Soft Magnetic Materials

Of the three common ferromagnetic elements, the most useful is iron, in various degrees of purity (plain carbon steels included). Nickel is used in transducers (magnetostrictive oscilla-

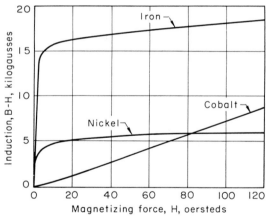

Fig. 107. Magnetization curves for commercially pure iron, nickel and cobalt, annealed 5 hr at 850 C (1560 F) in dry hydrogen

tors), because of its relatively high magnetostriction. Elemental cobalt has found no widespread use in magnetic devices. Iron, besides being plentiful, has a high magnetic saturation ($4\pi I_s = 21{,}600$) and relatively high permeability. Magnetization curves for pure iron, nickel and cobalt are given in Fig. 107; other typical properties are included in Table 57.

Table 57. Typical Magnetic Properties of the Commercially Pure Elements

Property	Nickel	Cobalt	Iron
Initial permeability, μ_0.	110(a)	70(a)	150(b)
Maximum permeability, μ_{max}	600(a)	250(a)	5,000(b)
Saturation, $4\pi I_s$, gausses.	6,100	18,200	21,600
Hysteresis at saturation(c), ergs/cu cm/cycle.	2,000	2,000	5,000
Coercive force(c), oersteds.	0.7	10	1.0
Curie temperature, C.	360	1120	770
Electrical resistivity, microhm-cm	7	9	10
Density, g per cu cm.	8.9	8.9	7.8

(a) Hydrogen annealed at 1000 C (1830 F). (b) Hydrogen annealed at 950 C (1750 F). (c) From saturation induction.

Iron Sheet and Plate. Commercially pure iron finds some use in small and large electromagnets. Low-carbon nonsilicon-bearing steel products have extensive use as low-cost electrical material in rotating machinery. Low-carbon steels (for example, AISI 1010) have somewhat higher magnetic saturation than silicon steels; this property has to be compromised when high silicon (up to 4.5%) is added for increased resistivity, which is required in alternating-current power equipment.

Commercially pure iron and low-carbon steels are made in the basic open-hearth furnace. Iron of higher purity may be obtained by electrolysis, melting in vacuum, melting in hydrogen, decomposition of iron carbonyl, or zone melting, but these varieties are too expensive for extensive commercial use.

Hot rolled carbon steel plates are used in the frames of rotating machinery, which are fabricated by welding. Hot rolled low-carbon sheets are used in motors as pole pieces or part of the pole support. Permeability of this material is improved by annealing in the range of 720 to 815 C (1300 to 1400 F). Cold rolled sheets are also used in fractional-horsepower motors. Some comparative magnetic data are given in Table 58. Material used for poles in generators is produced to a minimum direct-current permeability of 330 at 16 kilogausses.

Relatively pure iron in the form of solid cores is used for relays, contactors, electromagnets, and other devices working on direct current. This material is generally annealed to improve permeability and minimize the coercive force, H_c.

The maximum permeability of commercial magnetic iron is of the order of 5000 to 10,000. By hydrogen annealing, higher per-

Table 58. Magnetic Properties of Iron and Low-Carbon Steel

Material	Condition	H_{max}, oersteds $B = 10,000$	Remanence, B_r, gausses $B = 10,000$	Coercive force, H_c, $B = 10,000$	Core loss, w/lb at 60 cycles $B = 10,000$	$B = 15,000$
High-purity iron, 0.025 in. thick	14 hr at 845 C (1550 F)	...	...	...	1.72	4.80
Ingot iron, 0.025 in. thick	1 hr at 845 C (1550 F)	...	...	...	2.46	6.34
Ingot iron, 0.0375 in. thick	As received	3.42	8550	1.47	4.67	11.40
	1 hr at 760 C (1400 F)	2.30	8650	1.15	3.95	11.06
Cold rolled low-carbon steel,	As received	4.59	7990	1.74	5.96	14.25
0.050 in. thick	1 hr at 760 C (1400 F)	2.44	8225	1.08	4.82	13.90

Table 59. Magnetic Properties of Ferritic Stainless Steels

AISI type	Cr, %	C, %	Other, %	Condition	Rockwell hardness	H_{max}(a), oersteds	B_{max}, gausses	Remanence, B_r, gausses	Coercive force, H_c, oersteds	Maximum permeability
410	12	0.15 max		Annealed	B 80	...	...	...	...	800
416	12	0.15 max	0.07 S	Hardened	C 42	300	12,600	6,200	51	76
420	12	0.15 min		Annealed	B 90	200	16,200	10,600	7.6	674
				Hardened	C 52	300	12,500	6,500	59.5	71
430	17	0.12 max		Annealed	B 78	200	16,200	11,500	6.1	1400
				Annealed	B 87	300	14,600	5,100	9.8	962
				Hardened	B 95	300	15,300	7,700	23.0	278
431	16	0.20 max	2 Ni	Hardened	C 30	...	...	...	...	...
440B	17	0.85		Annealed	B 97	...	...	...	...	420
				Hardened	C 58	...	...	...	...	26

(a) Maximum value of H is used; induction, B, corresponds to this value of H. The values of B_r and H_c were obtained from these peak values.

meabilities can be obtained. Permeabilities as high as 320,000 have been measured. Hydrogen treatment is particularly effective, because it removes the magnetically harmful oxygen, sulfur, carbon, and nitrogen; moist hydrogen removes carbon most readily. The removal of these impurities also favors the coarsening of the grains, which in turn is conducive to higher permeabilities and lower hysteresis loss.

Iron Powder. Relatively pure, spherical, iron particles, often insulated from each other, have been used in the communications industry for some time. The over-all effect of compacting on the magnetization curve of iron is to give a material with low, but more constant, permeability.

The hydrogen-reduced iron powders and carbonyl irons are used mostly in the low, medium and high-frequency ranges; the upper limit is 1 megacycle. Trends in electronics have been to higher frequencies, and here the high-permeability ceramic ferrites with their low eddy-current losses have found favor.

The chief factors used in the evaluation of iron powders are the Q factor and permeability. The Q factor, which is governed by eddy currents and residual losses, is used to show the sharpness of resonance of a tuned electronic circuit. It is expressed as the ratio of reactance of a coil at resonance to the resistance of the coil:

$$Q = \frac{X_L}{R} = \frac{2\pi f L}{R} \tag{67}$$

where X_L is inductive reactance, L is inductance, f is frequency, and R is resistance. The higher the Q factor of the coil, the better the coil. For iron-core coils, Q for resonant circuits varies from 20 to 100. Iron powders have been used with and without insulation; with binders (oxide or plastic), higher values of Q are obtained.

The relationship between magnetic properties and the density of uninsulated iron powder compacts has been considered by Steinitz (278), who found that, in general, the coercive force is higher, and the remanence and permeability lower for porous material in comparison with solid.

Carbon Steels. Iron, in the form of wrought iron, cast iron, and later steel, was the precursor of all soft and permanent magnet material. The properties of steel, the cheapest of magnetic materials, are still of technical importance, for instance, in the

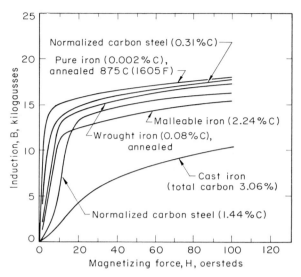

Fig. 108. Magnetization curves of some common ferrous materials

frames and shafts of motors and generators and as laminations for inexpensive, fractional-horsepower motors.

In carbon and low-alloy steels, carbon plays an important role. Depending on quantity and heat treatment, carbon may be present as martensite, pearlite, carbide, or graphite. Austenite is non-magnetic (paramagnetic). In soft magnetic materials, carbon should be eliminated or reduced to low amounts. In hard magnetic materials, high carbon is sought and treatments are used that give martensite. Carbon-produced constituents affect hysteresis loss in this order: largest effect, martensite; then, lamellar pearlite, granular pearlite, and graphite. Figure 108 gives the magnetization curves of some common ferrous materials; note the improvement of permeability with lower carbon.

The saturation induction of iron is reduced by carbon. This reduction is greater for quenched than for annealed alloys. The permeability of iron is depressed considerably by the addition of carbon and the form it is in. The effect of carbon on permeability is shown in Fig. 109 (279).

Cold rolling of carbon steels increases the hysteresis and coercive force, and decreases the permeability. Messkin (280) studied the magnetic properties of rolled 0.78% C steel, and found that the coercive force increased rapidly at first, then more

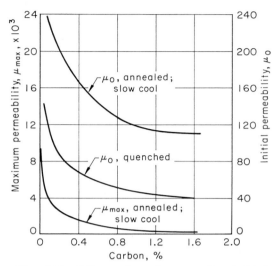

Fig. 109. *Effect of carbon on the initial and maximum permeability of quenched and annealed samples of iron. The maximum permeability of the quenched samples is only a fraction of the permeability of the annealed steel.*

slowly, and finally reached a value of 40. The maximum permeability is approximately halved by severe deformation.

Ferritic Stainless Steels. The commercial ferritic steels (AISI 400 series), also known as the magnetic stainless grades, are used in magnetic cores, solenoid switches, pole pieces, and relays, generally where corrosion or oxidation resistance is required. The ferritic stainless steels are magnetically inferior to iron or silicon iron; they have lower saturation, lower permeabilities, and higher coercive force. Eberly (281) and Stein (282) discussed the properties of ferritic steels. Some typical data are given in Table 59. Data on the austenitic stainless steels are given under nonmagnetic materials, at the end of this chapter.

Iron-Silicon Alloys

The most important of the soft magnetic alloys, in terms of general usefulness, tonnage, and dollar volume, are the iron-silicon alloys containing from about 0.5 to 4.5% Si. The iron-rich part of the iron-silicon diagram, cn which these alloys are based, is shown in Fig. 110. Note the closing up of the gamma loop with about 2.5% Si. The extent of the gamma loop is influenced greatly by the presence of carbon. In a carbon-free alloy (less than 0.01% C), the boundary between alpha-plus-gamma and al-

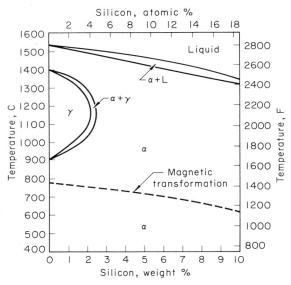

Fig. 110. Phase diagram of the iron-rich iron-silicon alloys

pha is at 2.5% Si, while the presence of only 0.07% C moves this boundary to about 3.5% Si.

In Fig. 111, the variation of several important magnetic quantities with silicon is shown. Note, in particular, the lowering of the Curie point and saturation magnetization with increasing silicon. The lowering of the Curie point is of academic interest, but the lowering of saturation is undesirable in a practical sense. The lowering of the anisotropy and magnetostriction is helpful in obtaining higher permeabilities; unfortunately, these properties are low only at high silicon contents, where the alloy is glass-brittle and hence unusable.

Iron-silicon alloys are the most widely used magnetic materials for power applications (generators, transformers, motors). The alloys are commonly referred to in the technology as electrical sheet, electrical steel, or silicon steel. These electrical steels are characterized by low core loss at fairly high flux densities. Although introduced over 50 years ago by Barrett, Brown, and Hadfield (283), the steels * are still undergoing improvement.

The presence of silicon allows the steel to undergo the cyclic variation of the magnetic field at power frequency (60 cps in America, 50 cps in Europe) without undue energy (heat) losses, in comparison with low-carbon steels. The silicon increases the resistivity, thereby reducing the high fraction of eddy currents that are part of the energy losses; hysteresis makes up most of

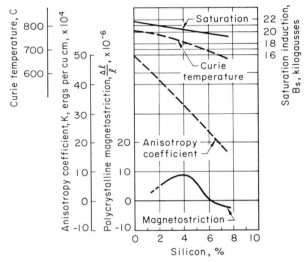

Fig. 111. Correlation of some magnetic quantities with composition in the iron-rich iron-silicon system

the remainder of the loss. Carbon steels deteriorate electrically due to aging, primarily through precipitation of carbon. Silicon steels show relatively low aging effects, as a result of the decrease in solubility of carbon in silicon ferrite.

Alloys containing 0.5 to 1.5% Si are used principally in cores of rotors and stators of motors and generators. The low end of silicon content is used for stationary field poles and magnetic circuits, where high permeability is required. Steels with about 1%

* Actually, it is more correct to refer to them as irons. Steel is often defined as a ductile alloy of carbon and manganese. The high-quality, grain-oriented iron-silicon alloys have virtually no carbon (less than 0.005%) and very little manganese (less than 0.10%).

Table 60. Typical Properties of Standard Electric Sheet
(Annealed 0.014-in. sheet. $B_m = 15,000$ gausses and $f = 60$ cps.)

Grade	Si, %	Saturation induction, $4\pi I_s$	Permeability, max	Coercive force, H_c, oersteds, ($B = 10,000$)	Core loss, watts per lb ($B = 15,000$)	Electrical resistivity, microhm-cm	Density, g per cu cm
Armature........	0.5	21,400	5,500	0.9	4.30	17	7.84
Electrical........	1.2	21,000	6,100	0.85	3.60	27	7.79
Motor...........	2.8	20,400	5,800	0.75	2.65	42	7.70
Dynamo.........	3.25	20,100	5,800	0.65	2.15	50	7.65
Transformer 1....	3.75	19,900	7,000	0.5	1.00	59	7.60
Transformer 52...	4.25	19,500	9,000	0.39	1.40	65	7.57
Grain-oriented ($\parallel$)(a)..........	3.25	20,100	55,000	0.08	0.60	47	7.65
Grain-oriented (#)(b).........	3.25	20,100	116,000	0.07	0.56	47	7.65

(a) ($\parallel$) is the symbol for cube-on-edge orientation, (110)[001], oriented parallel to the rolling direction. (b) (#) is the symbol for cube or doubly oriented material, (100)[100].

Si are used for reactors, relays, and intermittent-duty transformers.

Alloys with higher silicon (2.5 to 3.5% Si) are used for motors and generators of average to high efficiency and in medium-sized intermittent-duty transformers, reactors and motors.

The highest silicon alloys (3.2 to 5% Si) are used in high-efficiency motors and generators, as well as power transformers, radio transformers, and other radio equipment.

For high-efficiency transformers, either distribution or power, the grain-oriented 3.25% Si steels are used. Some typical magnetic properties of the various grades are given in Table 60. It should be recognized that the magnetic properties of all these grades vary greatly as a result of variations in composition, manufacture, and heat treatment.

Over the past ten years, annual production of these steels has averaged about 600,000 tons; about 30% of this tonnage is of the grain-oriented silicon steel (3.25% Si).

Silicon decreases the magnetic transformation (A_2 or Curie point) about 12 °C (22 °F) for each percentage point of silicon up to 4%. Pure iron has a Curie point of 780 C (1435 F) and 4% Si iron has one of 730 C (1246 F). Silicon increases the electrical resistivity linearly by 11.4 microhm-cm for each per cent of silicon. Silicon reduces the density linearly: 7.82 g per cu cm for pure iron and 7.57 for 4.5% Si iron. Unfortunately, it also reduces ductility and high-silicon alloys are very brittle. Silicon decreases the magnetic saturation, according to the relation

$$4\pi I_s = 21,600 - (480 \times \%\text{Si}) \tag{68}$$

Great improvements in lowering the core loss have been made in these steels since they were introduced commercially in 1907. The phenomenal reduction in losses has been achieved by reducing impurities, such as carbon, nitrogen, oxygen, and sulfur. The harmful effect of carbon, sulfur, and manganese is shown in their effect on hysteresis loss (expressed in ergs per cubic centimeter per cycle) at $B = 10,000$ gausses in a 4% Si alloy (279):

$$\begin{aligned} \Delta W_h &= 45,000 \times \%\text{C} \\ &= 10,000 \times \%\text{S} \\ &= 1,000 \times \%\text{Mn} \end{aligned} \tag{69}$$

Although in the past most silicon steel sheets were hot rolled in packs, it is now more common to cold roll the grades containing up to 3.25% Si. Cold rolled strip is made from a hot band that has been rolled to about 0.1 in. thick. The hot band is then cold reduced to the final thickness. High-silicon alloys (greater than 3.25% Si) are hot rolled from about ⅜-in. sheet bars. Sheets may be up to 48 in. wide and up to 120 in. long.

Electrical steel is classified by the method of production:

Hot rolled sheets (produced by pack rolling *)
Cold reduced (produced by continuous rolling). The production of grain-oriented steel is carried out by a definite schedule of cold rolling and annealing operations, and the process can be considered as a variation of the cold reduction method.

Cold reduced steel can be furnished either as fully processed or as semiprocessed steel. Semiprocessed steel is given a stress-relief treatment by the user. Users of electrical steel prefer to receive semiprocessed steel and anneal the material themselves to develop optimum magnetic quality; the resulting quality, of course, must meet the same core-loss requirement as fully processed steel. A substantial part of electrical steels is produced in the fully processed condition, with the magnetic properties fully developed by the supplier.

---

* Pack rolling is the process of hot rolling two or more sheets together to the final gage. Packs may be doubled, reheated, and rerolled a number of times, depending on the gage desired.

Table 61. Characteristics and Applications of the Various Silicon Steel Flat-Rolled Products

AISI type	Si, %	Characteristics	Typical applications
M-50(a)	0 to 0.6	Excellent ductility	For intermittently operated electrical apparatus. Pole pieces and relay cores.
M-45	0 to 0.6	Ductile. High core loss, but good permeability at high induction.	Same as for M-50
M-43	0.6 to 1.3	Ductile. High core loss, but good permeability at high induction.	For fractional-horsepower motors, pole pieces, relays
M-36	1.0 to 1.8	Ductile. Excellent permeability at high induction.	Used extensively for rotating machines including a-c and d-c motors
M-32	1.7 to 2.5	Ductile. Relatively good punching properties. Generally furnished as semiprocessed.	Small motors (less than 10 hp)
M-27	1.7 to 3.0	Ductile. Relatively good punching properties.	Continuous-duty high-efficiency motors. Small transformers operative at moderate induction.
M-22	2.5 to 3.5	Ductile. Relatively good punching properties.	Cores of high reactance, stator of high efficiency rotating electrical equipment, intermittent-duty transformers, magnetos
M-19	2.5 to 3.8	Usually more ductile than types of lower core loss. Moderately high permeability at all inductions.	Communication transformers and reactors. High-efficiency fractional-horsepower motors.
M-17	3.0 to 4.0	Fairly good core loss and intermediate values in other properties	Used occasionally for transformers of less than 1000 kva
M-15	3.0 to 5.0	Characteristics depend on annealing process used. Open-annealed lower-silicon steel is quite ductile.	Punchings requiring low core loss and excellent permeabilities at low and moderate induction
M-14	4.0 to 5.0	Lowest core loss in conventional grades. High permeability at low induction. Brittle.	Distribution and power transformers and rotating machines of high efficiency
M-7 M-6 M-5	2.9 to 3.25 2.9 to 3.25 2.9 to 3.25	Highly directional grain oriented. Very low core loss and high permeability in rolling direction.	Highest efficiency power and distribution transformers with lower weight per kva

(a) Not commonly subjected to magnetic test requirements.

Table 62. Maximum Core Losses in Some Flat-Rolled Electrical Steels at 60 Cps *

AISI type	Gage number		
	29	26	24
	Thickness, in.		
	0.014	0.0185	0.025

Fully Processed Hot and Cold Rolled Conventional Types
(Samples not annealed after shearing — AS)

Core Loss, Watts per Pound, at 15 Kilogausses

M-14	1.30	...	...
M-15	1.45	1.70	...
M-19	1.64	1.86	2.10
M-22	1.77	1.97	2.23
M-27	1.92	2.16	2.45
M-36	2.15	2.47	2.90

Core Loss, Watts per Pound, at 10 Kilogausses

M-14	0.52	...	...
M-15	0.58	0.68	...
M-19	0.67	0.76	0.91
M-22	0.73	0.83	0.98
M-27	0.81	0.93	1.10
M-36	0.92	1.06	1.27

Fully and Semiprocessed, Cold Rolled Conventional Types
(Samples stress-relief annealed — SRA)

Core Loss, Watts per Pound, at 15 Kilogausses

M-22	N.A.	1.90	2.10
M-27	N.A.	2.03	2.25
M-36	N.A.	2.35	2.70

Core Loss, Watts per Pound, at 10 Kilogausses

M-22	N.A.	0.80	0.93
M-27	N.A.	0.90	1.05
M-36	N.A.	1.02	1.21

Note 1. Core losses are determined according to ASTM A34 and A343.

Note 2. Core-loss data are specified at inductions of either 15 or 10 kilogausses, but not at both, on specimens half parallel and half transverse to direction of rolling.

Note 3. Gages most commonly used are No. 29 (0.014 in.), No. 26 (0.0185 in.), and No. 24 (0.0250 in.).

Note 4. Where annealing is carried out, the stress-relief temperature is 1550 F for approximately 1 hr.

Note 5. Core loss at 50 cycles may be approximated by multiplying losses shown at 60 cps by 0.79.

Note 6. N.A. Not available at press time.

* As of January 8, 1963

Organic-type coreplate is applied to the metal that will not be annealed. Inorganic coreplate is applied to the metal that will be stress-relief annealed.

The maximum core-loss requirements of the various AISI grades are given in Table 62. The AISI types use the prefix "M," for magnetic material, followed by a number. When the system was adopted, the number was approximately equal to ten times the core loss expressed in watts per pound at 15 kilogausses and 60 cycles for 29-gage (0.014-in.) metal. Regardless of the method of manufacture, flat-rolled electrical steel of any type is produced to meet certain magnetic requirements. The main criterion is core loss in watts per pound at 60 cycles and either 10 or 15 kilogausses, but not at both. Users may require certain other magnetic properties, as well as physical characteristics.

Table 62 gives two types of data: One set is for semiprocessed and fully processed steel that has been stress-relief annealed at 1550 F for approximately 1 hr, and the other set is for fully processed steel in the as-sheared condition. Some users anneal fully processed punchings to improve core loss by removing punching strains. The core loss maximums to which producers are adhering (1963), given in Table 62, will very likely be incorporated into the AISI manual on flat-rolled electrical steel, which is currently being revised.

Oriented Iron-Silicon Alloys. Just as it is possible to obtain preferred orientations in metals by cold rolling and annealing, so it is possible to do so with iron-silicon alloys, and, furthermore, it is possible to capitalize on this characteristic. By proper choice of cold rolling and annealing treatments, it is possible to obtain a high degree of orientation, approaching that of single crystals. Goss (284) demonstrated that a strong, preferred orientation can be developed in iron-silicon alloys.

It is possible to obtain two types of preferred orientation in silicon steels. Historically, the first orientation developed was the (110)[001], which to the crystallographer means that most of the grains of a polycrystalline sheet have their (110) planes parallel to the plane of the sheet, and that the [001] directions in these planes are parallel to the rolling direction. This orientation, known as the cube-on-edge texture, was developed without any idea of why or how the orientation occurred. Fortunately, the orientation is one that can be utilized in transformer construction, but steel has to be used in the rolling direction. For this reason, distribution transformer cores are made by coiling the strip. Large power transformers are made by stacking punchings cut in such manner that the flux is parallel to the direction of rolling. Figure 112 shows the normal magnetization curves for grain-oriented steel produced in 1944 and 1962, in comparison with dynamo grade 3.25% Si steel, which is an isotropic ma-

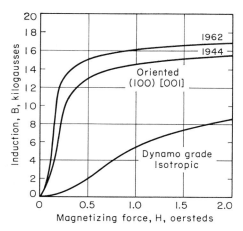

Fig. 112. Magnetization curves of grain-oriented 3.25% Si steel produced in 1944 and 1962, in comparison with isotropic 3.25% Si dynamo-grade steel

terial. Grain-oriented steel is sold to a core-loss specification. The limits on core loss at $B = 15,000$ gausses at 60 cps for two thicknesses are given in Table 63. The oriented steel is sold only on the basis of core loss at 15 kilogausses.

The (110)[001] or cube-on-edge orientation is produced in the following manner: Steel of the proper chemistry is carefully teemed into preheated molds. After sufficient soaking, the ingot is rolled to slabs. The slabs are reheated and rolled to hot band of about 0.08 in. The band is pickled and then cold rolled $65 \pm 5\%$ to 0.028 in. Next, the coil is annealed, to recrystallize the steel. The coil is further cold reduced $50 \pm 5\%$ to about 0.014 in. It is decarburized at about 815 C (1500 F). Finally, it is annealed at above 1100 C (2020 F) in dry hydrogen to develop orientation and excellent magnetic properties.

The second kind of orientation developed is the (100)[100] or cube texture (285). Here the (100) planes are parallel to the plane of the sheet, and the [100] directions are parallel to the rolling direction. However, by symmetry relations, it also follows that the direction at 90° to the rolling direction is also a direction of easy magnetization. Table 64 gives some magnetic properties of cube-oriented and singly (cube-on-edge) oriented 3% Si

Table 63. Core Loss Limits for Grain-Oriented Silicon Steel
(Loss in watts per pound at 60 cps)

AISI type	Core loss, w per lb B = 15 kilogausses	
	0.014-in.	0.012-in.
M-5	0.60	0.58
M-6	0.66	0.64
M-7	0.73	0.71
M-8	0.80	0.78
M-9	0.90	. . .
M-10	1.00	. . .

Note 1. Core-loss limits are based on specimens cut parallel to the rolling direction and tested after a suitable stress-relief anneal, usually 1 hr at 790 C (1450 F) in a protective atmosphere.
Note 2. Losses are determined according to ASTM A34 and A343.
Note 3. To convert above values from watts per pound to watts per kilogram, multiply values shown by 2.204.
Note 4. Core loss at 50 cycles may be approximated by multiplying losses shown by 0.79.
Note 5. Grades M-8, M-9 and M-10 are hardly considered commercial today.

steel (286). With this cube-textured material in a transformer, lower energy losses have been obtained at all inductions.

Mechanical properties of silicon steels are of secondary importance to magnetic properties. Some typical mechanical properties are given in Table 65. The requisites of silicon steels are that they should have good punching and shearing quality. Flatness is also an important requirement, not only because it promotes ease of punching and shearing, but also because flatness is generally conducive to low noise level in transformers.

Aging. The early manufacturers of electric sheet for transformers were troubled by the phenomenon of aging, which resulted from composition and temperature; magnetization had nothing to do with it. The introduction of silicon irons has materially reduced aging, possibly through the reduction of solubil-

Table 64. Comparison of Magnetic Properties of Cube and Cube-on-Edge Textured Materials

Property	Parallel to rolling direction		Right angles to rolling direction	
	Cube texture	Cube-on-edge texture	Cube texture	Cube-on-edge texture
Maximum permeability............	116,000	55,000	65,000	8,000
Coercive force, oersteds...........	0.07	0.08	0.08	0.27
Residual induction, gausses.......	12,200	9,500	11,500	1,750
B at $H = 2$ oersteds.............	16,600	16,300	16,000	11,000
Core loss, watts per lb,...........	0.56	0.60	0.65	1.60
$B = 15$ kilogausses and 60 cps				

Table 65. Nominal Mechanical Properties of Electrical Sheet
(All measurements in rolling direction)

Grade	Condition	Si, %	Density, g per cu cm	Yield strength, psi	Tensile strength, psi	Elongation in 2 in., %	Hardness, Rockwell B
Armature	HR	0.7	7.81	27,000	46,100	29	37
Electrical	HR	1.3	7.78	35,000	50,800	28	51
Electrical	CR	1.8	7.76	57,000	75,400	17	63
Motor	HR	2.80	7.68	46,400	63,300	21	66
Motor	CR	2.80	7.68	67,000	81,000	14	71
Dynamo	HR	3.25	7.65	51,300	69,000	18	74
Dynamo	CR	3.25	7.65	55,800	67,100	18	78
Oriented	CR	3.25	7.65	47,700	58,300	8	80
Transformer 72	HR	3.80	7.62	59,200	76,000	12	76
Transformer 72	CR	3.25	7.65	55,300	68,200	17	76
Transformer 65	HR	3.80	7.62	54,100	65,300	7	70
Transformer 58	HR	4.25	7.59	60,300	61,600	4	75
Transformer 52	HR	4.5	7.57	60,200	69,500	1.6	74

HR, hot rolled; CR, cold rolled

Table 66. Effect of Aging on Coercive Force of Iron Containing Various Amounts of Silicon

Composition, %		Coercive force, H_c, in oersteds, for $B = 10,000$ gausses		
C	Si	After annealing at 800 C (1470 F)	Aged 600 hr at 100 C (212 F)	Change, %
0.15	0.075	1.62	2.80	73
0.14	0.425	0.52	0.80	54
0.25	1.03	0.74	0.74	0
0.21	2.41	0.77	0.77	0
0.06	3.71	0.77	0.78	0
0.29	4.45	1.06	1.06	0

Table 67. Aging of Hot Rolled and Grain-Oriented Silicon Steel

Material	Treatment	Carbon, %	Aged	Hysteresis, ergs per cu cm per cycle
3.5% Si, ... hot rolled	Mill annealed	0.01 to 0.02	Not aged	1400
	Mill annealed	0.01 to 0.02	600 hr, 100 C	1420
	Reannealed, 1200 C	>0.01	Not aged	480
	Reannealed, 1200 C	>0.01	600 hr, 100 C	730
3.25% Si, ... grain-oriented	Annealed, 1100 C	0.007	Not aged	630
	Annealed, 1100 C	0.007	600 hr, 100 C	1350
	Reannealed, 1200 C	0.004	Not aged	365
	Reannealed, 1200 C	0.004	600 hr, 100 C	375

ity of carbon in the iron. Table 66 shows how effectively silicon reduces aging (287). Carbon contents above the solubility limit, up to 0.03 or 0.04%, can be tolerated, but the steel must be slowly cooled to precipitate, as carbide, as much carbon as possible. Significant aging can thereby be prevented.

For modern grain-oriented silicon steel, aging can occur if carbon is above 0.005%. If carbon is below that amount, no aging (increase in coercive force or watt loss) will occur. Above that amount, the iron will age roughly in proportion to the amount of carbon present. Table 67 shows how hot rolled silicon iron and grain-oriented steel can age (288).

Iron-Nickel Alloys

In the iron-nickel phase diagram, shown in Fig. 113, there are two ranges of composition, one at about 50% Ni and the other at about 78% Ni, that have served as the basis for the development of two important classes of iron-nickel magnetic alloys.

Figure 114 gives several magnetic properties plotted as a function of the iron-nickel content. The important iron-nickel magnetic alloys exist in the face-centered cubic structure, beyond about 28% Ni. At about 50% Ni, the saturation magnetization is the highest of the face-centered cubic iron-nickel alloys. In the 78% Ni alloys, the anisotropy and magnetostriction reach relatively low values. Because of these low values, the materials have unusually high permeabilities. Ordering has some influence on the anisotropy. The Curie temperature is of no particular concern in these materials.

Although small nickel additions to iron were studied at the

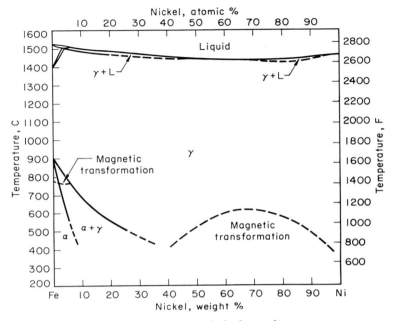

Fig. 113. *The iron-nickel phase diagram*

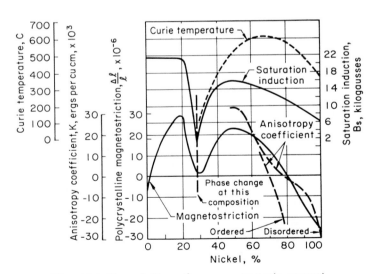

Fig. 114. *Correlation of some magnetic quantities with composition in the iron-nickel system*

turn of the century, it was not until Burgess and Aston (289) pointed out the attractiveness of the 47% Ni alloy for transformer construction that much attention was given to the alloys. A comprehensive study of the iron-nickel alloys was begun by Elmen in 1913, who, with others, demonstrated that alloys containing 30 to 90% Ni had initial permeabilities higher than any material known at that time; these alloys he called Permalloys (290). Some important iron-nickel alloys, along with high-purity iron and nickel, are compared in Table 68.

The iron-nickel alloys have unusually low core losses within the range of flux density at which they are used. The 50% Ni composition cannot compete with the 78% Ni composition for applications requiring the highest permeability.

These alloys are not used for power-frequency applications, because they saturate at low flux densities (16,000 gausses for 50% Ni, 12,000 gausses for 78% Ni). To use them for core materials in power applications would require large amounts of a relatively expensive material. The iron-nickel alloys are used largely for electronic and communications transformers.

The properties of iron-nickel alloys are profoundly affected by interstitial impurities, particularly carbon and nitrogen, but other elements, namely sulfur and oxygen, are also objectionable. Great improvements in properties were made in the past by re-

Table 68. Properties of Iron, Nickel and High-Permeability Iron-Nickel Alloys

Material	Permeability Initial	Permeability Maximum	Hysteresis, ergs per cu cm per cycle(a)	Saturation induction, gausses	Coercive force, oersteds(a)	Electrical resistivity, microhm-cm
Ingot iron (99 + % Fe)	250	7,000	5,000	21,600	1.0	11
45 Permalloy (45% Ni)	2,700	23,000	1,200	16,000	0.3	45
Hipernik (50% Ni)	4,500	100,000	100	16,000	0.03	45
Mumetal(b)	30,000	100,000	. . . .	8,000	0.05	42
4-79 Permalloy(c) . .	20,000	200,000	200	8,500	0.05	55
Supermalloy(d)	100,000	1,000,000	20	8,000	0.004	60
Nickel (99 + % Ni)	110	600	2,000	6,100	0.7	7

(a) For saturation value. (b) 75% Ni, 5% Cu, 2% Cr. (c) 79% Ni, 4% Mo. (d) 79% Ni, 5% Mo.

moving impurities by vacuum melting the charge and hydrogen annealing the finished product. The role of oxygen in Permalloys appears to be subtle. Nesbitt, Heidenrich and Williams (291) found that 63% Ni, 2% Mo Permalloy with low oxygen (0.0006%) did not respond to heat treatment in a magnetic field, as did a sample containing 0.077% O. The higher-oxygen sample gave an improved rectangular hysteresis loop.

The resistivity of iron-nickel alloys is relatively low, but other elements can be added to increase their electrical resistivity in order to obtain lower eddy-current losses. Chromium, molybdenum, and copper are added for this purpose. Aside from increasing the resistivity, these elements simplify the heat treatment required to attain high permeabilities. The additives make the order-disorder transformation sluggish. Up to 2% Mn is sometimes used in 50 Fe − 50 Ni to improve hot workability.

The effect of ordering on the magnetic properties of iron-nickel alloys at or near compositions corresponding to FeNi (50% Ni) and $FeNi_3$ (75% Ni) is pronounced. For optimum properties, a disordered lattice is desired; such a state is obtained by either rapid cooling or by introducing alloy elements (molybdenum or chromium) to reduce the order-disorder transformation rate so that even furnace cooling will retain the disordered lattice. In the 50% Ni alloy, furnace cooling (slow) gives a maximum permeability of 46,000 and a coercive force of 0.07 oersteds ($B = 10$ kilogausses); a rapid cool will give a maximum permeability of 77,000 and a coercive force of 0.04 oersteds. In 78.5% Ni Permalloy, slow cooling (5 °C per sec) gives a maximum permeability value of 50,000; a rapid cool (80 to 100 °C per sec) will give a permeability of 120,000.

The iron-nickel alloys are very sensitive to plastic strains. Even handling sometimes impairs their high permeability. Iron-nickel alloys are generally annealed in their final forms, after all fabricating and assembly are completed. On submarine cables, Permalloy is annealed after it has been wound on the conductor.

The iron-nickel alloys are very susceptible to neutron radiation (292). In Mumetal and the Permalloys, irradiation without a magnetic field caused a constriction of the hysteresis loop with a loss of remanence and an increase in coercivity. With a magnetic field and with irradiation, there was a directional ordering that gave square-loop properties, with increases in both remanence and coercive force.

50 Fe – 50 Ni Alloys. Elmen (290) found that 45 Permalloy was useful because it had a higher saturation induction than any of the other iron-nickel alloys above 30% Ni (Fig. 114).

Yensen made a significant contribution to the knowledge of the properties of 50% Ni alloys and developed the composition known as Hipernik (293). Although Yensen reported improvements due to vacuum melting, his great contribution was devising the practice of dry-hydrogen annealing at temperatures between 985 to 1310 C (1800 to 2400 F), a treatment that raised the maximum permeability of the 50% Ni composition by a factor of 2 to 5. The treatment was eventually found to remove carbon, sulfur, and oxygen.

Iron-nickel alloys containing 50% Ni are used in magnetic amplifiers, relays, transformers (audio, instrument, pulse, high-frequency power and current), motors, generators, gyrocompasses, and magnetic shielding. Considerable usefulness of the alloy is found for sensitive telephone relays and receivers. The material is available in thicknesses from about 0.014 in. to a fraction of a mil.

78% Ni – Fe alloys are characterized by unusually high initial and maximum permeabilities (Table 68). As mentioned, high permeabilities are associated with low anisotropy and magnetostriction that exist at about 78% Ni. The high initial permeability and low hysteresis loss of these alloys have made them very successful as materials for loading coils for land lines and submarine cables. Because ordinary submarine cables have a large capacitance as compared with inductance, there is much attenuation and distortion of the signals; as a consequence, the speed of transmission is affected. On land lines, the deficiency of inductance is corrected by putting loading coils at frequent intervals in the line. It is not practical to do this with submarine cables. For some time, the solution has been to load cables with a continuous wrapper of 78% Ni – Fe alloys of high permeability. This method of loading was not successful with iron or iron-silicon tapes, which have much lower initial permeability. The first Permalloy-wound cable was laid in 1924 between New York and the Azores; the Permalloy wrap increased the speed of transmission fivefold.

Land lines are loaded every 6000 ft or so. For this application, the Permalloy is generally powdered, mixed with an insulating material, pressed to a solid form, and annealed to develop the best characteristics. Although Permalloy is a ductile alloy, it can be made very brittle by the addition of sulfur, and hence, easily pulverized when cold. The sulfur-bearing alloy is readily hot rolled (294). Sulfur is removed by hydrogen annealing.

The high permeabilities of the Permalloys are developed by high-temperature annealing in dry hydrogen. The alloy is annealed in the form or shape in which it is to be used, because strains, elastic or plastic, will harm the properties. Annealing above about 1100 C (2010 F) in dry hydrogen, with a dew point of −50 C (−58 F) or lower, is necessary to obtain optimum quality.

Annealing iron-nickel compositions containing 65 to 70% Ni in a magnetic field in the temperature range of 400 to 600 C (750 to 1110 F) will further improve the permeability and decrease the hysteresis loss. The maximum permeability will ordinarily increase from about 10,000 to 270,000 by a magnetic anneal.

The magnetic properties of iron-nickel alloys are also influenced greatly by cooling rate. For instance, rapid cooling of Permalloy will increase the initial permeability from about 2000 (after a slow cool) to about 10,000.

The original Permalloy alloys suffered serious disadvantages. First, the heat treatment was complicated: only thin pieces could be cooled at an optimum rate to obtain the best properties, and special means had to be devised for thicker pieces. Also, the electrical resistivity was low, and thus the eddy currents were too high. This limitation was removed by the addition of molybdenum, chromium, and copper to Permalloy. The alloying elements not only increase the electrical resistivity, but allow the development of excellent magnetic properties by slow cooling from the annealing heat treatment. About 4% Mo is added to Permalloy containing 79% Ni. This composition is often referred to as 4-79 Permalloy. Mumetal, another alloy of the high-nickel class, has 75% Ni, 5% Cu, and 2% Cr.

Supermalloy contains 5% Mo. In this material, initial permeabilities as high as 125,000 and maximum permeabilities as high as one million have been obtained by annealing the material at 1200 to 1300 C (2190 to 2370 F). Figure 81 gives the hysteresis loops of Supermalloy and Molybdenum Permalloy in comparison with Armco iron. Note the small size of the loop for Supermalloy.

Oriented Iron-Nickel Alloys. Dahl and Pfaffenberger (295) were the first to observe a rectangular hysteresis loop in iron-nickel alloys containing 40 to 60% Ni. Snoek (296) and Dahl (297) were able to correlate the rectangular loop with grain orientation, which was produced by a large amount of cold rolling followed by annealing.

It is now known that rectangularity is readily achieved by rolling the alloys 95% or more, and annealing them in dry hydrogen

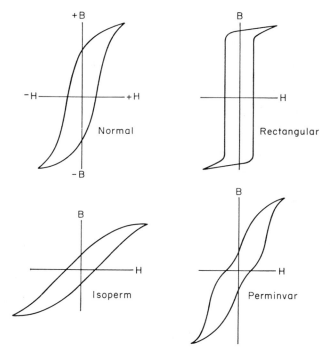

Fig. 115. Types of hysteresis loops

at above 800 C (1470 F). The resulting orientation is described as (010)[100]. Above 1100 C (2010 F), the rectangularity of the loop is lost, although the coercive force and permeability improve above this temperature, because of the elimination of impurities.

The oriented iron-nickel alloys are often used in tape-wound cores that are wound from strip from 6 to 0.5 mil in thickness (Fig. 105). The tapes are used for electronic computers, magnetic amplifiers, pulse transformers, and memory elements.

In the Permalloy-type alloys (78% Ni), a magnetic anneal produces rectangular hysteresis loops. The resulting domain orientation is responsible for the rectangular loop (298).

Perminvar. The iron-nickel alloys are strongly influenced by the addition of cobalt (299). The iron-nickel-cobalt alloys, called Perminvars, have a moderate permeability that is quite constant over a range of flux densities below about 500 gausses. At somewhat higher flux densities, a twin-section loop, constricted at the origin, develops; the material has little or no measurable remanence or coercive force. These alloys are also used for loading coils. The hysteresis loop for Perminvar is shown in Fig. 115.

The nominal alloy contains 45% Ni, 25% Co, remainder iron. The optimum properties are developed by annealing at 425 C (810 F), followed by slow cooling.

Isoperm. Another class of alloys of constant permeability over a range of B or H have been developed for loading-coil applications. Isoperm (300, 301) and Conpernik (302) contain 36 to 55% Ni; copper or aluminum may be added. Through heat treatment and working, the materials can be made with low retentivity, low hysteresis loss, and a permeability up to about 100. A hysteresis loop for Isoperm is shown in Fig. 115.

Iron-Cobalt Alloys

Iron and cobalt form a continuous solid solution (Fig. 116). The system possesses the highest known magnetic transformations (Curie temperatures). Cobalt itself has a Curie temperature of 1115 C (2039 F). An order-disorder transformation occurs at the 50 Co – 50 Fe composition.

Some important magnetic characteristics are plotted in Fig. 117. Note, in particular, the very high saturation of the alloys (the highest obtained at about 35% Co) and the Curie temperature. The magnetostriction and anisotropy nowhere reach low values simultaneously; hence, no unusually high permeabilities characterize the iron-cobalt alloys, at least to about 60% Co.

No large use has been made of iron-cobalt alloys thus far. Three types of iron-cobalt alloys have been studied: (a) the composition at 27% Co, (b) the composition at 35% Co, and (c) the composition at 50% Co. The 27% Co alloy is considerably more ductile after annealing than either the 35 or 50% Co irons. The trend toward miniaturization may favor the use of these alloys. Tape-wound cores of the 50% Co – Fe alloy have been used

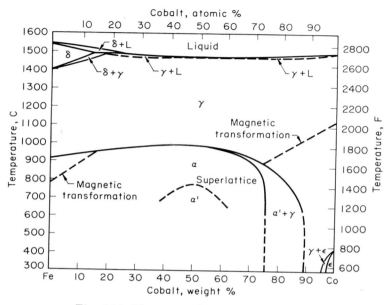

Fig. 116. The iron-cobalt phase diagram

with success in magnetic amplifiers and computer elements. Electromagnets have been made with pole pieces of 35% Co alloy. Experimental motors and generators have been built with frames and laminations made of the 35% Co alloy, but the cost for improved performance has not been justified.

The highest saturation induction known is obtained in an iron-cobalt alloy containing 35% Co; this induction is 24,200 gausses (303). The saturation remains high to 50% Co, where it is about 24,000 gausses, but, at higher levels of cobalt, the saturation decreases and becomes 17,900 gausses for the pure metal. Alloys above 30% Co are somewhat brittle in the hot rolled and the annealed conditions. In 1932, White and Wahl (304) succeeded in producing an alloy with good hot working properties by adding vanadium; after quenching, the alloy is ductile enough to cold roll. Stanley and Yensen (305) developed a workable alloy containing chromium. Unfortunately, alloys containing more than 30% Co become brittle after annealing for optimum magnetic properties.

The alloys of high saturation have relatively low permeability and high hysteresis loss, although these properties are considera-

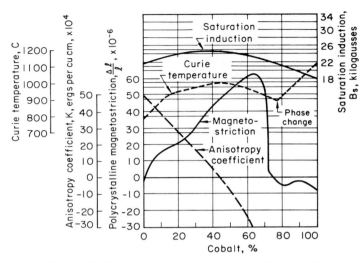

Fig. 117. Correlation of some magnetic quantities with composition in the iron-cobalt system

bly better at 50% than at 35% Co. The electrical resistivity of the binary alloy is low, although it can be increased by vanadium or chromium additions. Optimum magnetic properties are obtained by dry-hydrogen annealing in the range of 825 to 925 C (1515 to 1695 F). Annealing above the alpha-gamma phase transformation in this system does not improve magnetic properties; materials annealed at 1200 C (2190 F) actually have higher losses and lower permeabilities. The resistivity also varies widely with heat treatment, for example, 17.8 microhm-cm after a 700 C (1290 F) anneal to 25 microhm-cm after a 1100 C (2010 F) anneal. Some properties of iron-cobalt alloys are given in Table 69.

Table 69. Properties of Some Iron-Cobalt Alloys

Composition, %		Induction, B, gauss		Coercive force, H_c, oersteds, $B = 10,000$	Hydrogen heat treatment		
Co	Cr	$H = 10$	$= 100$		Hours	°C	°F
25	0.70	14,500	20,900	0.85	10	875	1605
30	0.70	14,500	21,100	0.69	50	875	1605
35	0.70	17,400	23,000	0.36	10	850	1560
40	0.70	16,500	22,800	0.63	50	825	1515
45	0.70	17,300	22,800	0.34	50	800	1470
50	0.70	20,400	23,300	0.24	10	850	1560

An alloy of 2% V, 49% Fe and 49% Co, vacuum melted to minimize interstitial impurities, has a maximum permeability of 66,000, a remanence of 21,150 gausses, a coercive force of 0.26 oersted, a saturation of 24,000 gausses, and a rectangular loop. This material is know as Supermendur (306).

The effect of temperature on the magnetic properties of these alloys was described in Chapter 5, page 249.

Other Soft Magnetic Materials

Iron-Aluminum Alloys. Although aluminum is known to have about the same effect on iron as silicon, with respect to electrical resistivity and magnetic properties, the alloys have never been developed to the same degree as those of the iron-silicon system. Iron-aluminum alloys are more ductile than iron-silicon alloys; to about 9% Al, they can be cold rolled. A 5% Al alloy can be rolled to tapes with as much as 99.5% cold reduction without difficulty. Iron-aluminum alloys are more oxidation resistant at elevated temperatures than any other soft magnetic material, and for this reason they may be used for high-temperature magnetic applications.

The magnetic properties of iron-aluminum alloys were first studied, along with iron-silicon alloys, by Barrett, Brown and Hadfield (283). The iron-aluminum alloys were abandoned in favor of the silicon alloys, probably because of the difficulty in melting and processing these steels, and their high cost at the time (aluminum cost $2.00 per lb).

Preferred orientation, either the cube-on-edge or the cube texture, can be developed in iron-aluminum alloys. Masumoto and Saito (307) made an extensive study of the magnetic properties of alloys containing up to 17% Al. Alloys in the range of 14 to 16% Al were found to be sensitive to cooling rate, because of the order-disorder transformation. Highest permeabilities (initial, 3,100 and maximum, 55,000) were obtained with an alloy containing 16% Al. Nachman and Buehler (308) have extended the work on 10 to 17% Al alloys and have developed the Alfenol alloys. To date no extensive commercial use has been made of the magnetic properties of iron-aluminum alloys.

Iron-Aluminum-Silicon Alloys. The Japanese (309) have developed an iron-aluminum-silicon alloy with 8 to 11% Si and 5 to 6.5% Al, which has good permeabilities. In the annealed condition, the alloy has the following magnetic properties:

Initial permeability ....Up to 35,000
Maximum permeability .....Up to 162,000
Hysteresis loss ....28 ergs per cu cm per cycle
at $B = 5000$ gausses
Magnetic saturation ....11,000 gausses

The alloy is very brittle and must be used as a powder. It has been given the name of Sendust. Sendust flake, produced by warm rolling the powder, indicates a possible usefulness of this material for powdered cores for high-frequency applications (310).

Materials of Constant Permeability. Although the permeability of ferromagnetic materials is not a linear function of B or H, their usage has not been restricted. However, applications exist where a magnetic material of constant permeability is required. Filter coils in radio and telephone circuits and loading coils for long distance lines must be wound of materials of constant permeability to avoid speech distortion. Powdered-iron cores were originally used for the constant-permeability requirement. Annealed, uninsulated 80-mesh electrolytic iron compressed into rings at 200,000 psi (but unsintered) had a constant permeability of about 75 up to $B = 100$ gausses; unannealed iron for the same conditions had a permeability of 50. The same powders insulated with shellac had permeabilities of 55 and 25, respectively. Carbonyl iron is still used for this purpose at radio-frequencies.

Higher permeabilities can be obtained with certain heat treated, cold rolled alloys. The Perminvars (299) (30% Fe, 45% Ni, 25% Co) have a constant permeability of about 400 up to $B = 1000$ gausses. Owing to this constancy of permeability, they have nearly zero hysteresis.

Isoperms (301), containing 35 to 55% Ni, 45 to 50% Fe, and 5 to 15% Cu, have a constant permeability of 50 to 60 over a wide range of $H = 0$ to 100, after proper heat treatment.

A novel method of obtaining constant permeability consists of welding thin plates of different compositions, having different thermal expansion and magnetostriction of opposite sign (311). Thus, 90 to 100% Ni iron which has a high negative magnetostriction, or even nonmagnetic austenitic stainless steel (18% Cr, 8% Ni), is used as the tension component. A 36 to

50% Ni iron, which has positive magnetostriction, is used as the compression member. After a proper amount of cold rolling and annealing, a laminated structure is produced. This bimetal has a constant permeability of 60 to 120 over $H = 0$ to $H = 150$.

Soft Ferrites

Since the Second World War, a new class of ferromagnetic materials, called ferrites, has been developed. These materials are derived from the spinel (ionic) structure of magnetite ($FeO \cdot Fe_2O_3$), and are at the same time magnetic materials and electrical insulators (313). The structural formula can be rewritten $Fe^{++}Fe_2^{+++}O_4^{--}$. There are one doubly ionized (divalent) iron atom, Fe^{++}, two triply ionized (trivalent) iron atoms, Fe_2^{+++}, and four doubly ionized oxygen atoms, O_4^{--}. All soft ferrites contain two trivalent iron ions and four oxygen ions. The divalent ion can be any atom small enough to be accommodated on the lattice: nickel, zinc, manganese, copper, cobalt or magnesium. Common systems are $NiO \cdot Fe_2O_3$, $ZnO \cdot Fe_2O_3$, $MnO \cdot ZnO \cdot Fe_2O_3$, $NiO \cdot ZnO \cdot Fe_2O_3$, and $NiO \cdot CuO \cdot ZnO \cdot Fe_2O_3$. These ferrites are unique in comparison with metals in that they possess moderate permeability combined with high volume resistivity. Because ferrites are produced by powder metallurgy techniques (no laminating is required to reduce eddy currents), they can be formed into many useful shapes.

Ferrites can be used as cores for switches, electronic transformers, antenna rods, recording heads, magnetic logic cores, tuning cores (adjustable inductors), traveling wave-guide tubes, and power transducers (magnetostrictive oscillators). Because of their chemical inertness and lower density than metals, ferrites have been used as stators and rotors in floated gyroscopes. Ferrites can be used to construct microwave conductors which offer virtually no resistance to the energy in one direction through the circuit, but which give rise to high resistance in the opposite direction.

The ferrites are made by mixing high-purity iron oxide (Fe_2O_3) with one or more pure divalent oxide (NiO, MgO, ZnO, CoO or MnO) and then sintering the mixture at 800 to 1200 C (1475 to 2190 F). The sinter is ground, mixed with lubricants and binders, and pressed into desired shapes. Final sintering is done at 1200 to 1650 C (2190 to 3000 F). Increasing the density, by compacting or sintering, or both, increases the initial permeability and lowers the coercive force (desirable effects).

Ferrites are commonly used for transformers. A typical example is the flyback transformer in a television receiver; this device pulls the electron-scanning beam very quickly to the starting line in the picture tube after each horizontal sweep. Ferrites are used for cores of receiving antennas of portable radios. The receiving antenna can be considered as the secondary coil of a transformer whose primary is the transmitting antenna.

Soft ferrites have magnetization loops that qualitatively resemble those of ferromagnetic metals. This form can be considered as a normal loop for any magnetic material. Quantitative differences between ferrites and metals exist, inasmuch as the saturation magnetization of ferrites ranges from about 2000 to 6000 gausses, and the saturation in common metals and alloys ranges from 6000 to 24,000 gausses. The coercive force of the ferrites extends from several thousand oersteds for the hard ferrites down to a few hundredths of an oersted for the soft, whereas, for metals, values down to a few millioersteds have been measured. The maximum permeability of the best ferrites is only about 6000, but that of the best magnetic alloys approaches one million. These differences in magnetic permeabilities have an effect only on the size of the hysteresis loop and have little effect on its form. The ferrites can be used up to frequencies of several megacycles per second, because of the high electrical resistivity, of the order of 10^5 microhm-cm (page 214); resistivities of metals will not exceed 60 microhm-cm (page 268).

The nickel-zinc ferrites have normal hysteresis loops, but, if small amounts of manganese and cobalt are added to that combination and if a certain sintering practice is used, a Perminvar-type loop develops (314). Such a loop is obtained when the structure contains both large and small crystallites. A uniform crystallite size, large or small, produces a normal loop (Fig. 115).

Compositions based on the $MgO \cdot MnO \cdot Fe_2O_3$ system can be readily made into materials with rectangular hysteresis loops. These materials are useful for magnetic memory cells in computers, switching, and automatic controls. Memory matrices for giant computers contain thousands of tiny ferrite cores.

Cooling nickel-zinc-cobalt ferrites in a magnetic field influences the type of hysteresis loop obtained. Cooling in a transverse field (H in the direction of the axis of the ring-shaped core) gives Isoperm-type loops. Cooling in the longitudinal (ring-shaped) field results in the formation of rectangular loops (Fig. 115).

Cadmium-manganese ferrites ($CdO \cdot MnO \cdot Fe_2O_3$), with a mole per cent of 20:40:40 and 20:35:45, have rectangular loops and have found usefulness in memory elements of high-speed computers. These cadmium-manganese ferrites have extremely high switching times, of the order of 0.1 microsec.

The nickel, nickel-copper, and nickel-cobalt ferrites exhibit large changes in dimensions on magnetization. The longitudinal magnetostriction of nickel ferrite is -27×10^{-6}; the magnetostriction for pure nickel, which is inordinately high by comparison to other metals, is -33×10^{-6}.

Garnets, the latest addition to the oxide magnet family, have the formula $3M_2O_3 \cdot 5Fe_2O_3$, where M_2O_3 can be one of the many rare earth oxides. These garnets are used in several types of microwave devices and are favored over the ferrites. The garnets are transparent magnetic materials.

Thin-Gage Materials — Tapes

Tapes are magnetic material under 0.012 in. thick. Common thin-gage tapes are 7, 5, 4, 2, and 1 mil and under. The frequency at which the tapes are used determines, in general, the thickness required. The manufacture of thin tapes requires cluster-type rolling mills having very small work rolls.

Tapes are used as core materials to frequencies of the order of 1 megacycle (312). Above this frequency, the soft ferrites find considerable use. Permeability of core steel decreases at high frequencies, depending on thickness. Oriented silicon steel and oriented iron-nickel alloys of 0.012 to 0.014 in. have excellent high permeability at low frequencies, but, unless thin laminations are used, this advantage disappears at frequencies of 20 to 40 kilocycles. By decreasing the thickness below 1 mil, the materials can be used up to 1 megacycle.

For frequencies from 400 to 2000 cps, tapes 4 to 7 mils thick are used; for frequencies of 2000 cycles and higher, 1 and 2-mil tapes are employed; and for frequencies over 1 megacycle, tapes under 1 mil are required. Some uses are given in Table 70.

Oriented 3.25% Si iron (down to 2 mils) and oriented iron-nickel alloys (even below 1 mil) are the bases for many thin

Table 70. Applications of Thin Electrical Steels

Thicknesses of 12 and 14 Mils
(Frequencies to 400 cycles)

Motors, generators, transformers

Thicknesses of 7, 5 and 4 Mils
(Frequencies of 400 to 2000 cycles)

400-cycle motors
  Automatic pilots and
    stabilizers
  Servo-mechanism motors
400-cycle converters
Television (5 mils)
  Deflection yoke cores
  Flyback or horizontal-
    sweep transformers
  Vertical-sweep transformers
Magnetic amplifiers
  (including seismographs
    and magnetometers)

Other electronic devices
  400-cycle power
    transformers
  Plate and filament
    transformers
  Filter chokes
  Swinging chokes
  Charging reactors
  Timing pulse generators
Radio
  Audiofrequency filters
  Voice-frequency modulators

Thicknesses of 2 and 1 Mil
(Frequencies of 2000 cycles and higher)

Pulse transformers
High-repetition rate-charging reactors
Intermediate-frequency transformers
Blocking oscillator-type pulse transformers
Timing pulse generators
Impulse storing and memory devices (and other devices that require a high rate of change in flux with respect to time)
Magnetic amplifiers (where small time constants are required with a rather low power input)

Thicknesses of 1 Mil and Under
(High-frequency, > 1 megacycle)

Transformers

---

tapes. Permalloy (78% Ni) and similar material (Supermalloy, Mumetal, Molybdenum Permalloy) are the alloys commonly used, although Hipernik (50% Ni) and related compositions (Deltamax, Orthonik and 4750) have had wide use. Silicon steels 1 and 2 mils thick compete with the Permalloys in low-current high-frequency transformers, as well as in pulse transformers.

Thin tapes from a fraction of a mil to 7 mils thick are the basis of magnetic amplifiers, which are being found in more and more electronic computers and machine-tool controls.

After rolling, the tapes of a required length are wound on ceramic mandrels or bobbins, with an insulating material to prevent sticking of the thin strip during high-temperature hydrogen annealing. Magnesia (MgO) is ordinarily used. The materials are annealed in very dry hydrogen, at a dew point of -40 C (-40 F) or less, at temperatures in the range of 1100 to 1200 C (2010 to 2190 F).

The annealed cores are extremely strain sensitive and must be handled very carefully. No deformation of any kind, not even dropping, is permissible. It is difficult, if not at times impossible, to reanneal damaged cores to recover properties.

After they are annealed, the tapes are carefully laid into close-fitting nylon, phenolic or aluminum boxes (hollow toroids), and sealed in silicone grease or oil to avoid damage to the core during winding and other handling.

Once each core is annealed and packed in a plastic box, it is tested for magnetic uniformity. This is one of the most expensive aspects of core production. Testing of individual cores is essential, because the chemistry, rolling, and annealing cannot be controlled to such an extent that magnetic quality can be predicted with high precision. Because cores are often matched in circuits, their individual performance must be accurately known.

Nonmagnetic Materials (315)

There are applications in which metals such as copper, brass, bronze, or aluminum are either too low in strength or too expensive, and nonmagnetic (nonferromagnetic) steels are required. Nonmagnetic steels are used to avoid the effect of a magnetic flux on the properties of the steel. A ferromagnetic material becomes magnetized in a magnetic field and will increase in temperature in an alternating-current field as a result of hysteresis effects. Hence, nonmagnetic materials are used in certain parts of electrical machinery (bushings on power transformers, retaining rings for generator rotor caps and wedges,* armature binding wire and strip), housings for electromagnets, measuring instruments, marine compasses, nonmagnetic ships in time of war (mine sweepers), armoring of alternating-current cables, and shells for induction melting furnaces.

Although all austenitic steels fulfill the condition of being nonmagnetic, consideration must be given to the stability of the structure on heating, welding and cold working. Table 71 shows

---

* The rings and wedges are used to restrict movement of the copper windings under centrifugal force.

Table 71. Magnetic Properties of Some Austenitic Steels in the Annealed and Cold Rolled Conditions

| AISI type | Composition, % | | | | | Magnetic permeability at 100 oersteds | | | | |
| | C | Mn | Cr | Ni | Others | Annealed | Cold reduced, % | | | |
							10	20	40	70
301	0.11	1.26	17.15	7.41	....	.... 1.010	1.56	6.64	21.3	40.0
302	0.09	0.49	18.30	8.34	....	.... 1.007	1.18	3.11	12.3	36.8
304	0.060	0.58	18.48	10.18	....	.... 1.004	1.006	1.038	1.36	2.9
316	0.06	1.82	17.32	12.54	2.3 Mo	.... 1.003	1.004	1.004	1.005	1.009
310	0.13	2.09	27.48	21.48	....	.... 1.005	1.004	1.004	1.004	1.007

| AISI type | Composition, % | | | | Remanence, B_r(a), gausses | | | Coercive field, H_c(a), oersteds | | |
| | C | Mn | Cr | Ni | Cold reduced, % | | | Cold reduced, % | | |
					70	80	90	70	80	90
302	0.05	0.63	18.85	8.80	....	3850	4800	5700	80	60	45
304	0.05	0.58	18.81	10.59	....	100	1000	2200	275	230	190

(a) $H_{max} = 400$.

the effect of cold rolling on permeability. The formation of ferrite or ferromagnetic carbides is objectionable. Note the stability of types 310 and 316; there is very little change in permeability even after 70% cold reduction.

Table 72 lists some nonmagnetic steels, which can be classified in the following manner:

Manganese (Hadfield) Steels. After water quenching from about 1000 to 1100 C (1830 to 2010 F), these steels are nonmagnetic. Tempering at about 400 C (750 F) precipitates carbides that are feebly magnetic. A proper selection of tempering temperature will give a truly nonmagnetic steel.

Manganese-Chromium Steels. The addition of 4% Cr and the increase of manganese to 18% allow the carbon to be reduced to 0.4% and the austenitic condition to be retained.

Chromium-Nickel Steels. All members of the AISI 300 series of stainless steels are austenitic. The 12% Cr, 12% Ni steels are particularly stable on severe cold working. The common 18% Cr, 8% Ni steel and its modifications (Types 302 and 304) are not stable, because cold work converts them into permanent magnet materials, which formerly were used for wire recording. Note high values of coercive force of these steels in Table 71. The reason for decrease of H_c with cold work remains unexplained. One of the principal uses of nonmagnetic stainless steel wire (type 304) coated with tin is in the banding of electric motor armatures. The wire is wound on the armature and then soldered.

Chromium-nickel-manganese steels use manganese as a substitute for some of the nickel. A steel containing 12% Cr, 9% Ni and 6% Mn is especially stable during cold working.

Table 72. Nonmagnetic Iron-Base Alloys

Material	C	Si	Mn	Cr	Ni	Others	Permeability of annealed material
Wrought Alloys							
Manganese steel	1.0 to 1.4	0.25 to 1.0	10.0 to 14.0	....	....	....	1.03 to 1.30
Mn 18	0.3 to 0.4	0.3 to 0.8	17.0 to 19.0	....	....	....	1.01
Mn + Bi	0.3 to 0.8	....	17.0 to 22.0	....	0 to 3	0.1 to 1.0 Bi, 0 to 3 Cu	1.003
MnCr 18	0.3 to 0.5	0.3 to 0.8	17.0 to 19.0	3.0 to 5.0	....	0.08 to 0.12 N	1.01
MnNiCr 14	0.45 to 0.65	0.3 to 0.8	13.5 to 14.5	3.3 to 3.8	5.5 to 6.5	....	1.01
CrNiMn 12-9	0.15 to 0.25	0.60	5.5 to 6.5	11.0 to 12.0	9.0 to 10.0	....	1.05
CrNi 12-12	0.10 max	1.00 max	2.00 max	11.5 to 13.5	12.0 to 14.0	....	1.01
MnCr 18-10	0.15 max	1.00 max	17.0 to 19.0	11.0 to 13.0	2.0 max	....	1.01
Lomu	....	....	8.0 to 12.0	1 max	6.0 to 10.0	0.4 to 0.6 Mo	1.062
88X	0.3	....	11.0	....	7.5	....	1.02
Jessop nonmagnetic	0.3 to 1.2	....	8.0	....	10	....	1.20
Type 304	0.08 max	0.75	2.00	18.0 to 20.0	8.0 to 11.0	....	1.01
Type 316	0.10 max	1.00	2.00 max	16 to 18	10 to 14	2 to 3 Mo	1.003
Type 310	0.25 max	1.50	2.00 max	24 to 26	19 to 22	....	1.005
Mn-Ni	0.25 to 0.40	....	10.5 to 12.5	7.0 to 8.5	7.0 to 8.5	....	1.003
Cast Alloys							
Mn 12	1.1 to 1.3	0.3 to 0.5	12.0 to 13.0	....	....	....	1.01
MnCr 18	0.3 to 0.50	0.3 to 0.8	17.0 to 19.0	3.0 to 3.5	....	0.08 to 0.12 N	1.01
Nonmagnetic cast iron	2.7	2.5	4.2	....	8.5	....	1.05
Nonmagnetic steel castings	0.25 max	0.5 max	10 to 12	....	5.5 to 6.5	....	1.008 to 1.03

Manganese-nickel steels find some commercial use because of their lower cost, compared with many of the other nonmagnetic materials (particularly the chromium-nickel steels). They contain 10.50 to 12.50% Mn, 7.00 to 8.50% Ni, and 0.25 to 0.40% C.

Titanium-nickel intermetallic compound with 54.5% Ni, remainder titanium, is nonmagnetic and has good corrosion and oxidation resistance. It can be heat treated to a hardness of Rockwell C 62.

Magnetic Temperature Compensation

The magnetic permeability of iron and its alloys decreases with a rise in temperature (except for low values of H). For certain instruments (for example, watt-hour meters), it is desirable to compensate for variations of ambient temperature. This can be done with certain alloys. To compensate for temperature errors, it is customary to shunt a certain part of the magnetic flux around the moving part of the meter by means of an alloy of unusually high magnetic temperature coefficient between 0 and 100 C. As the ambient temperature increases, the amount of shunted flux decreases and forces more of the flux through the moving member than would be possible otherwise.

Two types of alloys are used for temperature compensation: (a) 70 Ni – 30 Cu, with or without additions of 2% Fe, or 1% Mn and some silicon, (316); (b) 30 to 40% Ni, remainder iron, with small amounts of manganese, chromium and silicon (317).

Chapter 7

Permanent Magnet Alloys
and Their Applications

THE PURPOSE of a permanent magnet is to provide a constant source of magnetism without the application of outside power. Modern permanent magnets produce fields of considerable strength and permanency, and some of the newer magnets are replacing electromagnets in certain applications. For electronic gear, permanent magnets eliminate need for outside power. In loudspeaker construction, permanent magnets replace electrically energized coils. Magnets are also used in magnetos, electrical measuring instruments, magnetrons, and telephone receivers.

Permanent magnets are commonly used either with air gaps (for example, in meter movements) or where magnetic poles alone are used (for example, relays, lifting tools).

The functions of permanent magnets are as follows:

1 *Transformation of mechanical to electrical energy.* Here, permanent magnets are used to produce a magnetic field through which a conductor moves. Direct and alternating-current generators, magnetos, dynamic and velocity microphones are examples of this function of a magnet.
2 *Transformation of electrical to mechanical energy.* Mechanical motion can be produced by the passage of a current in a conductor that is placed in a magnetic field. Examples of this function of a magnet are electric motors, loudspeakers, and measuring and recording instruments (ammeters, voltmeters, galvanometers).

Probably the most important use of permanent magnets is in the construction of loudspeakers. In this application, the actual conversion of electrical to acoustical energy occurs when electric power is fed into a loudspeaker in which a movable member vibrates in accordance with the wave forms of the electrical in-

313

put. The movable member, which is in contact with air, transmits its vibrations into the air as sound waves.

The moving-coil loudspeaker is the most widely used type (Fig. 118). This type has a light coil of wire attached to a hollow cone of paper or composition. The coil is introduced into the annular gap in a permanent magnet. When a voltage is applied to the coil, the resulting current creates a magnetic flux at right angles to the flux in the air gap. The flux generated by the coil tends to move the coil and cone in the direction shown in Fig.

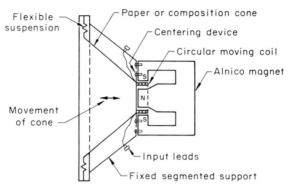

Fig. 118. Construction of a moving-coil loudspeaker

118. Actual movement of coil and diaphragm will be restricted by the flexible suspension and centering device. An alternating-current potential to the coil makes the system vibrate at the imposed frequency, and the amplitude of the movement will be directly proportional to the strength of the current and inversely proportional to the restraint imposed by the flexible support and centering device.

Permanent magnets are also basic in electrical measuring meters. Figure 119 shows a permanent magnet moving-coil direct-current instrument, commonly made with Alnico. The movement shown is that of D'Arsonval. A turning force is developed as a result of the current flowing in the moving coil. This torque acts in opposition to that of the spring. The pointer moves across a calibrated scale by an amount proportional to the current in the coil, the number of turns in the coil, and the flux density in the gap.

3 *Tractive effort.* The magnetic field of a magnet is also used to attract or repel other magnets or magnetic materials. Magnets are used for holding, as well as lifting. Common examples include: magnetic chucks, refrigerator and cabinet doors, magnetic separators, novelties and toys. Because like poles repel each other, magnets can be "floated" on one another. This effect is

used to replace springs in such devices as thermostats, pressure controls, and switches.

4 *Control of charged particles.* A magnetic field affects charged particles. When a flow of electrons or charged particles exists in a gas or vacuum, the magnetic field acts directly to deflect the particles from the original path. This effect is used in extinguishing electric arcs, operating magnetron tubes, constructing ion traps and focusing units for television and other cathode-ray tubes, and modifying electron or ion paths in cloud chambers and in mass spectrometers.

5 *Modification of the normal characteristics of matter.* The magnetic field can change normal physical properties of certain materials. Some properties affected by the application of a field are length and volume of ferromagnetic material (magnetostriction), electrical resistance (also known as magnetoresistance), elastic constants, rotation of the plane of polarization of light, and alternating-current permeability.

Most permanent magnets are used with an air gap. Therefore, the full residual induction is never available, because of the

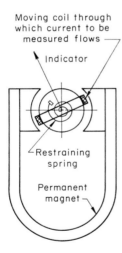

Moving coil through which current to be measured flows

Indicator

Restraining spring

Permanent magnet

Fig. 119. Permanent magnet moving-coil instrument. This D'Arsonval movement is commonly used in the direct-current instrument.

demagnetizing effect of the gap. The magnet is said to work down on the demagnetization curve. The most efficient portion of the curve at which to work, from the standpoint of maximum energy per unit volume, is the point at which the product of B and H is a maximum. The energy product, $(BH)_{max}$, is used almost universally as a criterion or index for magnetic quality. Representative permanent magnet materials are given in Table 73.

Table 73. Properties of Some Representative Permanent Magnet Alloys

Alloy	Composition, %	Residual flux density, gausses	Coercive force, oersteds	Maximum energy product, gauss-oersteds (millions)	Flux density, B_0(a), gausses	Fabrication and heat treatment
0.65% C steel	0.65 C, 0.85 Mn	10,000	42	0.18	6,500	Forged and quenched
1% C steel	1 C, 0.50 Mn	9,000	51	0.20	5,900	Forged and quenched
5% W steel	0.70 C, 5 W	10,500	70	0.33	7,000	Forged and quenched
1% Cr steel	0.60 C, 0.90 Cr, 0.45 Mn	9,500	52	0.23	6,500	Forged and quenched
6% Cr steel	1.1 C, 6 Cr, 0.40 Mn	9,500	74	0.30	6,200	Forged and quenched
9% Co steel	0.90 C, 9 Co, 1.25 W, 5 Cr	7,800	122	0.41	5,100	Forged and quenched
17% Co steel	0.70 C, 17 Co, 8.25 W, 2.5 Cr	9,000	170	0.65	5,900	Forged and quenched
36% Co steel	0.80 C, 36 Co, 3.75 W, 5.75 Cr	9,600	228	0.93	6,300	Forged and quenched
40% Co steel	0.70 C, 40 Co, 5 W, 4.25 Cr	10,000	242	1.03	6,500	Forged and quenched
Alnico I	12 Al, 22.5 Ni, 5 Co, rem Fe	6,600	540	1.40	4,100	Cast; cooled from high temperature; aged
Alnico II	10 Al, 18 Ni, 13 Co, 6 Cu, rem Fe	7,000	650	1.70	4,300	Cast; cooled from high temperature; aged
Alnico III	12 Al, 26 Ni, 3 Cu, rem Fe	6,400	560	1.35	3,900	Cast; cooled from high temperature; aged
Alnico IV	12 Al, 28 Ni, 5 Co, rem Fe	5,500	730	1.35	3,200	Cast; cooled from high temperature; aged
Alnico V(b)	8 Al, 15 Ni, 24 Co, 3 Cu, rem Fe	12,000	720	5.00	9,100	Cast; heat treated in magnetic field
Alnico V DG(b)	8 Al, 14.5 Ni, 24 Co, 3 Cu, rem Fe	13,100	700	6.50	11,000	Cast with directional grain; heat treated in magnetic field
Alnico V-7	8 Al, 14 Ni, 24 Co, 3 Cu, rem Fe	13,400	780	7.50	11,400	Cast with directional grain; heat treated in magnetic field
Alnico VI(b)	8 Al, 17 Ni, 23 Co, 3 Cu, 4 Ti, rem Fe	7,500	975	2.75	4,600	Cast; heat treated in magnetic field
Alnico VII(b)	8.5 Al, 18 Ni, 24 Co, 3.25 Cu, 5 Ti, rem Fe	7,500	1100	3.00	4,300	Cast; heat treated in magnetic field
Alnico VIII	7 Al, 15 Ni, 35 Co, 4 Cu, 5 Ti, rem Fe	8,700	1450	4.50	5,200	Cast; heat treated in magnetic field

Material	Composition					Treatment
Alnico XII	6 Al, 18 Ni, 35 Co, 8 Ti, rem Fe	6,100	1000	1.65	3,200	Cast; cooled from high temperature; aged
Nipermag	12 Al, 30 Ni, 0.4 Ti, rem Fe	5,600	660	1.34	3,400	Cast; cooled from high temperature; aged
Sintered Alnico II	10 Al, 17 Ni, 12.5 Co, 6 Cu, rem Fe	7,200	550	1.50	4,400	Sintered; cooled from high temperature; aged
Sintered Alnico IV	12 Al, 28 Ni, 5 Co, rem Fe	5,500	730	1.25	3,100	Sintered; cooled from high temperature; aged
Sintered Alnico V(b)	8 Al, 14 Ni, 24 Co, 3 Cu, 1 Ti, rem Fe	10,500	600	3.8	8,150	Sintered; heat treated in a magnetic field
Cunico I	50 Cu, 21 Ni, 29 Co	3,400	710	0.85	2,000	Rolled
Cunico II	35 Cu, 24 Ni, 41 Co	5,300	450	0.99	3,400	Rolled
Cunife I(b)	60 Cu, 20 Ni, 20 Fe	5,700	590	1.85	4,200	Rolled
Cunife II(b)	50 Cu, 20 Ni, 2.5 Co, 27.5 Fe	7,300	200	0.78	4,700	Rolled
Remalloy, Comol	12 Co, 17 Mo, rem Fe	10,000	230	1.10	6,900	Hot or cold worked; quenched and aged
Vectolite(b)	30 Fe₂O₃, 44 Fe₃O₄, 26 Co₂O₃	1,600	900	0.50	940	Sintered, heat treated in a magnetic field
Silmanal	86.75 Ag, 8.8 Mn, 4.45 Al	590	550	0.083	292	Cold worked; annealed and cold worked
Vicalloy I	9.5 V, 38.5 Fe, 52 Co	9,000	300	1.00	5,500	Hot or cold worked; aged
Vicalloy II(b)	13 V, 35 Fe, 52 Co	10,000	450	3.00	8,200	Hot or cold worked; aged
Permet, PF-1(c)	100 Fe	5,700	470	1.10	3,650	Compacted
Permet, PF-2(c)	30 Co, 70 Fe	6,000	625	1.52	3,830	Compacted
ESD iron(d)	100 Fe	7,000	670	2.15	....	Compacted, not sintered
ESD iron-cobalt(d)	65 Fe, 35 Co	7,900	1000	3.50	....	Compacted, not sintered
Bismanol(b)	79.2 Bi, 20.8 Mn	4,800	3650	5.30	2,640	Compacted
Platinum iron	77.8 Pt, 22.2 Fe	5,830	1570	3.07	3,400	Quenched and aged
Platinum cobalt	76.7 Pt, 23.3 Co	6,000	4300	7.5	3,240	Quenched and aged
New KS	3.7 Al, 17.7 Ni, 27.2 Co, 6.7 Ti, rem Fe	7,150	785	2.03	4,300	Quenched
Ferrimag I	BaO·6Fe₂O₃	2,100	1650	1.00	1,130	Sintered
Ferrimag V(b)	BaO·6Fe₂O₃	3,900	2000	3.50	....	Pressed in magnetic field; sintered

(a) B_0 is the flux density at the point of maximum energy product. (b) Directional magnetic properties. (c) Powder particles not elongated. (d) Elongated particles.

Martensitic Carbon Steels

The original permanent magnet materials were the plain, high-carbon steels. These steels are cast into ingots and are hot worked into bars and strip. The coercive force of iron can be increased by adding carbon and quenching from higher temperatures. Optimum results are obtained in steels containing 0.7 to 1.0% C that are quenched either in water or oil, but are not tempered. The remanence of these materials is high, but the coercive force is low. The magnets are comparatively unstable with respect to stray alternating-current fields, heat, vibration and aging.

The tungsten magnet steels, introduced after 1855, were an improvement over the plain carbon steels. Both the remanence and coercive force were increased. The steels contained 5 to 6% W and 0.5 to 1% C; a typical steel analyzed 6% W and 0.6 to 0.9% C. Tungsten steel was widely used at the time of the First World War.

When tungsten became difficult to obtain, chromium was found to be a cheaper and almost equivalent substitute. The chromium magnet steels contained from 1 to 6% Cr, but the 3% Cr, 0.90% C steel was one of the most popular compositions. For this material, a typical heat treatment was an austenitizing treatment at 800 to 850 C (1470 to 1560 F) followed by an oil quench; an aging treatment of about 24 hr at 100 C (212 F) gave a highly stable material.

The tungsten and chromium steels are more stable than the carbon steels from the standpoint of thermal changes and mechanical shock. Unfortunately, all three steels show variations in aging due to changes accompanying the decomposition of martensite. Because these steels have a relatively high remanence, they are used for applications requiring small cross-sectional areas.

In 1916, Honda in Japan introduced the KS Magnet Steel, better known as cobalt magnet steel (318). A typical composition is 0.7 to 1% C, 6 to 8% W, 1 to 4% Cr and 15 to 42% Co. The $(BH)_{max}$ of this steel was one million gauss-oersteds. A wide range of standard cobalt steel permanent magnet alloys has been developed; the principal ones contain 3, 9, 17 and 36% Co. Before the discovery of Alnico, the 36% Co alloy was the best permanent magnet alloy known. The alloys unfortunately are glass-brittle; they form cracks on quenching and the resulting martensite is readily transformed to a product of lower coercive force.

Precipitation-Hardening Magnets

In the early thirties, some carbon-free precipitation-hardening permanent magnet alloys were discovered. In 1930, Dean (319) patented iron alloys containing tungsten, molybdenum, tantalum or beryllium, tungsten and cobalt, or molybdenum and cobalt, which responded to solution and aging treatments. Koster (320) studied these alloys extensively. For iron containing 10 to 20% W or Mo and with up to 15% Co, an energy product of over one million gauss-oersteds was obtained. In 1934, Honda (321) reported that an alloy of 10 to 25% Ni, 8 to 25% Ti, and 15 to 36% Co had an energy product of two million gauss-oersteds.

Remalloy, or Comol, is an iron-base, carbon-free material containing about 12% Co and 17% Mo, with or without some chromium and tungsten. The alloy is most commonly made in hot rolled bars or sheet, which may be hot formed, sheared, punched, or machined to shape; the material does not cold form or cold roll. Magnetic properties are developed through precipitation hardening. The alloy is first quenched from 1200 C (2190 F) and then aged at 680 C (1256 F). After heat treating, only grinding is permissible as the heat treated alloy is fragile and brittle. The heat treated alloy has a remanence of 10,000 gausses, a coercive force of 230 oersteds, and a maximum energy product of 1.10 million gauss-oersteds.

A sintered product of this composition is called Indalloy. It is especially useful for low-cost production of small (less than 2 oz) magnets. Intricate shapes may be sand cast and machined before heat treatment.

Vicalloy (322) is a carbon-free material of about 38% Fe, 10% V, 52% Co, which belongs to the precipitation-hardening class of alloys. Ordering of the low-temperature phase may also contribute to magnetic hardening.

Vicalloy I contains 9.5% V, 38.5% Fe, and 52% Co. Properties of the following magnitude can be developed: remanence of 11,500 gausses, a coercive force of 200 oersteds, and a maximum energy product of 1.50 million gauss-oersteds.

Vicalloy II contains 13% V, 35% Fe, and 52% Co. By severe reduction (rolling to 0.002-in. tapes) and aging, the following properties are obtainable in the rolling direction only: remanence of 9000 to 10,500 gausses, a coercive force of 375 to 475 oersteds, and a maximum energy product of 1.70 to 3.40 million gauss-oersteds.

The alloy in its annealed single-phase state is ductile and can be worked by any ordinary shop operation. After the precipitation treatment, it is hard and brittle, comparable to a high martensitic hardness. It is available in bars, sheet, wire, strip, and tubing.

The alloy is usually solution treated at 925 to 1010 C (1700 to 1850 F) and quenched in oil for either cold working or prior to aging of the cast or hot worked metal. Aging is then performed for 1 to 4 hr at 595 C (1100 F).

Vicalloy is used for hysteresis motors, compasses, recording tape and wire, clock motors, and special holding magnets.

Nickel-copper-iron alloys can be hot and cold rolled and machined. Legat (323) found optimum magnetic properties at 15% Ni and 15% Cu. By quenching the alloy from 1095 to 1315 C (2000 to 2400 F) and subsequently aging it at 705 C (1300 F), Legat obtained a coercive force of 300 oersteds and a remanence of 1500 gausses.

Dahl and co-workers (324) obtained good properties in a copper-base alloy containing nickel and iron. An alloy with 60% Cu, 20% Ni, and 20% Fe developed the highest energy product. This was obtained by homogenizing the alloy at 1040 C (1900 F), aging at 595 C (1100 F), cold rolling 40 to 75%, and reaging at 595 C. Copper-nickel-iron alloys are known as the Cunife alloys.

Cunife I (60 Cu – 20 Ni – 20 Fe) is easily cold rolled and develops preferred orientation. It is machinable and easily cold formed. In the direction of rolling, the following magnetic properties can be developed: remanence of 5300 gausses, coercive force of 590 oersteds, and maximum energy product of 1.85 million gauss-oersteds. A modified alloy, Cunife II, contains about 2.5% Co. Surprisingly, the materials can be cold rolled, but they cannot be hot worked. An optimum range of size reduction between annealing and cold finishing is required to obtain the best magnetic properties. Best magnetic properties are developed in wires below 0.2 in. in diameter and in rectangular magnets about 0.625 in. wide and 0.04 in. thick.

The Cunifes respond to two heat treatments: One is a slow

cool from 1050 C (1920 F), followed by an aging treatment at 650 C (1200 F). The other is a quench from 1000 C (1832 F) and an aging treatment at 600 C (1110 F). After either of these heat treatments, the materials are cold rolled to a reduction of 70 to 90%.

Cunico magnets (50 Cu – 21 Ni – 29 Co) have magnetic and physical properties similar to those of Cunife. They are used as castings, sintered powder metallurgy products, and in the wrought condition. The alloys are malleable when cold, but cannot be hot worked. Wrought products are made by cold working (swaging or wiredrawing) the cast rounds or flats. Reheating for softening is often necessary. The highest coercive force in wire

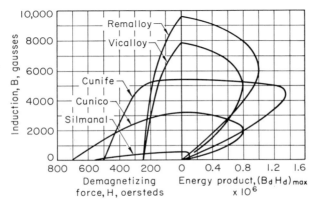

Fig. 120. Demagnetization and energy curves for various ductile permanent magnet materials

or strip is obtained by aging. The heat treatments used for Cunife can in general be used for Cunico. Typical properties are as follows: remanence of 3400 gausses, coercive force of 710 oersteds, and an energy product of 0.85 million gauss-oersteds.

Silmanal is a silver-base alloy in which manganese is the ferromagnetic component. It was discovered by Potter (325), who substituted silver for copper in the copper-manganese-aluminum Heusler alloy.

Silmanal is a ductile magnetic material containing 4.4% Al, 8.8% Mn and 86.8% Ag. The alloy requires high fields for magnetization and is extremely difficult to demagnetize.

The alloy is cast into small ingots, which are homogenized,

and then cold swaged to small rounds. The material is not hot workable. Cold working is necessary to develop magnetic properties. Silmanal is ductile, malleable, and machinable before and after heat treatment. Silmanal is aged at 200 to 300 C (390 to 570 F) to develop properties.

Silmanal has the following characteristics: remanence of 590 gausses, coercive force of 550 oersteds, and a maximum energy product of 0.08 million gauss-oersteds. Because of its cost and low output energy, Silmanal is used in special instrumentation exposed to alternating-current fields and other electrical demagnetizing influences.

The demagnetization and energy-product curves for the permanent magnet alloys just discussed (Remalloy, Cunife, Cunico, Vicalloy and Silmanal) are given in Fig. 120.

Alnico Permanent Magnet Alloys

The Alnico alloys are the most popular and most widely used of all permanent magnet materials. Alnico is a generic term describing the ternary alloys of nickel, aluminum, and iron discovered by Mishima (326) in 1931. These alloys have the highest energy products known, and are well suited for applications where a large force and small size are needed. Being glass-brittle, they are difficult to fabricate; however, they have sufficient strength for most applications. These alloys (25 to 30% Ni, 10 to 15% Al, remainder iron) correspond roughly to Fe_2NiAl. They are precipitation hardening, but they are important enough to be placed in a class by themselves.

The alloys are usually fabricated by sand or shell mold casting; a few are fabricated by powder metallurgy techniques. By heating some Alnico compositions close to the melting point, it has been possible to hot work the alloys. In general, vacuum-melted alloys hot work more easily than air-melted. The alloys have been extruded, rolled, and swaged. Properties of hot worked Alnico are similar to those of the cast product.

Some compositions can be heat treated in a magnetic field to give improved properties in the direction of the magnetizing field. Still other compositions are cast on chill plates to give directional grain structure; when heat treated in a magnetic field parallel to the grain, these alloys have very high energy products. Single crystal magnets are in the development stage; these offer considerable commercial promise for the future. Energy products of 10 to 11 million gauss-oersteds are predicted.

In 1938, anisotropic permanent magnets were obtained by heat treating the Ni-Al-Cu-Co-Fe material in a magnetic field (327). This work culminated in the period from 1940 to 1942 in the familiar cast alloys referred to as Alcomax in England, Ticonal in Holland, and Alnico DG in the United States. Further gradual improvement in alloying and heat treatment has occurred over the years, until at the present time numerous Alnico compositions are available (Table 73).

The original alloys made by Mishima, a student of Honda, were called Alni and their composition corresponded approximately to Fe_2NiAl (25% Ni, 12% Al, remainder iron). The alloy had the following excellent properties (superior to the best magnet steel then available, 36% Co): remanence of 6500 gausses, coercive force of 470 oersteds, and an energy product of about 1.3 million gauss-oersteds. This alloy was later incorporated into the Alnico family as Alnico III, but only after the development of the cobalt-containing Alnico I and II.

In the first cobalt-containing Alnico, cobalt replaced 5% of the nickel content of Alnico III. The properties of Alnico I are as follows: remanence of 6600 gausses, coercive force of 540 oersteds, and an energy product of 1.4 million gauss-oersteds.

It was next discovered that the coercive force could be improved without sacrifice of the residual induction by further increasing the cobalt and adding some copper. This alloy, known as Alnico II, had the following characteristics: remanence of 7000 gausses, coercive force of 650 oersteds, energy product of 1.7 million gauss-oersteds.

To meet the demand of a lower-cost alloy of high coercive force, where some sacrifice of the residual induction could be tolerated, the Alnico IV composition was devised. This alloy is similar to Alnico I, except that the nickel is increased from 20 to 28%. For some time, Alnico IV had the highest coercive force known (about 730 oersteds).

All of the preceding compositions (Alnico I, II, III and IV) have isotropic properties and hence can be magnetized just as effectively in one direction as another. In 1938, Oliver and Sheddon found that, if Alnico was solution treated and then cooled in a magnetic field, improved magnetic properties could be obtained in the direction of the field used in heat treating. Although the effect was not large, specialized heat treating eventually was to give highly anisotropic (and improved) magnets. Within a year, an energy product more than twice that of a standard alloy was produced. The properties in the direction transverse to the applied field used in heat treating are very poor.

The very popular Alnico V alloy resulted from the discovery that anisotropic properties could be obtained by this specialized heat treating. As a consequence of this treatment, along with improving the composition, the remanence was almost doubled and the energy product was trebled over the previously best permanent magnet alloys. For instance, one variety of Alnico V had a remanence of 13,200 gausses, a coercive force of 580 oersteds, and an energy product of 5.5 million gauss-oersteds (Table 74), the highest energy product known at that time.

For fixed air-gap apparatus, Alnico V was ideal, but, when the demagnetizing force exceeded about 500 oersteds, the induction decreased very rapidly (Fig. 121). This characteristic was undesirable for variable air-gap apparatus, and, to circumvent this drop, about 1% Ti was introduced to give a magnetization curve that had a less precipitous drop than Alnico V. Although the coercive force was improved, the remanence and energy product were lower. This alloy became known as Alnico VI.

Next on the scene was Alnico XII, with 24% Co and 8% Ti.

Table 74. Characteristics of Several Varieties of Alnico V

Alnico V variation	Composition, %					Energy product, $(BH)_{max}$, gauss-oersteds, millions	Remanence, B_r, gausses	Coercive force, H_c, oersteds	Induction, B_0, at $(BH)_{max}$, gausses
	Al	Ni	Co	Cu	Ti				
Random Grain									
1	8	15	24	3	..	5.00	12,000	720	9,100
2	8	14.5	24	3	..	5.50	12,500	685	10,000
3	8	14	24	3	..	5.50	12,700	650	10,400
4	8	13	24	3	..	5.50	13,200	580	11,200
5	8	14.5	23	3	0.5	4.50	11,000	700	8,400
Directional Grain (DG)									
6 ....Same as 2 above						6.50	13,100	700	11,000
7 ....Same as 3 above						6.50	13,300	685	11,250
8 ....Same as 3, but 100% DG						7.50	12,750	765	11,000
9 ....TK-8; exact composition not known; 100% DG						8.1	14,240	800	12,050

This composition was similar to Honda's New KS steel and developed a very high coercive force of 1100 oersteds. Alnico XII is now obsolete.

Subsequent modifications of Alnico VI were made by increasing the titanium; Alnico VII has 5% Ti. The new alloy, Alnico VIII, has higher cobalt (34%), but about the same titanium (5%). Coercive forces of the order of 1450 oersteds are attainable with Alnico VIII.

A major advance occurred in magnet technology when Hoselitz and McCaig (327) found that orienting the crystal axes

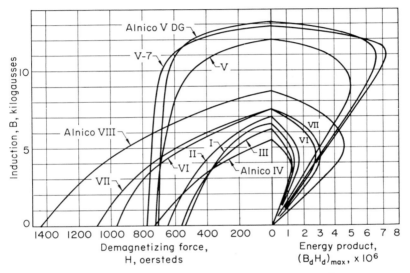

Fig. 121. *Demagnetizing and energy product curves for various Alnico alloys*

of the alloy during casting (growing columnar grains) improved the energy product by 20% or more. The columnar grains grow so that the favorable [100] direction is perpendicular to the chill face in the mold. Materials with columnar grains are known as DG (directional-grain) permanent magnet alloys. Typical properties of Alnico V DG are given in Table 74. Energy products of 6.5 million gauss-oersteds are obtained. Although 100% directional grain has been the goal, almost all DG magnets are only partially columnar, with the balance of the structure being constituted of equiaxed grains.

Only recently has the production of 100% directional grain been realized by special and secret foundry techniques, among which is the use of preheated molds. Alnico V compositions with 100% directional grain have energy products of 7.5 million gauss-oersteds or somewhat higher. These are called Alnico V-7.

The highest energy product attained with completely columnar Alnico compositions is about 11 million gauss-oersteds. The next important development probably will be in the production of single-crystal magnets of favorable composition.

Alnico magnets are essentially a foundry product; they can also be prepared by powder metallurgy methods. As a family, they are hard and brittle. The magnets are produced by casting (sand or shell molding) and grinding; they cannot be drilled or otherwise machined. When shell molding is used, grinding may not be necessary as tolerances can be held to about ±0.005 in.

Alnico permanent magnet alloys must be heat treated to obtain their optimum magnetic properties. The heat treatment, which is somewhat involved depending on grade, ordinarily consists of three stages:

1 High-temperature treatment for solution of the aluminum or titanium compounds, or both
2 Conditioning treatment, which is effected by controlled cooling of the alloys from certain critical temperatures with or without the influence of a magnetic field
3 Coercive aging treatment for the controlled reprecipitation of the compounds at some lower temperature

The isotropic, nondirectional grades are heat treated somewhat differently than the anisotropic materials. Each Alnico composition requires a unique cycle of its own. The treatment is encompassed within the following procedure: The isotropic alloys are solution treated at some definite, critical temperature between 900 to 1120 C (1650 and 2050 F). They are then carefully cooled in insulated chambers at a predetermined rate to a black color. Beyond a certain temperature, they are still-air cooled to room temperature. The alloys are then "coercive" aged in the temperature region of 540 to 650 C (1000 to 1200 F).

The anisotropic Alnico alloys formerly were solution treated for about 1½ hr at 1205 to 1315 C (2200 to 2400 F). As a result of the Hansen patents (328), it is now possible to solution treat these grades at 900 to 925 C (1650 to 1700 F). The Hansen patents use silicon or zirconium to suppress the formation of the undesirable gamma phase at above 900 C (1650 F), so that high-temperature annealing is not necessary. After being solution treated, the alloys are cooled in a strong magnetic field at a pre-determined rate. They then produce phenomenal characteristics in the direction of the applied field. Most directionalizing equipment consists of solenoids cooled with water jackets. Special directionalizing jigs are required for odd-shaped magnets. The directionalized alloys are "coercive" aged from 540 to 650 C (1000 to 1200 F).

Directional-grain Alnico alloys are anisotropic as a result of the columnar structure, and their anisotropy is accentuated by heat treating in a magnetic field. The heat treatment used is similar to that for the random-grain anisotropic alloys. The Alnico alloys, unlike martensitic steels, do not age at room temperature.

Sintered Alnico. Alnico magnets can be made by powder metallurgy, although they are more expensive than cast magnets for equivalent sizes. Sintered magnets are usually made in sizes weighing 1 oz or less. This product has improved mechanical strength resulting from fine particle size.

The most important type of sintered magnet is Alnico V (8% Al, 14% Ni, 24% Co, 3% Cu, 1% Ti, remainder iron). A properly processed sample will have a remanence of 10,500 gausses, a coercive force of 600 oersteds, and a maximum energy product of 3.8 million gauss-oersteds. A cast anisotropic magnet of this composition has a remanence of 12,700 gausses, a coercive force of 650 oersteds, and an energy product of 5.50 million gauss-oersteds.

The demagnetization and energy curves for the various Alnico alloys are given in Fig. 121.

Hard Ferrites

Ceramic permanent magnet materials or hard ferrites ($BaO \cdot 6Fe_2O_3$, $SrO \cdot 6Fe_2O_3$ or $PbO \cdot 6Fe_2O_3$) (329) have very high coercive forces, and, on an equal weight basis, they have maximum energy products equal to or better than those of some magnetic alloys. Because coercive forces up to about 3000 oersteds or higher are possible, the ceramic magnet can be designed with a short length; the flux density is low ($B_r = 3900$ gausses); hence magnets of high cross section are required. The hard ferrites have a high resistance to demagnetization; therefore, they can perform well with fairly large air gaps.

Both isotropic and anisotropic materials can be made. Isotropic materials generally have energy products of about 1.0 million gauss-oersteds, but the anisotropic ferrites can attain energy products of about 3.50 million gauss-oersteds.

The magnets are made by powder metallurgy techniques. A mixture of iron oxide and barium oxide (or carbonate) is calcined, ground, pressed, and fired. The anisotropic material is pressed in a strong magnetic field to align the magnetic particles. This alignment is preserved even after sintering. After sintering, the magnets have to be magnetized. Optimum properties in the oriented material are obtainable only by meticulous processing at every stage of the process. Particle size is a very important factor in obtaining highest energy product.

The ferrites have high electrical resistivity, up to one million ohm-cm. They are of low density, about 0.17 lb per cu in., which is about 30% lighter than metallic permanent magnet alloys. The ferrites are somewhat less expensive than Alnico. They are hard and brittle, but easily ground.

It is possible to bond the ferrite powder with various resins and plastics (polyethylene, styrene) to produce a soft, machinable and formable material. Properties of this bonded ferrite are as follows: remanence of 2100 to 2600 gausses, coercive force of 1300 to 2200 oersteds, and an energy product of 0.9 to 1.7 million gauss-oersteds.

Miscellaneous Permanent Magnet Materials

ESD (Elongated Single-Domain) Magnets. Although pure iron is usually considered the classic example of nonretentive ferromagnetic material, it can, if properly subdivided into particles that can accommodate only one domain, form a permanent magnet material. If the particles have an elongated, cigar-like shape (high shape anisotropy), energy products of 2.2 million gauss-oersteds can be obtained from pure iron (330, 331). Acicular particles of iron-cobalt (35% Co) have an energy product of 3.6 million gauss-oersteds, because cobalt increases the saturation of the iron (332). These ESD magnets are machinable.

The shaped particles are prepared by electrodepositing iron or iron-cobalt into mercury. After removal of the mercury, the particles are coated to prevent oxidation, and the binder also serves to consolidate the powder. Binders can be either plastics or metals such as lead.

Manganese-Bismuth Permanent Magnets (Bismanol). Although manganese and bismuth are not ferromagnetic by themselves, they form an intermetallic compound, MnBi, that is ferromagnetic (333). Bismanol is an anisotropic aggregate of crystals of the intermetallic phase MnBi and is produced by powder metallurgy techniques. The size, shape, and magnetic orientation of the magnet are obtained by hot pressing. The consolidated magnet is not sintered. Machining by drilling is considered feasible. A residual induction of 4800 gausses, a coercive force of 3650 oersteds, and an energy product of 5.3 million gauss-oersteds along the preferred magnetic axis have been reported.

This permanent magnet material has low corrosion resistance and a large temperature coefficient, experiencing a loss of magnetism at about -40 C (-40 F).

Vectolite is a nonmetallic magnet material composed of the oxides of cobalt and iron (334). It has high coercive force and is essentially a nonconductor of electricity. These two properties have made it useful in some high-frequency apparatus, speed indicators, and direct-current Selsyn motors. The oxides used are Fe_2O_3 (31%), Fe_3O_4 (43%) and CoO (26%). The magnets are sintered at about 995 C (1825 F). After sintering, the magnet is cooled in a magnetic field. In this preferred direction, the remanence is 1600 to 1900 gausses, the coercive force is 1100 to 1150 oersteds, and the maximum energy product is of the order of 0.75 million gauss-oersteds. The properties vary with density. The material is fragile and difficult to grind.

Precious Metal Permanent Magnet Alloys. Of more theoretical than practical importance are the binary alloys of platinum and iron or platinum and cobalt (335); materials containing about 77% Pt and 23% Fe or cobalt have very high coercive forces. Platinax II is said to have a maximum energy product of 9.2 million gauss-oersteds and the highest developed coercive force of all known materials, 4300 oersteds. The alloys are very ductile. The materials are aged between 500 to 800 C (930 to 1470 F) to develop the properties.

Manganese-Aluminum. An alloy, $Mn_{1.11}Al_{0.89}$, cooled 30 °C per min from 1150 C (2100 F) forms a two-phase tetragonal structure with good properties (336, 337). The swaged material has an energy product of 3.5 million gauss-oersteds, a remanence of 4280 gausses, and a coercive force of 2750 oersteds.

Rare Earth Alloys. Gadolinium alloyed with 60 to 70% Co shows a coercive force of several thousand oersteds (338).

Chapter 8

Developments that Cast
Their Shadows

MANY of the current ideas on the fundamental nature of electrical and magnetic phenomena need elaboration; comprehensive theories for explaining most observations remain to be developed. New knowledge, raising more questions than it is answering, is being developed in all areas at such a rate that computers are required to deal with it.* It is amazing how many applications can be made of phenomena that are not understood from first principles. Magnetism is a notable example.

Research budgets rise exponentially to astronomical sums. Research has become a basic industry and big business.** With this skyrocketing of research, scientists have gained popular respect and appreciation, which are long overdue.

Almost daily there is a new semiconductor discovery. Weekly, someone demonstrates a higher magnetic field in the cryogenic realm of superconductors. Monthly, a new alloy of unusual magnetic or electrical characteristics is announced. New knowledge in the field of electricity and magnetism is coming so fast that one cannot keep abreast of all the activity in his own specialty.

A cry has been raised by one editor to stop inventing and start producing. He singles out solid-state electronic devices, which, except for transistors, are not in commercial use. His point is that invention is only the beginning, and that time and hard work at the engineering stage are necessary before man can

---

* The number of scientific papers doubles every 12 years. In 1960, about two million papers were published; in 1972, four million are anticipated.
** It is estimated that the cost of research in the United States will be about $17.6 billion in 1963. Ten years ago, it was $5.1 billion, and by 1970 expenditures will probably be about $25 billion. Of this 1963 sum, the government is spending 60.5%; industry, 36.5%; and institutions, 3%.

enjoy the benefits of the discoveries. But, as he knows, there is no stopping, particularly with plentiful monetary encouragement, and new knowledge keeps accumulating.

With the space age at hand, a science of materials is coming into its own. Mechanical properties of metallic and nonmetallic materials were studied first, in an obvious attempt to attain high strength-to-weight ratios. Next, the thermal properties were examined, because of the re-entry problem. With the passing of the urgency of these problems, attention is being shifted to the solid-state physics, not only from the strength standpoint, but also from the point of view of electrical and magnetic properties in terms of fundamental structure. Strange types of materials are being added to categories of interest to the materials scientist (in contradistinction to the materials engineer): for example, thin films, semiconductors, ceramics with amazing electrical or magnetic properties, and superconductors. The new materials under study, and others to be developed on the basis of new principles, will become the bases or the critical elements of new products or systems.

Solid-state electronics will lead the electronics industry. News will be made for some time with either very small, very thin, or very cold devices. This is the fashionable trend in research today. Integrated circuitry and microelectronics will in time give highly reliable equipment of high quality, low cost, and great complexity.

The electronics industry has a rate of growth about five times that of the national economy. It is growing mainly because of the increase in the use of electronics commercially, by the military establishments and by the consumer. Dramatic achievements in the use of electronics in scientific, industrial, medical, defense, and space technology have resulted. In the consumer market, the major portion of electronic devices goes into radio, television, and phonographs. In industry, electronic devices are used in areas of automation, data handling and retrieval, and closed-circuit television. Military emphasis on missile development provides another area for electronic and electrical technology.

The electrical industry is seeking a solution on the total conditioning of home living space for ultimate comfort. This means automatic year-round control of living or working space with respect to temperature (heating or cooling), humidity, air circulation, dust collection, and lighting (color and intensity). Perhaps sterilization of the air (by ultraviolet light, and metering of ozone or disinfecting gases and vapors to provide an aseptic environment) will be available as extras. Such a total-comfort system would be an excellent load builder for the electric power companies; this they plan to exploit.

The following sections appraise the active research areas, and present some conjectures on applications. Work on computers, energy conversion, and superconductors is leading the research parade. They represent the glamorous facets of solid-state research.

Computers, Data Storage and Retrieval

Although calculators had been used for a long time, it was only in the late 1940's that automatic sequence-controlled calculators, better known now as computers, came onto the scene. In 1948, there were a half-dozen or so computers in use; in 1962, it is estimated, there are more than 10,000. In 1948, the Eniac computer was capable of 5000 additions per second and 300 multiplications. Today, if a computer cannot do 100,000 additions or multiplications per second, it doesn't rate.

It is naive to assume that the task of thinking can be referred to a computer. Nothing is further from the truth, because modern computers are not giant brains, but merely high-speed automotons.

Of course, it all depends on the definition of "thinking." Computers have a sort of artificial intelligence in the sense that they can prove mathematical theorems, calculate π to 100 or more places, expand a mathematical series, and so on. Admittedly, such ability is at least one attribute of an intelligent mind. On the other hand, computers cannot think intuitively, experience a stroke of genius, devise their own instructions, perceive external situations in terms of the senses, and interpret them and formulate action. The future will certainly see a fantastic evolution in computers. Even now, complex computers, simulating the millions of neurons of the human body, are planned. Such devices, after proper conditioning with solvable problems, might tackle difficult ones and make decisions on the basis of previous experience. Probably there will never be a mathematical monster that will out-think man, conclude that he must be destroyed, and act on the conclusion.

The move is on for progressively smaller components or assemblies. The Aerospace Industries Assoc. predicts that compaction will progress in the following evolutionary manner: At present, 50,000 equivalent circuit components can be assembled into 1 cu ft of space by printed circuitry; by 1965, with electronic modules, 200,000 can be assembled in the same space; by 1967, with thin films, three million components; and in 1970, with molecular electronics, 15 million components.

For computers, faster switching speed and smaller size, with a high degree of reliability, are the primary objectives. First, speeds of microseconds (10^{-6}), then nanoseconds (10^{-9}), and currently picoseconds (10^{-12}) * have been attained. The push for high-speed computers came from the military. Obviously, a fast acting computer is a necessity in missile interception systems. Germanium tunnel diodes have been developed that have switching times of the order of 5 picoseconds, faster than cryogenic and magnetic films. Development is in the direction of miniature and microminiature devices. The current aim in this type of research is reliability, through improved manufacturing techniques and statistical analysis.

The digital computer has been widely used since its introduction in 1957. It has found applications in scientific data processing, accounting, inventory management, control of industrial tools and processes, and military control systems.

The analog computer was in use as early as 1946, and airborne fixed-fire-control systems were built around it. Analog machines are less well suited for decision making than the digital type and, in general, are limited in precision and speed of response. Hybrid digital-analog computers are also available.

The reliability requirements of computers are increasing. Reliabilities of the order of one error per 10^{20} operations are not at all unreasonable. Unfortunately, high reliability goes with high cost.

Computers are expensive. A special-purpose digital computer designed for management problems has a price tag of $20,000. Process-control types cost from $100,000 to $350,000, including auxiliary equipment. One company has launched a low-priced analog computer that sells for $1800; weighing 50 lb, it is almost portable.

A giant computer at the Air Defense Headquarters in Colorado

* In one minute there are 60 trillion picoseconds.

Springs, Colorado, keeps track constantly of the orbit, speed, and position of every manmade object in space. At the press of a button, details on the 200 or so objects now in space are immediately available.

Work is progressing on automatic translating computer-type machines. One such machine is able to translate Russian into English or English into Russian with amazing accuracy.

Teaching machines are quite successful, and their usage is increasing tremendously. They will require programs, data storage and readout.

Information storage and retrieval from libraries or company statistics and inventory are receiving much attention of computer-oriented minds. Storing pictures and graphs poses some problems. The photographic approach is helpful in this instance.

The soft ferrite core will probably continue to be the building block in the memory equipment. The magnetic tape (plastic ribbon covered with ferromagnetic iron oxide) is the common storage medium for computers. About 24,000 units (bits) of information can be stored on a square inch of tape. The transfer rate from or into a computer is about 300,000 bits per second.

Systems of computers and data storage devices can now assist management in planning and directing corporate enterprise. Depending on available information, and making certain assumptions, it is possible to forecast the future when specific courses of action are adopted. Such a system is a powerful decision-making tool.

The suggestion has been made that the dissemination of information may even be a solution to the problem of war. Information was once disseminated by foot and boat, later by railroads, telegraph, automobiles, and telephones, later still by radio, television, and now by Telstar. Possibly, because of these modern communications media, there may come a time of understanding when thoughts of war as an instrument of national policy will become absurd.

Energy Conversion

It has irked man that he has had to generate electricity indirectly from heat—starting with coal, oil or nuclear fuel to produce steam to drive turbines to turn generators to produce electricity. Man is impatient to generate electricity directly from heat or to harness the energy of the sun. There are several ways of direct energy conversion; none is practical as yet. These methods employ thermoelectrics, photovoltaics (for example, silicon cells for solar conversion), thermionics, and magnetohydrodynamics. All of these processes are intimately connected with materials problems. Fuel cells are in the picture, but their operation depends on the free energy of a reaction rather than on direct heat. A spokesman for the Edison Electric Institute predicts that some of these unconventional methods of generating electricity may be in practical use within the next ten years.

Thermoelectricity. New thermoelectric materials of improved characteristics (high electrical conductivity and low thermal conductivity) continue to be developed. Current efforts are in the direction of improving reliability, decreasing cost, and increasing operating temperatures.

Thermocouples generate direct-current power. With static converters, employing semiconducting elements, direct current can be converted to alternating current with a high efficiency (85 to 95%). A thermocouple-converter system operated by a gasoline flame would serve well for a military and civilian emergency communications power supply.

A thermocouple system can be considered a truly reversible heat pump. For a given setting, a heat pump will cool or heat. Spot cooling by thermocouples is now used to cool some transistor circuitry. Small thermoelectric refrigerators have been marketed. Home gas-heating furnaces have been equipped with thermoelectric generators that power the blower motor after the flame is on for a short time.

For space probing, nuclear heat sources (small, 100-watt reactors) will provide heat for thermoelectric generators or for combined thermionic-thermoelectric units.

An effect related to thermoelectricity has been found in the Austin cell, which consists of sandwiches of certain metals separated by porcelain enamel. Such combinations can be used at elevated temperatures.

Thermionics. This type of generator — a high temperature cathode emitting electrons that are collected by an anode — is not practical as yet. A variety of devices have been developed. Because of the high temperatures used — 1650 C (3000 F) or higher — materials problems (oxidation, sublimation, leaks in seals, and internal corrosion if cesium is present) must be solved.

Their first use will probably be as a heat source in connection with nuclear reactors. The dispersion of thermionic generators throughout the nuclear core has been suggested. Single crystals of refractory metals, especially if cut on appropriate crystallographic planes, may give reduced sublimation and improved electron yields.

Photovoltaics (Solar Cells). Sunshine is free and, in many regions, plentiful. How convenient if it could be converted to electricity practically and cheaply! The silicon solar cell was a big step toward realizing this old dream. Improvements continue to be made in silicon cells. New cells are 10 to 100 times more resistant to damage from radiation — electrons and protons from the Van Allen belt; life expectancy is about 25 years, and is obtained with a sapphire cover. Higher conversion efficiencies will be attained.

Under development are solar-thermoelectric generators. In these, the sunlight is focused by parabolic mirrors onto a cluster of thermocouples. In one installation, 50 watts were developed within a bundle of 72 thermocouples. Solar-thermionic generators have also been considered.

Magnetohydrodynamics (MHD). The MHD generator is similar in principle to a conventional generator in which an electrical conductor moving through a magnetic field generates a voltage. In a MHD generator, plasma (high-temperature, highly ionized gas) is passed through a magnetic field perpendicular to the plasma stream; probes at right angles to the flow and field pick up a voltage. The main difficulty with these units is the temperature problem; even when the stream is seeded with easily ionized material, high temperatures are required to get a sufficiently ionized stream. It has recently been reported that one experimental MHD generator produced 1,350,000 watts of power; the unit operated over 100 hr at 2760 C (5000 F) using commercial power-plant fuel and potassium metal for seeding. A "cool" method of ionizing the gas without the use of heat has been discovered. This method, if proven out, could make the MHD generator practical.

Predictions have been made that a combination of the MHD generator and the conventional steam turbine apparatus will be the principal power source in central power plants of the future. Some such installations can be expected within the next 20 years.

Superconductivity

Applications using superconductivity are virtually here. The scientist is about to yield this fashionable research area to the engineer. Superconducting magnets will find application where high-intensity magnetic fields are required and where significant reductions in power consumption are economic in comparison to high-current generators. Such applications are particle accelerators, bubble chambers, and devices for containing plasma (highly ionized hot gases) in thermonuclear experimentation. Cryogenic computers are a possibility. By using thin films of a superconductor, switching times of 10 to 25 nanoseconds (10^{-9} sec) can be realized; these times are comparable to those obtained with semiconductors. Cryogenic transformers have been built with only the primary and secondary superconducting coils cooled; the magnetic core remains at ambient temperature.

Although columbium-tin has a potential field of about 200,000 gausses, other materials have been found that offer possibilities of attaining much higher fields. The compound, V_3Ga, appears to have a critical field in excess of 400,000 gausses! The search continues for other superconductors having higher transition temperatures or greater critical fields.

Extensive applications of superconductivity will be possible only if the cost of producing the low temperatures can be reduced significantly.

Less Spectacular but no Less Important

Semiconductors. Perhaps the most common commercial application of the semiconductor has been in transistorized radios. Transistorized television sets are already on the market; one portable with a 5-in. screen weighs 8 lb. It uses 24 transistors, including 3 epitaxial and 5 mesa, and 20 semiconductor diodes.

Additional characteristics of semiconductors are still being discovered. Recently a semiconductor microphone almost microscopic in size was announced. Transistors have been found to be pressure sensitive in the regions near the junctions. The device could lead to miniature hearing aids, high-fidelity phonograph needles, and space-age eavesdropping (supersleuths).

Interest continues high in gallium arsenide as a semiconductor material. Semiconductors are well-established detectors of energy, but one gallium arsenide diode generates modulated infrared, making possible transmission of television patterns on an infrared beam. In diodes of gallium arsenide, laser * action has been observed.

In nuclear physics, semiconductor devices are being used instead of bulkier and less efficient radiation counters. Doped silicon is finding increasing usage in nucleonics.

Medicine. The application of electronics to medicine is largely an untapped field. Electrical devices that use semiconductors are becoming quite common. One unit is being used to record the condition of critically ill and post-operative patients. The instrument makes a plot of the patient's temperature, pulse rate, respiration rate, and systolic and diastolic blood pressure. The circuitry will activate visual or audible alarms, depending on the settings of the various parameters measured. Under development is an electronic hypodermic needle which, when introduced into the blood stream, will continuously measure the acidity (pH) of the blood. The acidity can also be recorded readily.

Microphones connected to a transmitter are being taped to women in labor, and the heartbeats of the mother and fetus are picked up in the doctor's quarters by a radio receiver. Because this receiver is coupled to a strip-chart recorder or an oscilloscope, the progress of delivery can be followed continuously. Perhaps not too fantastic is the concept of cardiac, diabetic or epileptic individuals wearing a sensing transmitter. In case of an attack, the transmitter will flash a warning (sound or shock), and emergency measures can be resorted to until assistance arrives.

Ultrasonics are being used to outline organs, such as the heart, and to locate tumors.

A better understanding of the effect of magnetism on biological systems is needed. There are some poorly understood observations on this subject. A magnetic field of 4000 gausses appears to decrease antibody production in mice used for cancer study.

---

* Laser is an acronym, a term formed from the initial letters of the phrase, "light amplification by stimulated emission of radiation." In laser devices, energy is supplied by direct injection of electrons (and holes) into the diode. This laser does not use an external light source. It is possible to modulate the output radiation of the diode by modulating the incoming current and, in this way, avoid the problem of modulating the coherent light after it leaves the laser. The directional and coherent beam of infrared light is emitted from the junction-plane edges at carefully polished and precisely parallel sides of the crystal.

Bionics is the electronic replication of biological systems. For instance, microcomponents of high reliability will replace neurons of low reliability, and perhaps machines of amazing artificial intelligence can be built.

A Cyborg (a body on which machines are hitched or built into to perform or modify some functions of the body) is no longer a topic for science fiction writers. The publicized Pacemaker provides electrical stimulation to the heart and paces it back to a normal beat. Missing legs, arms and hands will be replaced with electronic prosthetic devices actuated by body muscles.

Properties of Materials. New characteristics of familiar elements are still being found. For instance, an anomaly has been discovered in the conduction of bismuth at low temperatures. As high-purity metals and alloys are prepared, new or intensified characteristics will be observed. Scientists at Bell Laboratories have found superconductivity in molybdenum and iridium, and now the search is on to check other purified elements for superconductivity. Zone refining in conjunction with electron beam melting may aid in the preparation of extreme-purity metals, particularly those of high melting point.

New knowledge can be expected from superpressure high-temperature (SPHT) conditions. The pressure-temperature diagram for bismuth reveals six new crystal structures. SPHT studies show transitions in semiconductor materials. More surprises will probably come from investigation of other highly purified metals and nonmetals.

Titanium capacitors are on the horizon. Rutile (TiO_2) has one of the highest dielectric capacities known and, if it is formed on thin titanium, it should make an excellent capacitor. Columbium capacitors that compete with tantalum capacitors have just been introduced.

Thin films have opened up a new technology; investigation of them has revealed a new set of startling properties. Thin films can be made into resistive, inductive, and capacitive circuit elements; they can be made into conductors, and they can have useful ferromagnetic and ferroelectric properties. The next move is to manufacture continuously uniform (in thickness and properties) ultra-reliable thin films.

Thin film semiconductors, in combination with the thin film circuit, will make practical the miniature and microcircuitry. The principal use will probably be in computers.

Magnetism. Discoveries of new magnetic materials continue to amaze all scientists. Because there is very little theory for guidance in the search for them, discoveries come from unexpected quarters as investigators stumble on them in other pursuits.

A transparent ferromagnetic material ($Ca_2Fe_{10}O_{17}$) has been discovered. This red, hexagonal product has a saturation magnetization of 142 gausses. It can be used for magneto-optical applications, such as conversion of electric signals to optical signals.

Single crystal Alnico magnets or polycrystal magnets of proper orientation are definitely in the future. With proper composition and structure (as reflected by heat treatment), these magnets should give energy products to about 15 million gauss-oersteds.

Proposals have been made to use superconductors as permanent magnets. With proper superconductor geometry, an energy product of over 25 million gauss-oersteds is obtained from Cb_2Sn at 4.2 K. Higher values are anticipated.

Ceramic ferrites, soft or hard magnetic types, can be made in sheets to a thickness of 0.012 in. Soft ferrites with holes and slots may be used in computers, and in memory and switching devices.

An electromagnetic metal-forming machine is now practical. One machine applies a magnetic field against a piece of metal in pulses of 10 to 20 millionths of a second creating peak pressures up to more than 50,000 psi.

Electrical Steels. In more mundane areas, electrical steels are experiencing a realignment in technology. In nonoriented types, the trend is to use cheaper (lower-silicon) grades. There will probably be a lowering of the core loss of iron, low-carbon steel and the silicon grades. The improvement (lowering of core loss and improving permeability) will come from the lowering of impurities (carbon, nitrogen and sulfur) or combining them into innocuous coarse precipitates (carbides and nitrides), by reducing the number of inclusions, and obtaining coarse grains.

With grain-oriented silicon steel, in the singly oriented (110)-[001] type, the lowering of core loss will continue. There is a likelihood of being able to produce material with controlled magnetostriction, which should allow operation of oriented steel in transformers at inductions in excess of 17,000 gausses without perceptible noise.

Doubly oriented (that is, (100)[100]) steel is on the verge of being announced commercially. It will replace some singly oriented steel and will find some use in rotating machinery.

Cryogenics pose no serious threat to usage of silicon steels for distribution purposes. There is a remote possibility of a central station using superconductors to reduce copper losses in the transformers. However, the cost of a plant for making liquid hydrogen or liquid helium would probably be in the millions of dollars. An extra helium plant would be required with elaborate, quick-acting switchgear to forestall the threat of an explosion if a transformer were to go resistive. Schemes for using transformers at low temperatures or only the windings at cryogenic temperatures have been worked out, but the practicality of a cryogenic central station remains to be demonstrated. To consider superconducting transformers for substations seems economically unwarranted with the present state of knowledge. There is also the possibility of using air core transformers (no silicon steel core) at low temperatures, but this approach appears to have less merit than an iron core transformer.

The study of the electrical and magnetic properties of metals is obviously basic to modern technology. The properties are important industrially, to produce goods and to generate electricity. The properties are responsible for electronic devices for the general public. Electronic gear plays an important part in the defense of societies.

The story of electrical and magnetic properties continues to be written, and no one can guess where new discoveries will lead

References

Chapter 1

1 W. F. Friedrich, P. Knipping and M. Laue, Interference Phenomena with Roentgen Rays, Akad Munchen Ber, 303 to 322 (1912); Le Radium, 10, 47 to 57 (1913)

2 W. H. Bragg and W. L. Bragg, Reflection of X-rays by Crystals, Proc Roy Soc, A88, 428 to 438 (1913)

3 C. S. Barrett, "Structure of Metals," McGraw-Hill Book Co., Inc., New York, 1952, p 1

4 R. Kiessling, Bonding in Metals, Met Rev, 2, 77 to 107 (1957)

5 M. Born and A. Landi, The Absolute Calculation of Crystal Properties with the Aid of the Bohr Atomic Model, Sitzb Kg Preuss Akad, 1048 to 1068 (1918); Ber Phy Ges, 20, 202 to 204 (1918)

6 C. S. Barrett, reference 3, p 225

7 W. Hume-Rothery, "The Structure of Metals and Alloys," Institute of Metals, London, 1936

8 W. Hume-Rothery, Electrons, Atoms, Metals and Alloys, Metals Technol, No. 2130, 16 p (1947)

9 P. Doyal and L. S. Darken, Migration of Carbon in Steel under the Influence of D.C., Trans AIME, 188, 1156 to 1158 (1950)

10 W. Hume-Rothery, The Electrolytic Migration of Carbon in Steels, J Iron Steel Inst, 188, 113 (1958)

11 L. Pauling, "The Nature of the Chemical Bond and Structure of Molecules and Crystals," Cornell University Press, Ithaca, N. Y., 1940, 326 to 330

12 F. C. Nix and W. Shockley, Order-Disorder Transformations in Alloys, Rev Mod Phys, 10, 1 to 71 (1938)

13 W. Hume-Rothery, "Atomic Theory for Students of Metallurgy," Institute of Metals, London, 1946

14 G. Hagg, Regularity in Crystal Structure in Hydrides, Borides, Carbides and Nitrides of Transition Elements, Z Phys Chem, B12, 33 to 56 (1931)

15 National Research Council Symposium on Imperfections in Crystals, 1950

16 H. E. Buckley, "Crystal Growth," Chapman and Hall, London, 1951

17 Y. Haven, Lattice Imperfections in Crystals, Studies on Alkali Halides, Philips Tech Rev, 20, 69 to 79 (1958–1959)

18 C. G. Darwin, The Theory of X-ray Reflection, Phil Mag, 27, 315 to 333, 675 (1914); 43, 800 (1922)

343

19 M. J. Buerger, The Lineage Structure of Crystals, Krist, **89**, 195 to 220 (1934); The Non-existence of a Regular Secondary Structure in Crystals, ibid, **89**, 242 to 267

20 J. J. Thomson, "Conduction of Electricity Through Gases," Cambridge University Press, 1903

21 R. Millikan, The Isolation of an Ion, a Precision Measurement of its Charge, and the Correction of Stokes' Law, Science, **32**, 436 to 448 (1911); Physik Z, **11**, 1097 to 1109 (1911)

22 P. Drude, Electron Theory of Metals, Ann Phys, **1**, 566 to 613 (1900); **3**, 369 to 402 (1900)

23 H. A. Lorentz, Motion of Electrons in Metals, Koninkl Akad Wetenschap Amsterdam, **7**, 438 to 453, 588 to 593, 684 to 691 (1905)

24 R. C. Tolman and T. D. Stewart, E.M.F. Produced by Acceleration of Metals, Phys Rev, **8**, 97 to 116 (1916); Mass of Electric Carrier in Copper, Silver and Aluminum, ibid, **9**, 164 to 167 (1917)

25 A. Somerfield, Electron Theory of Metals on the Basis of the Fermi Statistics, Z Physik, **47**, 1 to 32, 43 to 68 (1928)

26 F. Seitz, "The Physics of Metals," McGraw-Hill Book Co., Inc., New York, 1943

27 P. Longevin, Electronic Theory of Magnetism, Compt Rend, **139**, 1204 to 1207 (1904); Ann Chim Phys, **5**, 70 to 127 (1905)

28 P. Weiss, L'hypothese du champ moleculaire et la propriete ferromagnetique, J Phys, **4**, 661 to 690 (1907)

29 W. Heisenberg, Theory of Ferromagnetism, Z Physik, **49**, 619 to 636 (1928)

30 S. J. Barnett, Magnetization by Rotation, Phys Rev, **6**, 239 to 270 (1915); Gyromagnetic and Electron-Inertia Effects, Rev Mod Phys, **7**, 129 to 166 (1935)

31 S. Goudsmit and G. E. Uhlenbeck, Spinning Electrons and the Structure of Spectra, Nature, **117**, 264 to 265 (1926)

Chapter 2

32 Y. S. Borovik, Electrical Conductivity of Metals at High Current Density, Dokl Akad Nauk USSR, **91**, 771 to 774 (1953)

33 G. Wiedemann and R. Franz, Weber die Warme-Leitungsfahigkeit der Metalle, Ann Phys Chem (Pogg Ann), **89**, 493 to 531 (1853)

34 C. Kittel, "Introduction to Solid State Physics," John Wiley and Sons, New York, 1956, p 245

35 R. W. Powell and M. J. Hickman, The Physical Properties of a Series of Steels. Part II, Electrical Resistivities Up to 1300° C, J Iron Steel Inst, **154**, 99 to 105 (1946)

36 R. J. Wasilewski, Observations on Electrical Resistivity of Titanium, Trans AIME, **224**, 5 to 8 (1962)

37 S. V. Radcliffe and E. C. Rollason, The Electrical Resistivity of High-Purity Iron-Carbon Alloys, J Iron Steel Inst, **189**, 45 to 48 (1958)

38 V. P. Chernobrovkin, Changes in Electrical Resistance of Cast Iron in Connection with Graphite Formation, Phys Metals Metallog USSR, **4**, 153 to 155 (1957)

39 F. Pawlek and K. Reichel, Der Einfluss von Beimengungen auf die elektrische Leitfahigkeit von

Kupfer, Z Metallk, **47**, 347 to 356 (1956)

40 Private communication, L. A. Wiley, Aluminum Co. of America, 1959

41 L. W. Kempf, C. S. Smith and C. S. Taylor, Thermal and Electrical Conductivities of Aluminum Alloys, Trans AIME, **124**, 287 to 299 (1937)

42 F. Seitz, "Modern Theory of Solids," McGraw-Hill Book Co., Inc., 1940, p 45

43 E. F. Northrup, The Resistivity of Copper from 20 to 1450° C, J Franklin Inst, **177**, 1 to 21 (1914)

44 S. L. Ames and A. D. McOwillan, The Resistivity-Temperature-Concentration Relationship in Beta-phase Titanium-Hydrogen Alloys, Acta Met, **4**, 602 to 610 (1956)

45 D. K. C. Macdonald, Resistance of Metals at Low Temperatures, "Les Electrons dans les Metaux," R. Stoops, 1955, 89 to 113

46 N. F. Mott, Electrical Conductivity of Transition Metals, Proc Roy Soc, **A153**, 699 to 717 (1936); Resistance and Thermoelectric Properties of the Transition Metals, **A156**, 368 to 382 (1936)

47 R. W. Powell, Thermal Conductivities of Solid Materials at High Temperatures, Research, **7**, 492 to 501 (1954)

48 J. H. Dellinger, The Temperature Coefficient of Resistance of Copper, Nat Bur Std (US) Tech News Bull, **1**, 72 to 107 (1910)

49 J. G. Ball and W. B. H. Lord, History of the Early British Work in Plutonium Metallurgy, J Inst Metals, **86**, 369 to 379 (1958)

50 P. Saldau, Apparatus for the Measurement of Electrical Resistance of Material in the Solid State at High Temperature and the Determination of the Critical Points of Iron and Steel, Rev Soc Russe de Met, **I**, 655 to 690 (1915); Iron Steel Inst, Carnegie Scholarship Memoirs, 195 to 231 (1916)

51 P. Chiotti, "Thorium-Carbon System," Atomic Energy Commission, AECD-3072, June 1950, p 50

52 F. M. Jaeger, E. Rosenbohm and R. Fonteyne, Specific Heats, Electrical Resistance and Thermoelectric Behavior of Titanium and Their Dependence on Temperature, Rec Trav Chim, **55**, 615 to 654 (1936)

53 W. R. Ham and C. H. Samans, Electrolytic Conductivity as a Method for Studying Electronic Transitions in Elements — Application to Iron, Nickel and Cobalt, Trans ASM, **39**, 73 to 98 (1947)

54 R. N. L. Yon, "Liquid Metals Handbook," U. S. Government Printing Office, 1952; R. R. Miller, Chapter 2, Physical Properties of Liquid Metals, p 38

55 N. F. Mott, The Resistance of Liquid Metals, Proc Roy Soc (London), **A146**, 465 to 472 (1934)

56 L. G. Schulz and P. Spiegler, An Experimental Determination of the Electrical Resistivity of Liquid Alloys Hg-In, Hg-Tl, Ga-In, Ga-Sn, and of Liquid Gallium, Trans AIME, **215**, 87 to 90 (1959)

57 A. Matthiessen and C. Vogt, Weber den Einfluss der Temperatur auf die elektrische Leitungsfahigkeit der Legirungen, Ann Phys Chem (Pogg), **122**, 19 to 78 (1864)

58 E. Krantz and H. Schultz, Detection of Impurities and Cold Deformations in Sintered Tungsten by Residual Resistance Measurements, Z Metallk, 49, 399 to 403 (1958)

59 A. L. Norburg, Electrical Resistivity of Dilute Metallic Solutions, Trans Faraday Soc, 16, 570 to 596 (1921)

60 J. V. Linde, Electrical Properties of Silver Alloys, Ann Phys, 14, 353 to 366 (1932); Electrical Properties of Dilute Solid Solutions, ibid, 15, 219 to 248 (1932)

61 Le Chatelier, Les Alliages Metalliques, Rev Gen Sci, 30, 529 to 538 (1895)

62 N. S. Kurnakov and V. A. Nemilov, Alloys of Platinum with Copper, Z Anorg Allgem Chem, 210, 1 to 12 (1933); Alloys of Platinum with Ni, ibid, 210, 13 to 20 (1933); Hardness, Microstructure and Electrical Conductivity of Platinum-Silver Alloys, ibid, 168, 339 to 348 (1928); Alloys of Platinum with Copper, Ann Inst Platine, 8, 5 to 16 (1931); Alloys of Platinum with Nickel, ibid, 8, 17 to 24 (1931)

63 W. Guertler, On the Electrical Conductivity of Alloys, Z Anorg Chem, 51, 397 to 433 (1906); ibid, 54, 58 to 88 (1907); Law of Matthiessen Relating to the Temperature Coefficient of Electrical Conductivity of Metals; Z Phys, 9, 29 to 36 (1908)

64 W. Wien, editor, "Handbuch der Experimental Physik," Vol II, Part 2, Akod Verlogsgesellschaft, 1935; W. Meissner, Elktronleitung, p 89 to 90

65 H. G. van Bueren, Electrical Resistance and Plastic Deformation of Metals, Z Metallk, 46, No. 4, 272 to 281 (1955)

66 L. Guillet and M. Ballay, The Influence of Cold Work on the Resistivity of Metals and Alloys, Compt Rend, 176, 1800 to 1802 (1923); Rev Met (Paris), 20, 398 to 408 (1923)

67 G. Tammann and K. L. Dreyer, Die Erholung des elektrische Widerstandes und der Harte von Kupfer, Silber und Gold sowie von Platin und Palladium von der Folgen der Kallbearbeitung, Ann Physik, 16, 111 to 119 (1933)

68 R. Bardenhauer and H. Schmidt, The Effect of Cold Work and Heat Treatment on the Electric Conductance of Copper, Mitt Kaiser-Wilhelm-Inst Eisenforsch, 10, 193 to 212 (1928)

69 D. K. Crampton, H. L. Burghoff and G. T. Stacy, Effect of Cold Work upon the Electrical Resistivity of Copper Alloys, Trans AIME, 143, 228 to 245 (1941)

70 M. Balicki, A Study of Work-Hardening and Reannealing of Iron, J Iron Steel Inst, 151, 181 to 224 (1945)

71 T. P. Wong and E. T. Kubilins, The Metallurgical Aspects of Resistance, Electronic Industries, 16, 52 to 54, 120 to 122, 124 (1957)

72 E. Klokholm and B. Hyatt, The Effect of Plastic Deformation on the Resistivity of Copper-Palladium Alloys, Trans AIME, 215, 792 to 794 (1959)

73 F. E. Jaumot and A. Sawatzky, Order-Disorder and Cold Work Phenomena in Cu-Pd Alloys, Acta Met, 4, 127 to 144 (1956)

74 A. C. Damask, Some Resistivity Effects of Short-Range Order in Alpha Brass, J Appl Phys, 27, 610 to 616 (1956); Phys Chem Solids, 1, 23 to 26 (1956)

75 R. M. Bozorth, Magnetoresistance and Domain Theory of Iron-Nickel Alloys, Phys Rev, **70**, 923 to 932 (1946)

76 H. G. Muller, Recovery and Recrystallization of Cold Worked Nickel, Z Metallk, **31**, 161 to 167 (1939)

77 S. E. Maddigan and A. I. Blank, "Recovery and Recrystallization in Long-Time Annealing of 70-30 Brass," AIME Tech Pub 1166, 1940, 22 p

78 L. M. Clarebough, M. E. Hargreaves and G. W. West, The Density of Dislocations in Compressed Copper, Acta Met, **5**, 738 to 740 (1957)

79 R. F. Mehl and L. K. Jetter, The Mechanism of Precipitation from Solid Solutions and the Theory of Age-Hardening, "Symposium on Age-Hardening of Metals," American Society for Metals, Metals Park, Ohio, 1939, 342 to 412

80 N. F. Mott, discussion of paper by M. L. V. Gaylor, The Theory of Age Hardening, J Inst Metals, **60**, 249 to 283 (1937); discussion, 267 to 268

81 W. L. Fink, D. W. Smith, and L. A. Wiley, Precipitation of High-Purity Binary and Ternary Aluminum-Copper Alloys, "Symposium on Age-Hardening of Metals," American Society for Metals, Metals Park, Ohio, 1939, 31 to 53

82 L. J. Dijkstra, Elastic Relaxation and Some Other Properties of the Solid Solutions of Carbon and Nitrogen in Iron, Philips Res Rept, **2**, 357 to 381 (1947); Precipitation Phenomena in the Solid Solutions of Nitrogen and Carbon in Alpha Iron Below the Eutectoid Temperature, J Metals, **1**, 252 to 260 (1949)

83 W. Crafts and J. L. Lamont, Secondary Hardening of Tempered Martensitic Steel, Trans AIME, **180**, 471 to 512 (1949)

84 E. C. Roberts, N. J. Grant and M. Cohen, Creep-Tempering Relationships in Hardened 4.5% Chromium Steels, Trans ASM, **47**, 650 to 664 (1955)

85 W. H. Colner and O. Zmeskal, An Electrical Resistance Apparatus for Studying Transformations in Metals. Its Application to Transformations in Stainless Steels, Trans ASM, **44**, 1158 to 1168 (1952)

86 A. W. McReynolds, Electrical Observations in the Austenite-Martensite Transformation in Steel, J Appl Phys, **17**, 823 to 833 (1946)

87 A. H. Cottrell and A. T. Churchman, Change in Electrical Resistance during the Strain Aging of Iron, J Iron Steel Inst, **162**, 271 to 276 (1949)

88 P. W. Bridgman, The Resistance of 72 Elements, Alloys and Compounds, Proc Am Acad Arts, **81**, 165 to 251 (1952)

89 C. H. Johansson and J. O. Linde, Roentgenographic Determination of the Atomic Arrangement in the Mixed Crystal Series Au-Cu and Pd-Cu, Ann Phys, **78**, 439 to 460 (1925)

90 T. Muto and Y. Takagi, The Theory of Order-Disorder Transitions in Alloys, "Solid State Physics," Academic Press, 1955, p 252 to 261

91 A. E. Berkowitz, J. F. Donahoe, A. D. Franklin and R. P. Steijin, Phase Transformations in Iron-Platinum Alloys Near the Composition Fe_3Pt, Acta Met, **5**, 1 to 12 (1957)

92 D. K. C. Macdonald, Electrical Conductivity of Metals and Al-

loys at Low Temperatures, "Encyclopedia of Physics," Vol XIV, Springer-Verlag, Berlin, 1956, p 178

93 P. Kapitza, Study of the Specific Resistance of Bismuth Crystals and Its Change in Strong Magnetic Fields and Some Allied Problems, Proc Roy Soc, A119, 358 to 444 (1928); Electrical Conductivity in Strong Magnetic Fields, ibid, 123, 292 to 372 (1929)

94 W. Thomson, On the Electrodynamic Qualities of Metals, Phil Trans, 146, 649 to 751 (1856); Proc Roy Soc, 8, 546 to 550 (1857)

95 E. Justi and H. Scheffers, Change of Resistance of Aluminum Single Crystals in Strong Magnetic Fields at Low Temperatures, Physik Z, 39, 105 to 109 (1938)

96 F. Seitz, The Effects of Irradiation upon Metals, Trans AIME, 215, 354 to 367 (1959)

97 G. J. Dienes and G. H. Vineyard, "Radiation Effects in Solids," Interscience Publishers, Inc., New York, 1957

98 "Vacancies and Other Point Defects in Metals and Alloys," Institute of Metals, 1958

99 C. J. Meechan and S. Sosin, Recovery of Electrical Resistivity of Cu, Au, and Ni Following Cold Work at 4 K, J Appl Phys, 29, 738 to 739 (1958)

100 J. W. Kauffman and J. A. Koehler, Quenching-in of Lattice Vacancies in Pure Gold, Phys Rev, 97, 555 (1955)

101 C. Panseri, F. Gatto and T. Federighi, Quenching of Vacancies in Aluminum, Acta Met, 5, 50 to 52 (1957)

102 C. Panseri, F. Gatto and T. Federighi, Interaction between Solute Magnesium Atoms and Vacancies in Aluminum, Acta Met, 6, 198 to 204 (1958)

103 M. Faraday, Experimental Relations of Gold (and Other Metals) to Light, Trans Roy Soc (London), 147, 145 to 181 (1857)

104 R. B. Belser, Electrical Resistances of Thin Metal Films Before and After Artificial Aging by Heating, J Appl Phys, 28, 109 to 116 (1957)

105 J. Bardeen, "Modern Physics for the Engineer," McGraw-Hill Book Co., New York, 1954, p 400

106 R. K. Willardson and T. S. Shilliday, Where to Use the New Semiconductor Materials, Mater Methods, 47, 114 to 118 (1958)

107 T. R. Lawson, Jr., Semiconductors, Their Characteristics and Principles, Westinghouse Eng, 14, 178 to 182 (1954)

108 L. Esaki, New Phenomenon in Narrow Germanium p-n Junctions, Phys Rev, 109, 603 to 604 (1958)

109 J. Evans, "Fundamental Principles of Transistors," Heywood & Company, Ltd., London, 1957

110 H. L. Armstrong, Using Unusual Semiconductors, Electronic Industries, 18, 90 to 95 (1959)

111 H. P. R. Frederikse, Compound Semiconductors, J Metals, 10, 346 to 350 (1958)

Chapter 3

112 H. B. Michaelson, Work Functions of the Elements, J Appl Phys, 21, 536 to 540 (1950)

113 C. Herring and M. H. Nichols,

Thermionic Emission, Rev Mod Phys, **21**, 185 to 270 (1949)

114 D. A. Wright, A Summary of Present Knowledge of Thermionic Emitters, Proc Inst Elec Engrs, **100**, 125 to 142 (1953)

115 H. C. Reutschler and D. E. Henry, Photoelectric Emission, J Franklin Inst, **223**, 135 to 145 (1937)

116 H. Hertz, Ultra-Violet Light and Electric Discharge, Ann Phys Lpz, **31**, 983 to 1000 (1887)

117 W. Hallwachs, Ueber den Einfluss des Lichtes auf Electrostatich gelande Korper, Ann Phys, **33**, 301 to 312 (1888)

118 A. Einstein, A Heuristic Standpoint Concerning the Production of Transformation of Light, Ann Phys, **17**, 132 to 148 (1905)

119 H. C. Reutschler, D. E. Henry and K. O. Smith, Photoelectric Emission from Different Metals, Rev Sci Inst, **3**, 794 to 802 (1932)

120 H. Y. Fan, Theory of Photoelectric Emission from Metals, Phys Rev, **68**, 43 to 52 (1945)

121 W. Smith, Effect of Light on Selenium During the Passage of an Electric Current, Am J Sci, **5**, 301 (1873)

122 D. M. Chapin, C. S. Fuller and G. L. Pearson, A New Silicon p-n Junction Photocell for Converting Solar Radiation into Electrical Power, J Appl Phys, **25**, 676 to 677 (1954)

123 E. Becquerel, Studies of the Effect of Actinic Radiation of Sunlight by Means of Electric Currents, Compt Rend, **9**, 145 to 149 (1839)

124 L. O. Grondahl, The Copper–Cuprous Oxide Rectifier and Photoelectric Cell, Rev Mod Phys, **5**, 141 to 168 (1933)

125 B. Lange, New Kind of Photoelectric Cell, Physik Z, **31**, 139 to 140, 964 to 969 (1930)

126 W. Schottky, Origin of Photoelectrons in Copper Oxide Photoelectric Cells, Physik Z, **31**, 913 to 925 (1930)

127 W. Schottky, Simplified and Extended Theory of the Barrier Layer Rectifiers, Z Physik, **118**, 283 to 285 (1941)

128 H. Bruining and J. H. de Boer, Secondary Electron Emission, Physica, **5**, 17 to 30, 901 to 917 (1938); ibid, **6**, 823 to 839, 941 to 950 (1939)

129 W. Schottky, Cold and Hot Electron Discharges, Z Physik, **14**, 63 to 106 (1923)

130 V. E. Cosslett, "Introduction to Electron Optics," Oxford University Press, 1950, p 162

131 R. H. Fowler and L. Nordheim, Electron Emission in Intense Electric Fields, Proc Roy Soc, **119**, 173 to 181 (1928)

132 C. M. Slack and L. F. Ehrke, Field Emission X-ray Tube, J Appl Phys, **12**, 165 to 168 (1941)

133 R. P. Johnson and W. Shockley, An Electron Microscope for Filaments: Emission and Absorption by Tungsten Single Crystals, Phys Rev, **49**, 436 to 440 (1936)

134 T. J. Seebeck, Ueber die Magnetische Polarisation der Metalle und Erze durch Temperature-Differenz, Pogg Ann, **6**, 1, 133 to 160, 253 to 286 (1826)

135 D. Hadfield, Thermo-Electricity, Iron Steel (London), **21**, 478 to 482 (1948)

136 J. C. A. Peltier, Nouvelles Experiences sur la Caloricite des Courants Electriques, Ann Chem, **56**, 371 to 386 (1834)

137 Q. Icilius, Ueber die Temperaturveranderungen, welche im galvanischer Strom beim Durchgange durch die Beruhrunge-flache zweier heterogenen Metalle hervorbringt, Ann Phys Chem Pogg, 89, 377 to 402 (1853)

138 W. T. Thomson, Account of Researches in Thermoelectricity; On the Thermal Effects of Electric Currents in Unequally Heated Conductors, Proc Roy Soc (London), VII, 49 to 58 (1854)

139 C. Celent, Thermoelectricity, Electronic Industries, 18, 66 to 78 (1959)

140 D. F. Stoneburner, L. Yang and G. Derge, Measurement of the Thermoelectric Power of Several Molten Sulfide – Solid Tungsten Thermocouples, Trans AIME, 215, 879 to 880 (1959)

141 E. H. Hall, On a New Action of the Magnet on Electric Currents, Phil Mag, 9, 225 to 230 (1880)

142 J. Smit, Hall Effect in Ferromagnetics, "Les Electrons dans les Metaux," R. Stoop, 1955, p 321 to 328

143 E. M. Pugh and N. Rostoker, Hall Effect in Ferromagnetic Materials, Rev Mod Phys, 25, 151 to 157 (1953)

144 A. Komar and S. Sidorov, The Arrangement of Atoms in the Alloy AuCu$_3$ and the Hall Coefficient, J Tech Phys (USSR), 4, 552 to 554 (1941)

145 S. Foner, quoted by J. Goldman, Atomic Moments in Alloys, Rev Mod Phys, 25, 108 to 113 (1953)

146 L. L. Campbell, "Galvanomagnetic and Thermomagnetic Effects, The Hall and Allied Phenomena," Longmans, Green & Co., New York, 1923

147 S. W. Angrist, Galvanomagnetic and Thermomagnetic Effects, Sci Am, 205, 124 to 126 (1961)

148 A. Ettingshausen, Ueber eine neue polare Wirkung des Magnetismus auf die galvanische Warme in gewissen Substanzen, Wiedemann Ann, 31, 737 to 759 (1887)

149 J. O'Brien and C. S. Wallace, Ettingshausen Effect and Thermomagnetic Cooling, J Appl Phys, 29, 1010 to 1012 (1958)

150 D. Shoenberg, "Superconductivity," 2nd Edition, Cambridge University Press, Cambridge, England, 1950

151 H. K. Onnes, Disappearance of the Electrical Resistance of Mercury at Helium Temperatures, Proc Roy Acad (Amsterdam), 14, 113 to 115 (1911)

152 W. Meissner, Supraconductivity, Z Tech Phys, 15.12, 507 to 514 (1934); Physik Z, 35, 931 to 938 (1934); with R. Ochenfeld, Naturwissenschaften, 21, 787 (1933)

153 P. Debye, The Magnetic Approach to Absolute Zero of Temperature, "Science in Progress," 4th Series, Yale University Press, 1945, p 151 to 164

154 J. Bardeen, Electron-vibration Interactions and Superconductivity, Rev Mod Phys, 23, 261 to 270 (1951)

155 B. Matthias, Relations Between Superconductors and Ferromagnets, J Appl Phys, 31, 23S to 26S (1960)

156 R. M. Bozorth and D. D. Davis, Magnetic Properties of Ferromagnetic Superconductors, J Appl Phys, 31, 321S to 322S (1960)

157 T. Giaever, Energy Gap in Superconductors Measured by Electron Tunneling, Phys Rev, 5, 147, 148 (1960)

Chapter 4

158 D. E. Noble, The Future of Solid State Electronics, Western Electronic News, 9, 17 to 20 (1961)

159 J. S. Smart, Jr., A. A. Smith and A. J. Phillips, Preparation and Some Properties of High Purity Copper, Trans AIME, 143, 272 to 286 (1941)

160 P. H. Brace, Physical Metallurgy of Copper and Copper-Base Alloys, Elec Eng, 63, 11 to 17 (1944)

161 C. H. Samans, "The Engineering Metals and Their Alloys," Macmillan Co., New York, 1948, p 834

162 R. Eisler, "Technology of Printed Circuits," Academic Press, Inc., New York, 1959

163 J. Watkins, A Survey of Thin-Film Technology, Electronic Industries, 20, 102 to 108 (1961)

164 S. J. Elliott, Evaluation of Solderless Wrapped Connections for Central Office Use, Bell System Tech J, 36, 1033 to 1059 (1959)

165 Low Temperature Bonding, Electromechanical Design, 5, 30 to 32 (1961)

166 "Handbook of Power Resistors," Ward Leonard Electric Co., 1951

167 C. D. Starr, Criteria for Evaluating Electrical Resistance Alloys, Metal Progr, 72, 88 to 94 (1957)

168 G. Nordstroem, Alloys Good at Temperatures above 2100° F, Metal Progr, 28, 68, 69 (1935)

169 H. B. Sache, Thermistors. . . . 10 to 600 K, Electronic Industries, 18, 81 to 85 (1959)

170 MIT staff, "Magnetic Circuits and Transformers," John Wiley and Sons, Inc., New York, 1943

171 R. Lee, "Electronic Transformers and Circuits," John Wiley and Sons, New York, 1955

172 W. Dubilier, Development, Design and Construction of Electrical Condensers, J Franklin Inst, 248, 193 to 204 (1949)

173 W. C. Bloomquist, "Capacitors for Industry," John Wiley & Sons, New York, 1950

174 G. W. A. Dummer, "Fixed Capacitors," Sir Isaac Pitman & Son, Ltd., London, 1956

175 G. F. Straube, A Voltage Variable Capacitor, Electronic Industries, 17, 69 to 73 (1958)

176 W. H. Kohl, "Materials and Techniques for Electron Tubes," Reinhold Publishing Corp., New York, 1960

177 H. B. Michaelson, High Temperature Materials for Vacuum Service, Mater Methods, 38, 110 to 115 (1953)

178 J. J. Bowe, What Cathode is Best for the Job, Electronic Industries, 18, 84 to 89 (1959)

179 W. T. Millis and J. F. Stephens, Copper-base Anodes Reduce Power Input by 40%, Mater Design Eng, 49, 132 to 134 (1959)

180 V. K. Zworkykin and E. G. Ramberg, "Photoelectricity," John Wiley and Sons, New York, 1956

181 W. G. Dow, "Fundamentals of Engineering Electronics," John Wiley and Sons, New York, 1952, p 429

182 H. C. Torrey and C. A. Whitmer, "Crystal Rectifiers," Mc-

Graw-Hill Book Co., Inc., New York, 1948

183 E. Gottlieb, Using the Tunnel Diode, Electronic Industries, 19, 110 to 113 (1960)

184 J. M. Carroll, What's New in Semiconductors, Electronics, 34, 90 to 120 (1961)

185 S. W. Herwald and S. J. Angello, Molecular Electronics, Westinghouse Engr, 21, 40 to 43 (1961)

186 J. Bardeen and W. H. Brattain, Nature of the Forward Current in Germanium Point Contacts, Phys Rev, 74, 231, 232 (1948)

187 N. B. Hannay, "Semiconductors," Reinhold Publishing Corp., New York, 1959

188 D. M. Warschauer, "Semiconductors and Transistors," McGraw-Hill Book Co., Inc., New York, 1959

189 R. E. Moe, Tubes or Transistors, Electronic Industries, 18, 58 to 63 (1959)

190 J. Bardeen and W. H. Brattain, Physical Principles Involved in Transistor Action, Phys Rev, 75, 1208 to 1225 (1949)

191 W. G. Pfann, Zone Melting, Met Rev, 2, No. 5, 29 to 76 (1957)

192 W. J. Grubbs, Hall Effect Devices, Bell System Tech J, 38, 853 to 876 (1959)

193 T. R. Lawson, Jr., The Hall Effect and Its Uses, Westinghouse Engr, 17, 71 to 73 (1957)

194 R. Holm, "Electrical Contacts," Hugo Gebers Forlag, Stockholm (in English), 1948; "Electrical Contacts Handbook," 3rd Edition, Springer, Berlin, 1958

195 L. B. Hunt, "Electrical Contacts," Johnson Matthey and Co., Ltd., London, 1946

196 C. A. Clark, Improved Nickel-base Alloys for Magnetostrictive Transducers, J Acoust Soc Am, 33, 930 to 933 (1961)

197 C. C. Perry and H. R. Lissner, "The Strain Gage Primer," McGraw-Hill Book Co., Inc., New York, 1955

198 R. C. Wallace, "Relays for Electronic and Industrial Control," Chapman & Hall, London, 1953

Chapter 5

199 P. L. Kapitza, Method of Producing Strong Magnetic Fields, Proc Roy Soc, 105, 691 to 710 (1924)

200 F. Bitter, Design of Powerful Electromagnets, Rev Sci Instr, 10, 373 to 381 (1939)

201 H. C. Oersted, Experimenta circa effectum conflictus electrici in acum magneticam, Ann Phil, 16, 273 to 276 (1820)

202 M. Faraday, "Experimental Researches," Vol. III, 1839, p 497

203 P. Curie, "Theses Pris a la Faculte des Science de Paris," 1895

204 P. Langevin, Magnetism and Electron Theory, Ann Chim Phys, 5, 70 to 127 (1905)

205 W. Pauli, Paramagnetism of a Degenerate Gas, Z Physik, 41, 81 to 102 (1926)

206 J. H. Van Vleck, "Theory of Electric and Magnetic Susceptibilities," Clarendon Press, Oxford, 1932

207 H. Bizette, C. F. Squire and B. Tsai, Transition Point of Magnetic Susceptibility of MnO, Compt Rend, 207, 449, 450 (1938)

208 C. F. Squire, Antiferromagnetism in Some Manganese Com-

pounds, Phys Rev, **56**, 922 to 925 (1939)

209 E. W. Gorter, Saturation Magnetization and Crystal Chemistry of Ferrimagnetic Oxides, Philips Tech Rev, **9**, 295 to 320, 321 to 365, 403 to 443 (1954)

210 "American Institute of Physics Handbook," McGraw-Hill Book Co., Inc., New York, 1957, p 5 to 217

211 J. J. Went, G. W. Rathenau, G. W. Gorter and G. W. Van Oosterhout, Ferroxdure, A Class of New Permanent Magnet Materials, Philips Tech Rev, **13**, 194 to 208 (1952)

212 L. Néel, Theory of Constant Paramagnetism. Application to Manganese, Compt Rend, **203**, 304 to 306 (1936); Magnetic Properties of Ferrites: Ferrimagnetism and Antiferromagnetism, Ann Phys, **3**, 137 to 198 (1948)

213 J. S. Smart, The Néel Theory of Ferrimagnetism, Am J Phys, **23**, 356 to 370 (1955)

214 T. J. Swoboda, W. H. Cloud, T. A. Bither, M. S. Sadler and H. S. Jarrett, Exchange Inversion in $Mn_{2-x}Cr_xSb$, Phys Rev Letters, **4**, 509 (1960); "AIEE Conference on Magnetism and Magnetic Materials," New York, 1960

215 F. Heusler, W. Starck and E. Haupt, Some Magnetic Alloys of Manganese, Deut Phys Ges Verh, **5**, 220 to 223, 224 to 232 (1903)

216 J. C. Slater, The Ferromagnetism of Nickel, Phys Rev, **49**, 537 to 545 (1936); Ferromagnetism of Nickel, II, Phys Rev, **49**, 931 to 937 (1936)

217 C. Zener, Interaction between the d Shells in the Transition Metals, Phys Rev, **81**, 440 to 444 (1951); Ferromagnetic Compounds of Manganese with Perovskite Structure, ibid, **82**, 403 to 405 (1951); Calculation of the Weiss Factors in Fe, Co and Ni, ibid, **83**, 299 to 301 (1951)

218 F. Bitter, On Inhomogeneities in the Magnetization of Ferromagnetic Materials, Phys Rev, **38**, 1903 to 1905 (1931)

219 H. J. Williams, R. M. Bozorth and W. Shockley, Magnetic Domain Patterns on Single Crystals of Silicon Iron, Phys Rev, **75**, 155 to 178 (1949)

220 H. J. Williams and W. Shockley, A Simple Domain Structure in an Iron Crystal Showing a Direct Correlation with the Magnetization, Phys Rev, **75**, 178 to 183 (1949)

221 L. Mayer, Electron Mirror Microscopy of Magnetic Domains, J Appl Phys, **28**, 975 to 983 (1957)

222 C. Kooy, Direct Observation of Weiss Domains by Means of the Faraday Effect, Philips Tech Rev, **19**, 286 to 289 (1958)

223 L. Landau and E. Lifshitz, On the Theory of the Dispersion of Magnetic Permeability in Ferromagnetic Bodies, Phys Z Sowjetunion, **8**, 153 to 169 (1935)

224 V. E. Legg, Survey of Square Loop Magnetic Materials, IRE Trans, **CP-4**, 106 to 109 (1957)

225 J. L. Snoek and F. K. duPré, Several After-Effect Phenomena and Related Losses in Alternating Fields, Philips Tech Rev, **8**, 57 to 64 (1946)

226 L. Néel, Influence of Thermal Fluctuations on the Magnetization of Very Fine Ferromag-

netic Particles, Compt Rend, **228**, 664 to 666 (1949)

227 C. P. Bean, Hysteresis Loops of Mixtures of Ferromagnetic Micropowders, J Appl Phys, **26**, 1381 to 1384 (1955)

228 H. Honda and S. Kaya, Magnetization of Single Crystals of Iron, Sci Rept Tohoku Univ, **15**, 721 to 753 (1926)

229 S. Kaya, On the Magnetization of Single Crystals of Nickel, Sci Rept Tohoku Univ, **17**, 639 to 663 (1928)

230 S. Kaya, On the Magnetization of Single Crystals of Cobalt, Sci Rept Tohoku Univ, **17**, 1157 to 1177 (1928)

231 J. B. Goodenough, Summary of Losses in Magnetic Materials, "AIEE Conference on Magnetism and Magnetic Materials," Boston, 1956, p 368

232 J. Snoek, "New Developments in Ferromagnetic Materials," Elsevier Publishing Co., New York, 1949, p 14

233 D. A. Leak and G. M. Leak, Influence of Impurities on the Magnetic Properties of High Purity 3% Silicon Iron, J Iron Steel Inst, **187**, 190 to 194 (1957)

234 T. D. Yensen and N. A. Ziegler, Effect of Carbon, Oxygen, and Grain Size on the Magnetic Properties of Iron-Silicon Alloys, Trans ASM, **24**, 337 to 358 (1936)

235 D. A. Leak and G. M. Leak, Solubility and Diffusion of Carbon in a Silicon-Iron Alloy, J Iron Steel Inst, **189**, 256 to 262 (1958)

236 R. W. Cole, Effect of Elastic Bending on Magnetic Properties of Oriented Silicon Iron, J Appl Phys, **29**, 370, 371 (1958)

237 J. K. Stanley, The Effect of Plastic Deformation on the Core Loss of Oriented Steel, "AIEE Conference on Magnetism and Magnetic Materials," Boston, 1956, p 401 to 407

238 E. Kneller, The Effect of Plastic Deformation on the Magnetic Properties of Ferromagnetic Crystals, "Ber der Arbeitsgemeinschaft Ferromagnetismus," D. Riederer Verlag, Stuttgart, 1958, 33 to 42

239 T. Muto and Y. Takagi, The Theory of Order-Disorder Transitions in Alloys, "Solid State Physics," Academic Press, 1955, p 252 to 261

240 E. M. Grabbe, Ferromagnetic Anisotropy, Magnetization at Saturation, and Superstructure in Ni_3Fe and Nearby Compositions, Phys Rev, **57**, 728 (1940)

241 J. E. Goldman and R. Smoluchowski, Magnetostriction and Order-Disorder, Phys Rev, **75**, 140 to 147 (1949)

242 G. W. Wiener, P. A. Albert, R. H. Trapp and M. F. Littman, Cube Texture in Body-Centered Magnetic Alloys, J Appl Phys, **29**, 366 to 367 (1958)

243 J. L. Walter, W. R. Hibbard, H. C. Fiedler, H. E. Grenoble, R. H. Pry and P. G. Frischmann, Magnetic Properties of Cube-Textured Silicon Iron Magnetic Sheet, J Appl Phys, **29**, 363 to 365 (1958)

244 R. M. Bozorth, Review of Magnetic Annealing, "AIEE Conference on Magnetism and Magnetic Materials," Boston, 1957, p 69

245 M. Goertz, Iron-Silicon Alloys Treated in a Magnetic Field, J Appl Phys, **22**, 964 to 965 (1951)

246 H. H. Helms, "Adaptability of Iron-Silicon Magnetic Alloys for Special Environments," Nav WEPS Report 7331, 1960

247 E. M. Terry, The Effect of Temperature upon the Magnetic Properties of Electrolytic Iron, Phys Rev, 30, 133 to 160 (1910)

248 M. Pasnak and R. Lundstan, Effects of Ultrahigh Temperatures on Magnetic Properties of Core Materials, Trans AIEE, 78, 1033 to 1039 (1960)

249 J. J. Clark, Effect of Temperature on the Permeability and Core Loss of Electrical Steels, "AIEE Conference on Magnetism and Magnetic Materials," Pittsburgh, 1955, p 329 to 333

250 J. J. Clark and J. F. Fritz, "The Effect of Temperature on the AC Magnetic Properties of Iron-Nickel Alloys," WADC Tech Note 58–277; ASTIA Doc No. AD 203397, Aug 1938

251 J. J. Clark and J. F. Fritz, Effects of Temperature on Magnetic Properties of Cobalt-Iron Alloys, Electro-Technology, 68, 93 to 96 (1961)

252 R. E. Alley, Jr., and V. E. Legg, Effects of Hydrostatic Pressure on Properties of Magnetic Materials, J Appl Phys, 31, 239S to 240S (1960)

253 C. A. Neugebauer, J. B. Newkirk and D. A. Vermilyea, "Structure and Properties of Thin Films," John Wiley and Sons, Inc., New York, 1959

254 J. C. Lloyd and R. S. Smith, Structure and Magnetic Properties of Permalloy Films, J Appl Phys, 30, 274S (1959)

255 A. H. Geisler, Structure of Permanent Magnet Materials, Trans ASM, 43, 70 to 104 (1951)

256 A. H. Geisler, Property Changes during Aging, Trans AIME, 180, 230 to 254 (1949)

257 A. J. Bradley, W. L. Bragg and C. Sykes, The Structure of Alloys, J Iron Steel Inst, 141, 63 to 142 (1940)

258 A. J. Bradley, X-ray Evidence of Intermediate Stages during Precipitation from Solid Solution, Proc Phys Soc, 52, 80 to 85 (1940)

259 H. Neumann, A. Buchner and H. Reinboth, Mechanically Soft Iron-Nickel-Copper Permanent Magnet Alloys, Z Metallk, 29, 173 to 185 (1937)

260 E. A. Nesbitt and G. A. Kelsall, Vicalloy, a Permanent-Magnet Material, Phys Rev, 58, 203 to 204 (1940)

261 I. Antik and T. Kubyschkina, On Hysteresis Loss in Liquid Ferromagnetics, Wiss Ber Univ Mosk, 11, 143 to 150 (1934)

262 C. Guilland, Thesis, "Ferromagnetics of Binary Alloys of Manganese," Strasbourg, 1943

263 C. Kittel, Theory of Structure of Ferromagnetic Domains, Phys Rev, 70, 965 to 971 (1946)

264 L. Néel, Properties of a Cubic Ferromagnetic Having Small Grains, Compt Rend, 224, 1488 to 1490 (1947)

265 E. C. Stoner and E. P. Wohlfarth, Mechanism of Magnetic Hysteresis in Heterogeneous Alloys, Trans Roy Soc (London), A240, 599 to 644 (1948); Nature, 160, 650 (1947)

266 K. Hoselitz and M. McCaig, Cause of Anisotropy in Permanent Magnet Alloys, Proc Phys Soc (London), B62, 163 to 170 (1949)

267 D. A. Oliver and J. W. Shed-

den, Cooling of Permanent Magnet Alloys in a Constant Magnetic Field, Nature, 142, 209 (1938)

268 A. H. Geisler, Structure and Properties of the Permanent Magnet Alloys, Elec Eng, 69, 37 to 44 (1950)

269 R. K. Tenzer, Effects of Temperature Variations on the Remanence of Permanent Magnets, "AIEE Conference on Magnetism and Magnetic Materials," Boston, 1956, p 203; Materials and Techniques for High-Temperature Components, Electromechanical Design, 4, 48 to 51 (1960)

270 J. L. Snoek, A Permanent Magnet Which Can Lift 3500 Times Its Own Weight, Philips Tech J, 5, 195 to 198 (1940)

271 D. I. Gordon, Magnetic Cores and Permanent Magnets in Hyper-Environments, Proc Inst Environ Sciences Nat Mtg (1960)

272 C. Zener, The Impact of Magnetism Upon Metallurgy, Trans AIME, 203, 619 (1955)

273 B. S. Chandrasekhar, The Anomalous Thermal Expansion of Some Rare Earth Elements, Acta Met, 6, 212 to 214 (1958)

274 W. Thomson, Effects of Magnetization on Electrical Conductivity of Nickel and Iron, Proc Roy Soc (London), 8, 546 to 550 (1857)

275 P. Weiss and A. Piccard, On a New Magnetocaloric Phenomenon, Compt Rend, 166, 352 to 354 (1918)

276 J. P. Remeike, $GaFeO_3$: A Ferromagnetic-Piezoelectric Compound, J Appl Phys, 31, 263S to 264S (1960)

277 P. H. Fang and R. S. Roth, Ferroelectric and Ferrimagnetic Properties of $(Ba_{6-2x}R_{2x})$ $(Nb_{9-x}Fe_{1+x})O_{30}$, J Appl Phys, 31, 278S (1960)

Chapter 6

278 R. Steinitz, Magnetic Properties of Iron-Powder Compacts, Metals Technol, 15, TP 2335 (1948)

279 T. D. Yensen, Magnetic Properties of Ternary Fe-Si-C Alloys, Trans AIEE, 43, 145 to 175 (1924)

280 W. S. Messkin, Influence of Cold Working on the Magnetic Properties of a Carbon Steel, Arch Eisenhuttw, 3, 417 to 425 (1929)

281 W. S. Eberly, How Fabrication Affects Stainless Magnetic Properties, Iron Age, 183, 106 to 108 (1959)

282 W. A. Stein, The Magnetic Properties of Stainless Steels, Trans AIEE, 67, 1534 to 1537 (1948)

283 W. F. Barrett, W. Brown and W. A. Hadfield, Conductivity and Permeability of Iron Alloys, Sci Proc Roy Dublin Soc, 7, 67 to 126 (1900)

284 N. P. Goss, New Development of Electrical Strip Steels Characterized by Fine Grain Structure Approaching the Properties of a Single Crystal, Trans ASM, 23, 511 to 544 (1935); U S Patents 1,965,559, 2,084,-336, and 2,084,337

285 G. W. Wiener and K. Deitert, Cube Oriented (Silicon Iron) Magnetic Sheet, J Metals, 10, 507 to 508 (1958)

286 J. L. Walter, W. R. Hibbard, Jr., H. C. Fiedler, H. E. Grenoble, R. H. Pry and D. G. Frischman, Magnetic Properties of

Cube-Textured Transformer Sheet, J Metals, 10, 509 to 511 (1958)

287 E. Gumlich, The Magnetic Properties of Iron-Carbon and Iron-Silicon Alloys, Trans Faraday Soc, 8, 98 to 114 (1912)

288 T. D. Yensen, Hipersil — A Greatly Improved Transformer Iron, J Appl Phys, 16, 379 to 385 (1945)

289 C. F. Burgess and J. Aston, The Magnetic and Electrical Properties of the Iron-Nickel Alloys, Met Chem Eng, 8, 23 to 26 (1910)

290 F. D. Arnold and G. W. Elmen, Permalloy, An Alloy of Remarkable Magnetic Properties, J Franklin Inst, 195, 621 to 632 (1923); Phys Rev, 21, 707 (1923)

291 E. A. Nesbitt, R. D. Heidenrich and A. J. Williams, Necessary Factor for Heat Treatment of Permalloys in a Magnetic Field, J Appl Phys, 31, 2285 to 2295 (1960)

292 A. I. Schindler and E. I. Salkovitz, Effect of Applying a Magnetic Field During Neutron Irradiation on the Magnetic Properties of Fe-Ni Alloys, J Appl Phys, 31, 2455 to 2465 (1960)

293 T. D. Yensen, Permeability of Hipernik Reaches 167,000, Elec J, 28, 386 to 388 (1931); U S Patent 1,807,021

294 W. C. Ellis and E. E. Schumacker, Magnetic Materials, A Survey in Relation to Structure, Metals & Alloys, 5, 269 to 276 (1934); 6, 26 to 28 (1935)

295 O. Dahl and J. Pfaffenberger, Anisotropy in Magnetic Materials, Z Physik, 71, 93 to 105 (1931)

296 J. L. Snoek, Magnetic Investigation of New Kind of Pupin Coil, Physica, 2, 403 to 412 (1935); J. L. Snoek and W. G. Burgers, Structures of Rolled and Recrystallized Fe-Ni Alloys, Z Metallk, 27, 158 to 160 (1935)

297 O. Dahl and F. Pawlek, Effect of Fiber Structure and of Cooling in a Magnetic Field on Magnetization, Z Physik, 94, 504 to 522 (1935)

298 G. A. Kelsall, Permeability Changes in Ferromagnetic Materials Heat Treated in Magnetic Fields, Physics, 5, 169 to 172 (1934)

299 G. W. Elmen, Magnetic Properties of Perminvar, J Franklin Inst, 206, 317 to 338 (1928)

300 W. Six, J. L. Snoek and W. G. Burgers, New Magnetic Material for Pupin Coils, Ingenieur (Hague), 49, 195 (1934)

301 O. Dahl, J. Pfaffenberger and H. Sprung, New Materials for Cores of Induction Coils, Materials with New High Magnetic Stability, Elek Nachr Tech, 10, 317 to 332 (1933); Metallwirtschaft, 13, 527 to 530, 543 to 549, 559 to 563 (1934)

302 T. D. Yensen, Conpernik, Iron Age, 121, 534 (1928)

303 P. Weiss and R. Forrer, Absolute Saturation of Ferromagnetics and Law of Approach as a Function of H and T, Ann Physique, 12, 279 to 374 (1929)

304 J. H. White and C. V. Wahl, U S Patent 1,862,559, 1932

305 J. K. Stanley and T. D. Yensen, Hiperco — A Magnetic Alloy, Trans AIEE, 66, 714 to 718 (1947)

306 H. L. B. Gould and D. H. Wenny, Supermendur, A New

Rectangular-Loop Magnetic Material, "AIEE Conference on Magnetism and Magnetic Materials," Boston, 1956, p 675 to 678

307 H. Masumoto and H. Saito, On the Effect of Heat Treatment on the Magnetic Properties of Iron-Aluminum Alloys I, II, III, Sci Rept Res Inst Tohoku Univ, 3A, 521 to 534 (1951); 4A, 321 to 337 (1952); 4A, 338 to 346 (1952)

308 J. F. Nachman and W. J. Buehler, "Fabrication and Properties of Alfenol Alloys (Al-Fe) containing 10 to 17% Aluminum," NAVORD Report 4130, 1955

309 H. Masumoto, On a New Alloy "Sendust" and Its Magnetic and Electrical Properties, Sci Rept Tohoku Imp Univ, Sec 1, 388 to 402 (1936)

310 W. M. Hubbard, E. Adams and J. F. Haben, Sendust Flake — A New Magnetic Material for Low-Frequency Application, "AIEE Conference on Magnetism and Magnetic Materials," Boston, 1956, p 445 to 451

311 S. Schweizerhof, A New Improved Laminated Material with a Rectilinear Magnetization Curve, Z Metallk, 33, 175 to 185 (1941)

312 G. H. Cole, Very Thin Electrical Sheet for High-Frequency Components, Elec Mfg, 38, No. 6, 104 to 107, 190 to 200 (1946)

313 Ferrites Issue, Proc IRE, 44, No. 10 (1956)

314 M. Kornetzki, J. Brackman, J. Frey and W. Gieseke, Measurements of Highly Permeable Ferrite Grains, Z Angew Phys, 3, 5 to 9 (1951); 4, 371 to 374 (1952)

315 W. Gross, Development and State of the Art in Nonferromagnetic Steels, Stahl Eisen, 75, 1558 to 1562 (1955)

316 I. F. Kinnard and H. T. Faus, Self-Compensating Temperature Indicator, Trans AIEE, 49, 949 to 951 (1930)

317 L. R. Jackson and H. W. Russell, Temperature-Sensitive Magnetic Alloys and Their Uses, Instruments, 11, 280 to 282 (1938)

Chapter 7

318 K. Honda and S. Saito, On K. S. Magnet Steel, Sci Rept Tohoku Imp Univ, 9, 417 to 422 (1920); U S Patents 1,-338,132, 1,338,133 and 1,338,-134; Phys Rev, 16, 495 to 500 (1920)

319 R. S. Dean, U S Patent 1,904,-859, 1930

320 W. Koster, Permanent Magnet Materials on the Basis of Precipitation Hardening, Stahl Eisen, 53, 849 to 856 (1933)

321 K. Honda, H. Masumoto and Y. Shirakawa, On a New K. S. Magnet Steel, Sci Rept Tohoku Imp Univ, 23, 365 to 373 (1934)

322 G. A. Kelsall, U S Patent 2,-190,667, 1940; E. A. Nesbitt, U S Patent 2,298,225, 1942

323 H. Legat, Magnetically Hard, Low-Carbon Copper-Nickel Steels, Metallwirtschaft, 16, 743 to 749 (1937)

324 O. Dahl, J. Pfaffenberger and N. Schwartz, On Iron-Nickel Alloys, Metallwirtschaft, 14, 665 to 670 (1935)

325 H. Potter, Some Magnetic Alloys and Their Properties, Phil Mag, 12, 255 to 264 (1931)

326 T. Mishima, Nickel-Aluminum Steel for Permanent Magnets, Ohm, **19**, 353 (1932); U S Patents 2,027,994, 2,027,995, 2,027,996, 2,027,997, 2,027,-998, 2,027,999 and 2,028,000.

327 K. Hoselitz and M. McCaig, Anisotropic Permanent Magnet Alloys, Nature (London), **164**, 581 (1949)

328 W. Hansen, U S Patents 2,-499,860 and 2,499,861

329 A. L. Stuijts, G. W. Rathenau and G. H. Weber, Ferroxdure II and III, Anisotropic Permanent Magnet Material, Philips Tech Rev, **16**, 141 to 147 (1954–1955)

330 R. B. Falk, G. D. Hooper and R. J. Studders, Recent Developments in the Field of Elongated Single-Domain Iron and Iron-Cobalt Magnets, J Appl Phys, **30**, supp, 1328 to 1335 (1959)

331 L. I. Mendelsohn, F. E. Luborsky and T. O. Paine, Permanent-Magnet Properties of Elongated Single-Domain Iron Particles, J Appl Phys, **26**, 1274 to 1281 (1955)

332 F. E. Luborsky, L. I. Mendelsohn and T. O. Paine, Reproducing the Properties of Alnico Permanent Magnet Alloys with Elongated Single-Domain Co-balt-Iron Particles, "AIEE Conference on Magnetism and Magnetic Materials," Boston, 1956, p 133 to 144

333 E. Adams, "Bismanol Permanent Magnets, Evaluation and Processing," NAVORD Report 2686, Jan 1953

334 Y. Kato and T. Takei, Permanent Oxide Magnet and Its Characteristics, J Inst Elec Engr (Japan), **53**, 408 to 412 (1940)

335 W. Jellinghaus, New Alloys with High Coercive Forces, Z Tech Physik, **17**, 33 to 36 (1935)

336 A. J. J. Koch, P. Hokkeling, M. G. v.d. Steeg and K. J. De-Vos, New Material for Permanent Magnets on a Base of Mn and Al, J Appl Phys, **31**, 755 to 775 (1960)

337 R. J. Campbell and C. A. Julien, Ferromagnetic Phase of Mn-Al, J Appl Phys, **32**, 3465 to 3475 (1961)

338 W. M. Hubbard, E. Adams and J. V. Gilfrich, Magnetic Moments of Alloys of Gadolinium with Some of the Transition Elements, J Appl Phys, **31**, 3685 to 3695 (1960)

339 J. G. Ferguson, Dimensions of Resistivity, Elec Engr, **68**, 470 (1949)

Appendix

Dimensions of Resistivity (339)

"Resistivity is defined as the resistance between opposite faces of a cube of unit dimensions. In the cgs system, this becomes ohms for a centimeter cube. For a long time, this was abbreviated to ohms per cm^3, sometimes written ohm/cm^3 or ohm-cm^3. No division or multiplication was implied, and the centimeter cube was not intended to be cc or it would have been written that way. This form of abbreviation caused considerable confusion. It is not correct dimensionally and has now been almost entirely discarded in favor of ohm-cm, which is dimensionally correct and is equally so in any other system, as the mks system where it would be ohm-m. However, it does not in itself furnish an adequate definition of resistivity.

"Another unit is in popular use, the resistance of a length of one foot having an area of one circular mil. It is open to question whether this should be considered a unit of resistivity at all, because none of the three units involved belong in the same system, and the units of length and area are not even commensurate. It is a purely arbitrary unit, but still a very popular and useful one. Like the ohm per centimeter cube, it has been abbreviated to ohm per circular mil foot, as a description abbreviation, no multiplication or division being implied. When abbreviated to ohm/mil ft, it is obviously incorrect dimensionally and no mathematics will make it correct. The only two solutions are to take it as a descriptive term and to forget about the dimensions, or educate the user to the term ohm-circular mil/ft, which has the advantage of being not only dimensionally correct, but is in itself a complete definition of resistivity in terms of this arbitrary unit."

Relations Among the Systems of Electrical and Magnetic Units

Quantity	Mksa (absolute) system	Old international system	Equivalents in other systems		
			Cgs esu system	Cgs emu system	Gaussian system
Permeability of empty space, μ	$1.2566(10)^{-6}$ henry/m ($mks^{-2}a^{-2}$)	$1.2560(10)^{-6}$ international henry/m	$1.1126(10)^{-21}$ ($cm^{-2}s^2$)	1 (dimensionless)	1 (dimensionless)
Potential difference, V	1 volt ($m^2ks^{-3}a^{-1}$)	0.999670 international volt	$3.336(10)^{-2}$ statvolts ($cm^{1/2}gm^{1/2}s^{-1}$)	$(10)^8$ abvolts ($cm^{3/2}gm^{1/2}s^{-2}$)	$3.336(10)^{-2}$ statvolts ($cm^{1/2}gm^{1/2}s^{-1}$)
Current, I	1 ampere (a)	1.000165 international amperes	$2.998(10)^9$ statamperes ($cm^{3/2}gm^{1/2}s^{-2}$)	0.1 abampere ($cm^{1/2}gm^{1/2}s^{-1}$)	$2.998(10)^9$ statamperes ($cm^{3/2}gm^{1/2}s^{-2}$)
Resistance, R	1 ohm ($m^2ks^{-3}a^{-2}$)	0.99505 international ohm	$1.1126(10)^{-12}$ statohms ($cm^{-1}s$)	$(10)^9$ abohms (cms^{-1})	$1.1126(10)^{-12}$ statohms ($cm^{-1}s$)
Capacitance, C	1 farad ($m^{-2}k^{-1}s^4a^2$)	1.000495 international farad	$8.988(10)^{11}$ centimeters (cm)	$(10)^{-9}$ abfarad ($cm^{-1}s^2$)	$8.988(10)^{11}$ centimeters (cm)
Magnetic field strength, H	1 ampere-turn/m ($m^{-1}a$)	1.000165 international ampere-turn/m	$3.767(10)^8$ statoersteds ($cm^{1/2}gm^{1/2}s^{-2}$)	$1.257(10)^{-2}$ oersted ($cm^{-1/2}gm^{1/2}s^{-1}$)	$1.257(10)^{-2}$ oersted ($cm^{-1/2}gm^{1/2}s^{-1}$)
Magnetic flux density, B	1 weber/m^2 ($ks^{-2}a^{-1}$)	0.999670 international volt s/m^2	$3.336(10)^{-7}$ statmaxwells/cm^2 ($cm^{-1/2}gm^{1/2}$)	$(10)^4$ maxwells/cm^2 ($cm^{-1/2}gm^{1/2}s^{-1}$)	$(10)^4$ gausses ($cm^{-1/2}gm^{1/2}s^{-1}$)

In the above table, m is meter, k is kilogram, s is second, a is ampere.

Values of Some General Physical Constants

Quantity	Value
Avogadro's number, N	6.025×10^{23} g per mol
Electronic charge, e	-4.802×10^{-10} esu
Electron rest mass, m	9.107×10^{-28} g
Planck's constant, h	6.624×10^{-27} erg sec
Velocity of light, c	2.9979×10^{10} cm per sec
Specific charge of the electron, e/m	1.759×10^{7} emu per g
Boltzmann's constant, k	1.38×10^{-16} erg per deg
Energy associated with 1 ev	1.602×10^{-12} erg

Conversion Units

Temperature Conversion

$$°C = 5/9(°F - 32)$$
$$°F = 1.8 \times °C + 32$$

Coefficient of Electrical and Thermal Conductivity

$$\alpha/°C = \alpha/°F \times 1.8$$
$$\alpha/°F = \alpha/°C \times 5/9$$

Electrical Conductivity

$$\text{Per cent IACS} = \frac{1.7241}{\text{microhm-centimeters}} \times 100$$

Electrical Resistivity

$$\text{Microhm-cm} \times 6.015 = \text{ohm per cir mil-ft}$$

Magnetic Quantities

$$\text{Kilogausses} = \frac{\text{maxwells per sq in.}}{6.450}$$
$$\text{Oersteds} = \frac{\text{ampere-turns per in.}}{2.02}$$
$$\text{Webers} = \frac{\text{maxwells}}{100 \text{ million}}$$
$$\text{Webers per sq m} = \frac{\text{kilogausses}}{10}$$
$$\text{Webers per sq m} = \frac{\text{maxwells per sq in.}}{64,500}$$
$$\text{Watts per lb} = \frac{10^{-4}fW_h}{2.205\rho}$$
$$\text{Watts per kg} = \frac{10^{-4}fW_h}{\rho}$$

Here f is the frequency in cycles per second, W_h is the hysteresis loss in ergs per cu cm per cycle, and ρ is the density in grams per cu cm.

Some Important Multiplying Factors

Multiply	By	To Obtain
cm	0.0328	ft
cm	0.3937	in.
cu cm	0.3531×10^{-4}	cu ft
cu cm	0.0610	cu in.
cu ft	28,317	cu cm
cu ft	1,728	cu in.
cu in.	16.387	cu cm
cu in.	0.5787×10^{-2}	sq ft
ft	30.48	cm
g	2.2046×10^{-3}	lb
g/cu cm	0.03613	lb/cu in.
in.	2.540	cm
mm	0.03937	in.
lb/cu in.	27.68	g/cu cm
sq cm	0.1550	sq in.
sq in.	6.452	sq cm
watts/cm/°C	0.2389	cal/sec/cm/°C
watts/cm/°C	0.1926	btu/sec/sq ft/°F/in.
microhm-cm	6.015	ohms/cir mil-ft
microhm-cm	0.3937	microhm-in.
microhm-cm	0.01ρ(a)	ohms/meter gram
ohms/cir mil-ft	0.1662	microhm-cm
ohms/meter-gram	$39.37/\rho$	microhm-cm
ohms	10^6	microhms
microhms	10^{-6}	ohms
volts	10^6	microvolts
volts	1000	millivolts
microvolts	10^{-6}	volts
millivolts	0.001	volts

(a) ρ = density in g per cu cm.

Symbols and Abbreviations Used in the Text

In some instances, one symbol is used to represent several different properties; this situation obtains from the wide scope of the electric and magnetic technology. To the purist, this situation may prove annoying, but long-time usage virtually dictates the use of accepted symbols. Where editorial license permitted, the author has adopted symbols and abbreviations best suited to his purpose.

A Angstrom unit
A area
B flux density; B_r, remanence
C degrees Centigrade
C Curie constant
E energy
F degrees Fahrenheit
F force, leakage flux
G conductance
H magnetic field; H_c, coercive force
I current (amperes), intensity of magnetization
K degrees Kelvin
L Lorenz number, length, inductance
M magnetic moment
N number of free electrons, carrier concentration, Avogadro's number, turn ratio, grains per square millimeter
P Peltier coefficient or voltage
Q quality factor
R resistance, reflection coefficient, Hall coefficient
S Seebeck coefficient
T temperature
W core loss; W_e, eddy-current loss; W_h, hysteresis loss

X electric field; X_L, inductive reactance
Z atomic number, thermoelectric figure of merit

a ampere
a interatomic distance
c velocity of light
d diameter
e charge on the electron, Ettingshausen coefficient
f frequency, leakage flux
g gram
h Planck's constant
i current density
k Boltzmann's constant
l mean free path, length
m meter, prefix for milli-
m mass of the electron, pole strength
n number of turns or turns per unit length
r radius
s second
t thickness, time
w watt

AISI   American Iron and Steel Institute
ASTM American Society for Testing Materials

AWG	American Wire Gage	a, β	coefficients
IACS	International Annealed Copper Standard	γ	conductivity, Poisson's ratio
OFHC	oxygen-free high-conductivity	δ	secondary emission coefficient
		ϵ	elongation, strain
ac	alternating current	θ	Curie temperature, volume fraction
bcc	body-centered cubic		
cgs	centimeter-gram-second	κ	thermal conductivity, volume susceptibility
cir mil-ft	circular mil-foot		
cm	centimeter	λ	wave length, magnetostriction
cph	close-packed hexagonal		
cps	cycles per second	μ	permeability, magnetic moment, electron mobility, micron
dc	direct current		
emu	electromagnetic units		
emf	electromotive force	ν	average velocity, frequency
ev	electron volt	π	3.1416
fcc	face-centered cubic	ρ	electrical resistivity, density
ft	foot	σ	electrical conductivity
in.	inch	ϕ	work function, lines of flux
kg	kilogram	χ	mass susceptibility; χ_A, atomic susceptibility; χ_M, molar susceptibility
kv	kilovolt		
kva	kilovolt-ampere		
kw	kilowatt		
mv	millivolt	Θ	Debye characteristic temperature
psi	pounds per square inch		
sec	second	τ	average time

Index

367